FERRIES
BRITISH ISLES AND NORTHE

ISBN 978-1-906608-83-5

Ferry Publications, PO Box 33,
Ramsey, Isle of Man IM99 4LP

Email: ferrypubs@manx.net   Website: www.ferrypubs.co.uk

europe's **leading** guide to the ferry industry

contents...

Seatruck Panorama (*Gordon Hislip*)

europe's **leading** guide to the ferry industry

introduction...

T his is the twenty-seventh edition of this book, which first appeared in 1983 as the 24-page 'home published' *'Car Ferries from Great Britain and Ireland'*. The book aims to list every passenger/vehicle ferry in Great Britain and Ireland, ro-ro freight vessels which operate regular services between Great Britain and Ireland and to nearby Continental destinations and major passenger/vehicle ferries in other parts of Northern Europe. The coverage of Northern Europe is not fully comprehensive (to make it so would probably triple the size of the book) and does not include freight-only operations and vessels - although freight-only vessels have been included where the operators also run passenger services. Ro-ro vessels engaged in 'deep-sea' trade and those operated solely for the carriage of trade cars or paper are also not included.

Each operator is listed alphabetically within sections - major operators, minor operators, freight-only operators, chain, cable and float ferries, passenger-only ferries, other North European passenger operators and vehicle/passenger vessels owned by companies not currently engaged in operating services. After details relating to each company's management, address, telephone numbers, email, website and services, there is a fleet list with technical data and then a potted history of each vessel with previous names and dates.

Each operator was sent the draft text relating to them a few weeks ago. Where they have not responded, I have attempted to ensure that any telephone, fax and email details match what is quoted on their website but management details may not be 100% accurate.

The last 18 months has seen the delivery of three splendid new LGN ferries for Fjord Line and Viking Line and more Visentini built ships have entered service from UK ports. TransEuropa Ferries has gone but LD lines has re-entered the UK market in their own right. With all the vessels built in the ro-ro boom of the late seventies and early eighties now departed from Northern Europe, it has been a quiet time on the freight front, with few new deliveries. Whilst the easing of the recession is seeing both passenger and freight traffic increasing, operators now face the new challenge of meeting the stretching new emissions regulations which come in at the start of 2015. Whatever solution is adopted - cleaner fuel or scrubbers - will inevitably lead to greater costs and could lead to some routes disappearing (Harwich - Esbjerg is the first but others may follow). It would be ironic indeed if attempts to curb air pollution on the empty seas led to an increase in polluting and congesting trucks on land where people actually live.

Nick Widdows

Whitstable, Kent

July 2014

europe's **leading** guide to the ferry industry

foreword...

Fjord Line's dream has become reality

Fjord Line is a challenger in the ferry market linking Norway and the EU. Our dream in recent years has been to expand this market with daily journeys between three major Norwegian ports and Hirtshals in Denmark – a service benefiting travellers and cargo shippers alike. To realize the dream, our owners have invested in two large, modern, environmentally friendly cruise ferries. The MS *Stavangerfjord* and MS *Bergensfjord* are identical vessels, specially designed to cope with the North Sea's whims. These cruise ferries are the largest in the world powered solely by liquefied natural gas (LNG). By a wide margin, they comply with the strict emissions rules about to be implemented in European shipping. It is a great honor and distinct pleasure to be able to present them in this edition of Ferries 2015.

The two multipurpose ferries were built by Bergen Group Fosen (now NorYards Fosen). The MS *Stavangerfjord* began sailing in July 2013 and the MS *Bergensfjord* in March of this year. Before the service began, we were sometimes asked if market demand on the Bergen-Stavanger-Hirtshals and Hirtshals-Langesund routes was sufficient to justify two vessels of such capacity. Had the feedback from passengers and shipping industry experts been negative, we would doubtless have begun to wonder whether the dream was realizable. But from the start, our philosophy has been that by introducing ships with outstanding design, superior comfort and advanced technological and logistical systems – and of course high regularity – we could unlock a large, untapped potential market. In our communications we have made sure to address segments of the retail and corporate markets that previously had not considered using our transport services. The prize awarded to Fjord Line at the opening of the Nor-Shipping 2013 trade fair – a prize saluting the energy efficiency and eco-friendliness of our cruise ferries' propulsion system – is visible evidence of the fresh, innovative approach we took in developing the MS *Stavangerfjord* and the MS *Bergensfjord*. Further confirmation of the global shipping industry's acclaim came in 2014, with Shippax Awards for best design and largest LNG ferry.

So far, everything we've learned from operating our cruise ferries suggests our strategy has been successful. We have documented that passenger demand is driven largely by the quality of service we at Fjord Line are able to provide. That's true for mini-cruise customers as well as for travellers who favour the sea route to holiday destinations on land. It's also the case for companies that book our floating hotels for courses and conferences, and for the goods transporters who value our efficient and environmentally friendly services to carry heavy vehicles and freight.

Fjord Line's dream of two new ships has become reality, and we can already see the venture bearing fruit. The danger is that our sense of progress and success could turn into complacency. Our operational model will therefore be subject to continuous evaluation and improvement. New and exciting journeys are in store.

Ingvald Fardal

CEO

a **guide** to using
this book

Sections Listing is in seven sections. *Section 1* - Services from Great Britain and Ireland to the Continent and between Great Britain and Ireland (including services to/from the Isle of Man and Channel Islands), *Section 2* - Domestic services within Great Britain and Ireland, *Section 3* - Freight-only services from Great Britain and Ireland and domestic routes, *Section 4* - Minor vehicle ferries in Great Britain and Ireland (chain and cable ferries etc), *Section 5* - Major passenger-only operators, *Section 6* - Major car ferry operators in Northern Europe, *Section 7* - Companies not operating regular services possessing vehicle ferries which may be chartered or sold to other operators.

Order The company order within each section is alphabetical. Note that the definite article and words meaning 'company' or 'shipping company' (eg. 'AG', 'Reederei') do not count. However, where this is part of a ship's name it does count. Sorting is by normal English convention eg. 'Å' is treated the same as 'A' and comes at the start, not as a separate character which comes at the end of the alphabet as is the Scandinavian convention. Where ships are numbered, order is by number whether the number is expressed in Arabic or Latin digits.

Listing of Ships When a ship owned by a company listed in this book is on charter to another company listed, then she is shown under the company which operates her. When a ship owned by a company listed in this book is on charter to another company not listed, then she is shown under the company which owns her.

IMO Number All ships of 100t or greater (except vessels solely engaged in fishing, ships without mechanical means of propulsion (eg. chain ferries), pleasure yachts, ships engaged on special service (eg. lightships), hopper barges, hydrofoils, air cushion vehicles, floating docks and structures classified in a similar manner, warships and troopships, wooden ships) are required to be registered by the International Maritime Organisation (IMO), an agency of the United Nations. The number is retained by the ship throughout her life, however much the vessel is rebuilt. This number is now required to be displayed on the ship externally and on top so that it can be read from the air. The scheme is administered by Lloyd's Register-Fairplay, who maintain a database of all ships in excess of 100t (with some exceptions), not just those classified through them.

Company Information This section gives general information regarding the status of the company. That is, nationality, whether it is public or private sector and whether it is part of a larger group.

Management The Managing Director and Marketing Director or Manager of each company are listed. Where these posts do not exist, other equivalent people are listed. Where only initials are given, that person is, as far as is known, male.

Address This is the address of the company's administrative headquarters. In the case of some international companies, British and overseas addresses are given.

Telephone and Fax Numbers are expressed as follows: + [number] (this is the international dialling code which is dialled in combination with the number dialled for international calls (00 in the UK, Ireland and most other European countries); it is not used for calling within the country), ([number]) (this is the number which precedes area codes when making long-distance domestic calls - it is not dialled when calling from another country or making local calls (not all countries have this)), [number] (this is the rest of the number including, where appropriate, the area dialling code). UK '08' numbers are sometimes not available from overseas and the full number must be dialled in all circumstances.

Internet Email addresses and **Website** URLs are given where these are available; the language(s) used is shown. The language listed first is that which appears on the home page when accessed from a UK based computer; the others follow in alphabetical order. In a few cases Email facility is only available through the Website. To avoid confusion, there is no other punctuation on the Internet line.

Routes operated After each route there are, in brackets, details of 1 normal journey time, 2 regular vessel(s) used on the route (number as in list of vessels) and 3 frequencies (where a number per day is given, this relates to return sailings). In the case of freight-only sailings which operate to a regular schedule, departure times are given where they have been supplied. Please note that times are subject to quite frequent change and cancellation.

Winter and Summer In this book, Winter generally means the period between October and Easter while Summer means Easter to October. The peak Summer period is generally June, July and August. In Scandinavia, the Summer peak ends in mid-August whilst in the UK it starts rather later and generally stretches into the first or second week of September. Dates vary according to operator.

Spelling The convention is used in respect of town and country names is that English names are used for towns and areas of countries where such names exist (eg. Gothenburg rather than Göteborg) and English names for countries (eg. Germany rather than Deutschland). Otherwise local names are used, accented as appropriate. In a few cases, English names have slipped out of common usage and the local name is more commonly used in Britain, ie Dunkerque not Dunkirk, Helsingør not Elsinore and Vlissingen not Flushing. Many towns in Finland have both Finnish and Swedish names; we have used the Finnish name except in the case of Åland which is a Swedish-speaking area. In the case of Danish towns, the alternative use of 'å' or 'aa' follows local convention. The following towns, islands and territories are expressed using their English names - the local name is shown following: Antwerp - Antwerpen/Anvers, Fyn - Funen, Genoa - Génova, Ghent - Gent, Gothenburg - Göteborg, Hook of Holland - Hoek van Holland, Jutland - Jylland, Copenhagen - København, Ostend - Oostende, Oporto - Porto, Seville - Sevilla, Sealand - Sjælland and Venice - Venezia.

Terms The following words mean *'shipping company'* in various languages: Redereja (Latvian), Rederi (Danish, Norwegian, Swedish), Rederij (Dutch), Reederei (German) and Zegluga (Polish). The following words mean *'limited company'*: AB - Aktiebolaget (Swedish) (Finnish companies who use both the Finnish and Swedish terms sometimes express it as Ab), AG - Aktiengesellschaft (German), AS - Aksjeselskap (Norwegian), A/S - Aktie Selskabet (Danish), BV - Besloten Vennootschap (Dutch), GmbH - Gesellschaft mit beschränkter Haftung (German), NV - Naamloze Vennootschap (Dutch), Oy - (Finnish), Oyj - (Finnish (plc)) and SA - Société Anonyme (French).

Types of Ferry

These distinctions are necessarily general and many ships will have features of more than one category.

Car Ferry Until about 1970, most vehicle ferries were primarily designed for the conveyance of cars and their passengers and foot passengers. Little regard was paid to the conveyance of lorries and trailers, since this sort of traffic had not begun to develop. Few vessels of this type are still in service.

Multi-purpose Ferry From about 1970 onwards vehicle ferries began to make more provision for freight traffic, sharing the same ship with passengers and cars. Features usually include higher vehicle decks, often with retractable mezzanine decks, enabling two levels of cars or one level of freight and coaches, and separate facilities (including cabins on quite short crossings) for freight drivers.

Cruise Ferry In the 1980s the idea of travelling on a ferry, not just to get from A to B but for the pleasure of the travel experience, became more and more popular and ferries were built with increasingly luxurious and varied passenger accommodation. Such vessels also convey cars and freight but the emphasis is on passenger accommodation with a high level of berths (sometimes providing berths for all passengers).

Ro-pax Ferry A vessel designed primarily for the carriage of freight traffic but which also carries a limited number of ordinary passengers. Features generally include a moderate passenger capacity - up to about 500 passengers - and a partly open upper vehicle deck. Modern ro-pax vessels are becoming increasingly luxurious with facilities approaching those of a cruise ferry.

Ro-ro Ferry A vessel designed for the conveyance of road freight, unaccompanied trailers and containers on low trailers (known as 'Mafis' although often made by other manufacturers). Some such vessels have no passenger accommodation but the majority can accommodate up to 12 passengers - the maximum allowed without a passenger certificate. On routes where there is a low level of driver-accompanied traffic (mainly the longer ones), ordinary passengers, with or without cars, can sometimes be conveyed. On routes with a high level of driver-accompanied traffic, passenger capacity will sometimes be higher but facilities tend to be geared to the needs of freight drivers eg. lounge with video, high level of cabins on routes of three hours or more. Technically such vessels are passenger ferries (having a passenger certificate) but are included in the freight section when exclusively or mainly conveying freight drivers.

Con-ro Many ro-ro vessels are capable of having ISO (International Standards Organisation) containers crane-loaded on the upper 'weather' deck. In this book the term con-ro applies only to vessels whose upper deck can only take containers and has no vehicle access.

Fast Ferry Streamlined vessel of catamaran or monohull construction, speed in excess of 30 knots, water jet propulsion, generally aluminium-built but some have steel hulls, little or no freight capacity and no cabins.

Timescale Although the book goes to press in June 2014, I have sought to reflect the situation as it will exist in early Summer 2014 with regard to the introduction of new ships or other known changes. Vessels due to enter service after July 2014 are shown as '**Under Construction**'. The book is updated at all stages of the production process where this is feasible, although major changes once the text has been paginated are not possible; there is also a 'Late News' section on page xxx for changes which cannot be incorporated into the text.

List of vessels

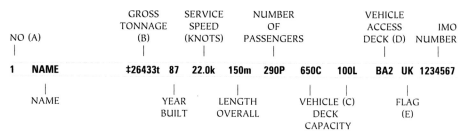

NO (A)	GROSS TONNAGE (B)	SERVICE SPEED (KNOTS)	NUMBER OF PASSENGERS		VEHICLE ACCESS DECK (D)	IMO NUMBER
1 NAME	‡26433t 87	22.0k	150m 290P	650C 100L	BA2	UK 1234567
NAME	YEAR BUILT	LENGTH OVERALL	VEHICLE (C) DECK CAPACITY		FLAG (E)	

(A) » = fast ferry, ● = vessel laid up, F = freight-only vessel (max 12 passengers), F‡ = freight-only vessel (with passenger certificate), p = passenger-only vessel

(B) C = Cars, L = Lorries (**15m**), T = Trailers (**13.5m**), r = can also take rail wagons, - = No figure quoted.

(C) B = Bow, A = Aft, S = Side, Q = Quarterdeck, R = Slewing ramp, 2 = Two decks can be loaded at the same time, C = Vehicles must be crane-loaded aboard, t = turntable ferry.

AG = Antigua and Barbuda	DE = Germany	IT = Italy	PA = Panama
	DK = Denmark	IR = Irish Republic	PT = Portugal
AL = Åland Islands	EE = Estonia	LU = Luxembourg	PL = Poland
AU = Australia	ES = Spain	LT = Lithuania	RU = Russia
BB = Barbados	FO = Faroes	LV = Latvia	SG = Singapore
BE = Belgium	FI = Finland	MD = Madeira	SE = Sweden
BM = Bermuda	FR = France	MT = Malta	UK = United
BS = Bahamas	GI = Gibraltar	NL = Netherlands	Kingdom
CY = Cyprus	IM = Isle of Man	NO = Norway	

(D) The following abbreviations are used:

In the notes ships are in CAPITAL LETTERS, shipping lines and other institutions are in *italics*.

Capacity In this book, capacities shown are the maxima. Sometimes vessels operate at less than their maximum passenger capacity due to reduced crewing or to operating on a route on which they are not permitted to operate above a certain level. Car and lorry/trailer capacities are the maximum for either type. The two figures are not directly comparable. Some parts of a vessel may allow cars on two levels to occupy the space that a trailer or lorry occupies on one level, some may not; some parts of a vessel with low headroom may only be accessible to cars. All figures have to be approximate.

Ownership The ownership of many vessels is very complicated. Some are actually owned by finance companies and banks, some by subsidiary companies of the shipping lines, some by subsidiary companies of a holding company of which the shipping company is also a subsidiary and some by companies which are jointly owned by the shipping company and other interests like a bank, set up specifically to own one ship or a group of ships. In all these cases the vessel is technically chartered to the shipping company. However, in this book, only those vessels chartered from one shipping company to another or from a ship-owning company unconnected with the shipping line are recorded as being on charter. Vessels are listed under the current operator rather than the owner. Charter is 'bareboat' (without crew) unless otherwise stated. If chartered with crew, vessels are 'time-chartered'.

Gross Tonnage This is a measure of enclosed capacity rather than weight, based on a formula of one gross ton = 100 cubic feet. Even small alterations can alter the gross tonnage. Under old measurement systems, the capacity of enclosed car decks was not included but, under the 1969 Convention, all vessels laid down after 1982 have been measured by a new system which includes enclosed vehicle decks as enclosed space, thereby considerably increasing the tonnage of vehicle ferries. Under this Convention, from 1st January 1995 all vessels were due to be re-measured under this system. Tonnages quoted here are, where possible, those given by the shipping companies themselves.

The following people are gratefully thanked for their assistance with this publication, many of them in ferry companies in the UK and abroad: John Bryant, Cees de Bijl, Dick Clague, Andrew Cooke, Matthew Davies, Ian Hall, William Mayes, Willie Mackay, Pekka Ruponen, Ian Smith (Camrose Media), and DW Jones Ltd, Swansea.

Whilst every effort has been made to ensure that the facts contained here are correct, neither the publishers nor the writer can accept any responsibility for errors contained herein. We would, however, appreciate comments from readers, which we will endeavour to reflect in the next edition which we plan to publish in summer 2015.

The Stavangerfjord *makes an impressive view as she passes under Sotrabrua Bridge inward bound to Bergen. (Miles Cowsill)*

FJORD LINE COMES OF AGE: 21 YEARS ACROSS THE SKAGERRAK

The Longest Winter

Northern European ferry operation is no longer a natural habitat for that rarest of maritime species: an optimist. The long, harsh winter of the 2008 – 2011 recession still casts a chill over the industry that has seen historically record low levels of growth and an enduring lack of investment in customer service and fleet replacement. Since the closing years of the last decade, genuine large-scale investment has been extremely sporadic: P&O at Dover, Viking Line at Turku, Scandlines at Gedser and Stena Line at Harwich, Cairnryan and Gdynia are rare and comforting lights in an otherwise gloomy seascape.

However, one company perhaps stands above all the rest in making a genuinely game-changing investment in new ships and services that have transformed their previously sleepy operation into one of the powerhouses of the modern industry. June 2014 represents the culmination of over half a decade's work of planning, endeavour and, of course, setbacks which will see the company's four ferries in service together for the first time. By far the biggest change for the company has been the arrival of the *Stavangerfjord* and *Bergensfjord* in July 2013 and March 2014 respectively and the inauguration of the new daily service between Langesund near Oslo, across the Skagerrak to Hirtshals in Denmark before sailing up the West Coast of Norway to Stavanger and Bergen. Not content with revolutionising their existing route, the company has also established a new operation between Sandefjord and Strömstad, using the massively rebuilt *Oslofjord*, and competing head-to-head with Color Line on this lucrative, duty-free service.

This represents a fitting coming-of-age for Fjord Line, one of the more recent entrants to the ferry scene, which this year celebrates twenty-one years since the start of their Bergen – Denmark service. It hasn't always been plain sailing for the operator which, almost since its inauguration, has been buffeted by regulatory changes, competitive dynamics and challenging markets. Nonetheless, the modern Fjord Line demonstrates what can be achieved when a small, local company invests to grow and serve its community.

Destination Skagerrak

Fjord Line's origins can be traced back to the 1950s when Rutelaget Askøy-Bergen (RA-B) was founded as a local bus and ferry operator in and around Bergen. In 1988, the company introduced its first modern vessel, the *Kystveien*, onto the service to Askøy. This route lasted for five years, until a bridge was opened to the island in 1992, thus making the service redundant. RA-B then took the bold decision to launch themselves onto the international ferry market with the establishment of a service between Bergen, Stavanger, Egersund and Hanstholm in Northern Denmark. The company sold the *Kystveien* to Arabian interests and placed an order for a new vessel with the Fosen Shipyard at Rissa. This ship was launched as the *Bergen* in January 1993, with the construction of her hull being subcontracted to a yard at Landskrona.

She was one of the first of the new generation of 'ro-pax' vessels, a type of combined freight and passenger ferry which first appeared in the late 1980s with the likes of TT-Line's *Nils Dacke* and Brittany Ferries' *Barfleur*. In reality, such vessels have long been a feature of the industry with the Atlantic Steam Navigation Company being early pioneers. Nonetheless, the modern interpretations of the design provided operators with the freight capacity to sustain a route year-round with sufficiently sizeable passenger accommodation to offer a genuinely comfortable tourist service. Indeed, the *Bergen* was the final ship in a series of five vessels, each built to slightly different specifications: the *Kaptan Burhanettin Isim* and *Kaptan Abidin Doran* were built for Turkish Cargo Lines whilst the *Stena Challenger* and *Stena Traveller* went to Stena. The *Bergen* was a somewhat shortened and heightened version of the class with significant additional passenger accommodation reflecting her owner's requirement for over 500 cabin berths.

The *Bergen* entered service in June 1993 on her new route, providing for the first time in several years a dedicated year-round service. For several years prior to Fjord Line's arrival, summer-only services had been operated somewhat half-heartedly by Color Line and their predecessors Fred. Olsen mostly using the *Bolero* which was latterly named the *Jupiter*. The *Bergen* represented a dramatic change over

Jupiter arriving North Shields (*Matthew Punter*)

Bergen and Jupiter at Bergen (*Matthew Punter*)

Grieg Gourmet on Stavangerfjord *(Matthew Punter)*

Fjord Lounge Bar on Bergensfjord *(Matthew Punter)*

Commander Buffet on Bergensfjord (*Matthew Punter*)

Deck 7 stairwell on Bergensfjord (*Matthew Punter*)

the old order. She presented an ungainly, blocky profile (most notoriously featuring outside cabins with fine views over the funnel casing), resplendent in a modified RA-B livery. Inboard, her public spaces were arranged over a single deck (three) offering the 'Holberg' buffet restaurant forward, flowing aft via an arcade lounge into the Café Nille and finally into the Jeppe Bar. A modest tax free shop was also available.

Unfavourable comparisons with the *Bolero* could be made but what these ignored was that for the first time, the service had a ferry with a future. As fine a ship as the *Bolero* was, she was from an elegant but unsustainable past. The future was here and the future was ro-pax.

Fjord Line's next major move was the acquisition of the Bergen – North Shields service from Color Line in December 1999. The service, at the time operated by the *Color Viking* (ex-*Wellamo*, *Dana Gloria* and *King of Scandinavia*), was a legacy of the Fred. Olsen-Bergen Line operation dating back to the early 20th Century. The new route was quickly integrated with the ship taking the name *Jupiter* and Fjord Line marking this latest phase of their existence with an elegant new black and turquoise livery. Now serving both the UK and Denmark from their Bergen base, Fjord Line were establishing something of a regional power-base with Color Line focusing on their services from Southern Norway to Denmark and Germany.

The company started the new millennium in an apparently secure position, with a small but significant network of routes, and with encouraging traffic growth figures. After a decade of service, it was apparent that the *Bergen* was no longer large enough for the route and so in 2003, a new vessel was acquired from TT-Line of Australia. She was the *Spirit of Tasmania*, originally constructed as the *Peter Pan* (by TT-Line of Germany) and, in her new guise, she was renamed the *Fjord Norway* for the services to Denmark. The *Bergen* meanwhile, was chartered to DFDS as the *Duchess of Scandinavia*.

However, within a year, the company was starting to feel the pressure. The *Fjord Norway* was rather too large for her new service and financial trouble was looming, driven by diminishing traffic figures, largely as a result of the growth of the low cost airline network as well as changes to Norwegian subsidy arrangements for local crews. In 2004, the company explored a merger plan with Smyril Line (who were in even worse financial difficulties), the aim being to establish a new 'North Atlantic Ferries' pooling arrangement across the two companies' extensive combined network. Although the two identities would remain, the Fjord Line vessels would be reflagged to the Faroe Islands. This plan was superseded by a direct takeover offer of Fjord Line by Smyril in 2005 although this was rejected by the former company's shareholders.

By April 2005, the situation had deteriorated further with Color Line establishing their own service between Bergen/Stavanger and Hirtshals using their cruise ferry *Princesse Ragnhild*, which siphoned off significant amounts of traffic from Fjord Line. In order to stem the losses, in late 2005 Fjord Line switched the *Fjord Norway* to the North Shields service and re-introduced the *Duchess of Scandinavia* back onto its original route, this time as the *Atlantic Traveller*. This failed to fundamentally change the situation and so in September 2006, the company sold the North Shields route (together with the *Fjord Norway*) to DFDS and were also apparently seeking to sell the *Atlantic Traveller* to Swansea Cork Ferries. Eventually, the *Atlantic Traveller* was switched to Danish registry and crew to stem costs. However, it was a case of too little, too late and by December of that year, the company was facing bankruptcy.

Rebirth

The long road to recovery began in early 2007 when Fjord Line secured fresh investment from Frode and Ole Teigen, Norwegian shipping entrepreneurs. Ingvald Fardal was installed as the company's Chairman (later Managing Director) and immediately began a recovery programme for the beleaguered operator. To mark the start of the new era, the *Atlantic Traveller* returned from overhaul renamed *Bergensfjord* and wearing an attractive new crimson and gold livery. The company was repositioned as a 'ro-pax' operator with a strategy of establishing the single ship operation on a sustainable basis whilst trimming costs significantly.

In 2008, the company restructured further, merging with Master Ferries who had inaugurated a fast ferry service between Kristiansand and Hanstholm in 2005 using the *MasterCat*, formerly the *Cat-Link V*, which was then renamed the *FjordCat*. This was largely in response to the arrival of the new 'Superspeed' class of high quality day ferries which Color Line introduced early that year to transform their own services from Hirtshals to Larvik and Kristiansand. Later that year, the ro-pax service saw

Full speed ahead – on green gas

Fjord Line is leading the way through its commitment to the market's most environmentally friendly fuel.

The new cruise ferries MS Stavangerfjord and MS Bergensfjord are the first ships of such a large size to run on solely natural gas (LNG), allowing our passengers to choose the greenest sea route between Norway and the EU.

THE ENVIRONMENTAL BENEFITS INCLUDE:

92 % reduction in NOx emissions.
23 % reduction in greenhouse gas emissions.
98 % reduction in particle emissions.
100 % reduction in sulfur emissions.

Photo: Espen Gees

fjordline.com

further significant change when the Danish terminal was moved to Hirtshals and the calls at both Egersund and Haugesund were dropped in favour of the new Risavika terminal at Stavanger.

However, the following year saw the company prevented from sailing into Kristiansand, whose port authority insisted on a year-round operation which Fjord Line were unwilling (and the *FjordCat* almost certainly unable) to provide. This led to lengthy legal proceedings under European competition law and eventually the craft returned from 2010, but with the Danish terminal consolidated with the ro-pax sailings at Hirtshals.

At the end of this, still turbulent period, it appeared that Fjord Line were settling down into a rhythm of operation that would enable the company to start to plan for the future. If the route was to indeed be sustainable, at some stage, the company would need to respond to the Color Line 'Superspeed' operation in addition to ever rapacious airline services.

Invest to grow

In March 2010, Fjord Line announced a €206 million order for a pair of new cruise ferries from Bergen Group Fosen. The new order was designed to provide a wholly game-changing response to their market situation, with the pair of vessels enabling Fjord Line to provide a 'southern extension' to the Hurtigruten service whilst transforming their onboard passenger experience.

Having searched unsuccessfully in the second hand market for a replacement for the *Bergensfjord*, the company chose to build afresh in order to ensure they had superlative tonnage that precisely met their needs. The new ships would be comparatively small as contemporary cruise ferries go, with an overall length of 170 metres and passenger capacity for 1,500. Bergen Group Fosen were chosen as the designers and builders of the vessels. They subcontracted construction of the hulls to Stocznia at Gdansk whilst fitting out would be completed at the Norwegian yard at Rissa. During the design phase, great emphasis was placed on minimising the vessels' environmental impact with the hull form enabling low fuel consumption at service speed. The ships would also be trendsetting in their dual-fuel propulsion system which would use LNG as well as conventional marine diesel. Additionally, they would offer a heat waste recovery system; a very efficient propulsion system that minimized energy loss from engine to propellers; enhanced insulation in the windows; LED lighting and a steam turbine to utilize heat loss from the engine to produce electricity for the passenger accommodation. Marintek were responsible for the testing of the design of the sisters, which would become the most energy efficient ships ever constructed.

The names *Stavangerfjord* and *Bergensfjord* were chosen for the vessels during late 2011. Both names explicitly commemorated Norwegian American Lines vessels: the *Stavangerfjord* of 1918 and two later *Bergensfjord*s (plus of course the existing ferry). It was also announced that the new ships would sail on a roster that would include a Hirtshals to Southern Norway leg, with Langesund eventually being selected over Kristiansand. At the same time, the date of the first ship's maiden voyage was set for 1st October 2012.

The *Stavangerfjord* was duly launched on 12th April 2012 and subsequently towed to Rissa whilst construction started on the new *Bergensfjord*. However, in a surprise announcement during the summer, the company announced that both ships were to be converted, prior to entering service, to run solely on LNG. This was due to the recently announced marine sulphur emissions directive from the European Commission which would come into force in January 2015. Therefore, Fjord Line took the expedient option to lengthen the delivery time in order to avoid having to subsequently modify the ships during their first few operational years. As a result of this change, the delivery dates were put back by six months, although subsequent delays in the conversion pushed her inauguration back to July 2013.

Eventually, the new *Stavangerfjord* was christened at Rissa on 6th June by Janne Johnsen and arrived at Bergen for berthing trials on 9th July prior to heading to Denmark. Amidst much fanfare, she departed, on schedule at 2100 on 14th July 2013 on her maiden voyage from Hirtshals. However, despite the euphoria, even as the ship was heading north against the midnight sun, clouds were gathering which were to have serious repercussions for her operation over the coming months. In addition to the teething troubles that any new ship will experience, the Norwegian authorities were prohibiting passengers from remaining onboard whilst the ship refuelled in Risavika, which (as the middle port of the voyage) necessitated the entire ship's complement disembarking whilst she took on bunkers. A revised timetable was issued to allow additional time at here, as well as Hirtshals where

Oasis Café servery on Bergensfjord (*Matthew Punter*)

Oasis Café entrance and arcade on Bergensfjord (*Matthew Punter*)

she also refuelled. This situation continued throughout the summer with increasing delays to the circuit but later in the autumn, the authorities relented, routines were mastered, and the vessel was ultimately allowed to revert to her planned schedules.

By this time, construction of the new *Bergensfjord* was well advanced, whilst it was also announced that the existing *Bergensfjord* would be used to start a new day service across the southern Oslofjord between Sandefjord and Strömstad. She would be rebuilt at Rauma in Finland as a day ferry and take the name *Oslofjord*.

The new *Bergensfjord* arrived in Bergen for her own christening on 6th March 2014 and she entered service on 17th March, displacing her older namesake for conversion. The 'southern Hurtigruten' was at last complete with a true nightly liner service in operation between Bergen, Stavanger, Hirtshals and Langesund. The last phase in the Fjord Line expansion was completed on 20th June 2014 when the new *Oslofjord* took up her station at Sandefjord on the new Swedish service.

The 'Lifestyle Liners: Stavangerfjord and Bergensfjord

The design commission, both general arrangement and interior design, was given to Falkum Hansen, a firm of Norwegian naval architects who were also responsible for most of Color Line's recent newbuildings. The vessels offer a unique maritime product: a state-of-the art car and freight ferry with a stylish-yet-intimate cruise ferry ambience, with the company advertising them as 'Lifestyle Liners'. After years of Scandinavian operators raising the stakes with ever increasing glitz and impact in their newbuilds, it marks a dramatic departure to step aboard the Fjord Line twins and their elegant, understated interiors. Both vessels are essentially identical with almost all public passenger facilities situated on Deck Seven. Given the limitations of the vessels' dimensions, they offer a wide selection of eating and entertainment options, decorated throughout in a stylish, modern aesthetic that avoids resorting to either pastiche or brashness to make an impact.

The forward part of this deck houses the 'Fjord Lounge', the main entertainment venue for the vessels, affording magnificent views over the bows through full height windows. This space is slightly tiered with seating and tables looking forward, behind which is situated an oval dance floor with a small stage to port backed by a floor-to-ceiling screen. At the rear of the space is situated the main bar, stylishly fitted out in white and black whilst the rest of the décor is dominated by mid-tone wood and glass for the tables and grey-blues for the seating fabric. Inlaid into the floor is a display of sand and beach accompaniments. The lounge acts as the main focal point for the vessels' entertainment programme with bingo and other activities during the day and a singing group and dancing during the night. To port, there is a small extension to this area which can be closed off for conferences and which proudly displays a large model of the 1956 *Bergensfjord*, on the sister whose name she bears. On the starboard side of the vessel, the 'Havana Cigar Club' offers a small venue for the smokers onboard.

Moving astern on the starboard side, the 'Fjord Lounge' opens out into the reception area. The striking, curved, red desk is backed by large portholes unifying the vessel, its crew and the passing seascape. Adjacent to this is '24 to Go', a small kiosk offering newspapers, magazine, books, small gifts and hot drinks in addition to a wide variety of frozen meat, ever popular on Norwegian services due to the large tax differentials. The kiosk is manned by the reception desk, thus offering crew efficiencies.

Opposite the reception/kiosk is the 'Bungalow Wine & Tapas' bar, offering a range of table and bar seating and providing a surprisingly good range of tapas as well as a variety of alcoholic and hot and cold drinks. Decorated in a mixture of blacks, greys and stone effect, the area is somewhat open plan to the main thoroughfare of the vessels, but distinct enough to offer a relaxing environment in which to enjoy the food and the ambience. The 'Bungalow' also has a small stage area, taken up with a grand piano for additional entertainment.

Continuing astern into the middle section of the vessels, passengers pass through a semi-circular vestibule displaying large murals of Norwegian landscapes which opens out into the 'Oasis Garden Café'. A thoroughfare through the ship is lined with large illuminated containers out of which shoot imitation 'Mother-in-law's Tongue' plants. To starboard lies the main seating area of the café, the main feature of which is a series of gnarled trees which twist up to the ceiling, providing an idiosyncratic, yet ultimately stylish garden aesthetic. To port are two function rooms (named 'Apple' and 'Pear') which can act as an overflow of the cafeteria or for private hire. Astern of these in the centre of the ship is the servery, fitted out in brilliant white.

Eating area on Bergensfjord *(Matthew Punter)*

Additional Fjord Lounge seating on Bergensfjord *(Matthew Punter)*

Beer, wine and spirits merchandising on Stavangerfjord *(Matthew Punter)*

The supermarket area on the Stavangerfjord *(Matthew Punter)*

Mini-Delux cabin *(Fjord Line)*

Suite cabin on the Stavangerfjord *(Fjord Line)*

Passengers then continue to pass astern through an arcade with the ships' galleys occupying much of the width of the deck, passing 'Kids' Planet', before opening out again into a foyer off which is situated the 'Grieg Gourmet' à la carte in the centre of the vessel and the 'Commander Buffet' occupying the full width of the vessel's stern. The 'Grieg Gourmet' offers sixty-six covers with a view of the chef working in the galley. Again, décor is stylish, yet muted with teals, greys and dark wood seating off-setting a rough wood-effect floor. The areas display striking photo collages by British artists Malcolm Martin and Gaynor Dowling and featuring Edvard Grieg along with several well-known European buildings and artists and artistes from the mid-twentieth century. The 'Commander Buffet' centres on a large circular seating area with more conventional table seating at the edges of the room adjacent to the windows. It is decorated in warm hues of reds, greys and teak effect, whilst the circular area is flanked by two striking illuminated nude statues by Lars Widenfalk.

There are two main decks of cabins: on decks eight and nine, the former of which offers twenty-four 'Luxe' cabins whilst the latter offers sixteen suites. The only other public areas are the large tax free ship on deck six and a 'Sky Deck Lounge' on deck ten. This can also be used as a conference reception area and on either beam of this are large reclining seat lounges which can be utilized as conference theatres.

Throughout the accommodation, in addition to the specific pieces outlined above, is a wide range of contemporary artwork, sourced for the company by ICART, a Norwegian corporate art consultancy. Pride of place on the main stairwell on deck ten of the *Bergensfjord* is a vast painting entitled *Dromenes Reiser* ("Dream Journeys") that was commissioned from the Norwegian artist Per Krohg for the 1956-built Norwegian American Lines vessel *Bergensfjord*. The painting was rescued by a former Fjord Line employee who kindly donated it to the company for restoration and display on the new vessel of that name.

The vessels boast large outside deck spaces, with small 'boat deck' areas on deck seven. Deck nine features a dramatically wide area ready for helicopter evacuation at the stern whilst deck ten offers a large selection of outside seating, screened by large panels affording excellent views of the passing scenery. Above the bridge on deck ten is a further sundeck providing a superb panorama forward – although with no seating.

Catering on board is of the highest quality: the 'Grieg Gourmet' is Fjord Line's flagship offering with Michelin-equivalent food and a tempting array of dishes. The *maître d'* on both vessels have been recruited from the cruise industry in order to give superlative service whilst the menus have been developed in collaboration with the Gastronomisk Institutt of Norway. The 'Commander' offers a wide selection of Scandinavian delicacies and the 'Bungalow' provides an authentic and deliciously varied tapas selection. Throughout the vessel, the crew are friendly, obliging and above all, immensely proud of their ship and what their company has achieved. On several occasions during this author's visit, crew members stopped to comment on one thing or another that had captured the attention.

The vessels are powered by four Rolls-Royce engines, two of which drive each of the twin propeller shafts and the *Stavangerfjord* proudly displays the words "Powered by Rolls-Royce" on her funnel. The choice of LNG for the propulsion makes the twins amongst the most environmentally friendly vessels in the world. Unlike the *Viking Grace*, the fuel tanks are inboard under the car deck. Bunkers are taken on in Risavika and Hirtshals; currently delivered by a road fuel tanker, although a pipeline is currently under construction from the nearby LNG processing plant adjacent to the Risavika terminal. This will save significant time during refuelling which currently takes two hours.

If there is anything wanting from the new cruise ferry operation, it is difficult to find. The 'Sky Deck Lounge' is perhaps the most lacklustre space onboard; similar spaces on other vessels present light, airy interiors and superb views, whilst this looks like an afterthought that is neither a convincing conference facility nor a sundeck space. Additionally, in contrast to most other overnight ferries from Scandinavia in recent decades, the vessels lack any spa or sauna facilities, a surprising move, given the popularity of these in the region. Aesthetes may well find fault with the outside deck arrangements with the side "wings" of the funnel impeding clear views aft from the midships area. The "POWERED BY LNG" ventilation shafts also have an unfortunately mesmerizing affect for passengers in the main outside deck area. However, despite these onboard sundeck irritations, the vessels' profile is sleek and modern when viewed from a distance, although the lack of a prominent funnel (or two) ultimately

Apple & Pear function rooms on Stavangerfjord *(Matthew Punter)*

Bungalow Wine & Tapas on Stavangerfjord *(Matthew Punter)*

Upper car deck on Bergensfjord *(Miles Cowsill)*

Stavangerfjord approaching Askøy *(Matthew Punter)*

Bergensfjord passing Haugesund (*Matthew Punter*)

Oslofjord at Hirtshals (*Matthew Punter*)

detracts from their overall appearance. However, all of these points are very minor issues on what are otherwise superlative vessels.

OSLOFJORD ups the ante

If Fjord Line's investment was limited to their new cruise ferries, that would be impressive enough, but 2014 also saw the inauguration of not only a day return service to Langesund from Hirtshals, but even more excitingly, a new short tax free shopping service across the southern Oslofjord. The redundant *Bergensfjord* has been expensively and dramatically reconstructed in a €30 million contract that went to STX in Rauma prior to the yard closing. The work has almost entirely reconfigured her accommodation, converting her from an elderly overnight ro-pax for 900 passengers into a stunningly modern day ferry for 1,800. Her new route between Sandefjord and Strömstad sees her operate two round trips per day and represents a massive challenge to Color Line's incumbent operation.

The former deck three has been utterly transformed, most notably featuring a large extension to the stern of the vessel in which is housed the 'Fjord of Coffee' bar area, complete with large domed skylight and floor-to-ceiling windows from which passengers can watch the passing scenery. The previous lounge bar and cafeteria amidships has been transformed into the 'Oasis Garden Café' whilst the former buffet has been retained as the 'Commander Buffet', but has also been comprehensively refitted, including large new rectangular windows forward and portholes on the sides of the ship.

Deck four now almost entirely comprises a vast duty free shop that replaces the previous cabins. Due to the low headroom, much of the ceiling space in this area is a black painted void, although notably it features two small atria which offer views from the deck above into the retail space. Deck five has also been stripped of its cabins and provides extensive additional seating and a bar area, designed to provide greater capacity on the busiest sailings. This area has adopted the 'Bungalow Snack Bar' branding.

Externally, the vessel's funnel has been given the 'Stavangerfjord' treatment with side "wings" and extensive new outside seating has been installed on both the stern of deck four as well as on deck six.

The "new" *Oslofjord* has been very impressively rebuilt and will offer accommodation and facilities on a par with her overnight fleet mates. Fjord Line will be anticipating taking a significant market share of this lucrative service and their new vessel offers some of the most attractive day ferry space currently afloat.

A Norwegian Renaissance

The recent story of Fjord Line since their resurrection in 2007 must surely represent one of the most dramatic turnarounds in maritime history. From teetering on the brink of bankruptcy, the company has invested, grown and become the operator of one of the finest fleets of ferries in Northern Europe. The quality of fittings and attention to detail across each of the three main units makes each a serious destination for the tourist, the enthusiast and the ferry industry in general. In particular, the *Stavangerfjord* and the *Bergensfjord* represent a new era in small cruise ferry design, whilst the *Oslofjord* shows the way in ferry reconstruction.

Of course, what matters now is that the new Fjord Line delivers for its owners; the investment has been made and now the route must grow. With daily departures in each direction, plus a Color-competing day return up to Langesund, in addition to attracting a large slice of the Oslofjord traffic, the future is certainly full of potential. Fjord Line's new ships and their crews are on track for a very successful future.

Matthew Punter

Acknowledgements: With thanks to Friedrich Schweitzer and Ingvald Fardal of Fjord Line for their assistance with this article

REVIEW 2013/14 - BRITISH ISLES

The following is a review of passenger and freight ferry activities during 2013 and the first half of 2014.

EAST COAST & THAMES

During the year, DFDS embarked on a plan to install scrubbers on all their North Sea freight vessels. This was to meet new emissions regulations coming into effect in 2015.

DFDS Seaways' Rosyth - Zeebrugge service started 2013 in the hands of the ex-Finnlines *Finlandia Seaways* but in March she was replaced by the chartered *Longstone*. This continued until May 2014 when the *Longstone* went off charter and the *Finlandia Seaways* returned. The company's Newcastle - Ijmuiden service, primarily a passenger route, continued to carry good loads. However, the two vessels used are now quite elderly and what happens in 2015 when new emissions rules come in remains to be seen.

In January the *Wilhelmine*, chartered from Cobelfret Ferries, replaced the *Norsky* on P&O's Teesport - Rotterdam route. She had initially operated on the Zeebrugge - Tilbury service but had proved too slow for the more intensive service.

North Sea Ro-Ro, a company set up by shippers dissatisfied with the prices charged by DFDS on their Immingham - Gothenburg service, ceased operations in March 2013, and traffic returned to the Danish company. The two vessels used, the Foreland Shipping vessels *Beachy Head* and *Longstone*, were taken over by DFDS Seaways. The former was deployed in the Mediterranean and the latter, initially on the Immingham - Cuxhaven route and then on the Rosyth - Zeebrugge until the charter ended in May 2014.

The increase in traffic on the Gothenburg route caused the company to switch back the three lengthened 'Flower class' vessels - the *Begonia Seaways*, *Freesia Seaways* and *Ficaria Seaways* - from the Ghent - Gothenburg route, to which they had been switched in May 2012, following a drop in traffic on the Immingham service and a rise in that to and from Ghent.

In July Cobelfret Ferries' *Clementine* returned from a brief charter to RMR Shipping for their service to Lagos and was chartered by DFDS Seaways for their Immingham - Cuxhaven service.

In late 2104, the Norwegian company Sea-Cargo cancelled the order for two LNG powered ConRo vessels from Bharati Ratnagiri Ltd, Mumbai, India as it became increasingly apparent that it was unlikely they would ever be delivered. Only one of an earlier order of two from this yard ever materialised (Sea-Cargo Express) and this was six years late! In May 2014 they announced the purchase of the *Express* from Eckerö of Finland. She is to be re-engined and modified for side loading.

P&O's usual practice during the winter refit period is to maintain a daily service on their Hull Rotterdam route, using a Hull - Zeebrugge vessel when a Rotterdam vessel was in dock and reducing the Zeebrugge service to alternate days, using a freighter on the other days. In 2013 the *Norqueen*, retired from the Tilbury - Zeebrugge route, did the business but in 2014 it was not possible to provide a vessel from their own recourses and they chartered *L'Audace* from Lineas Suardiaz, generally used as car carrier, but built with hoistable car decks to enable her to carry trailers and containers.

DFDS Seaways' *Britannia Seaways* and *Selandia Seaways* both undertook NATO charters, as part of the Danish/German ARK project during 2013. All went well until shortly after 19.00 on Saturday 16 November, a violent blaze started on the *Britannia Seaways'* weather deck, around 70 nautical miles off the Norwegian coast. Fortunately it was at the very front of the vessel, well away from the accommodation block, bridge and engine room. The vessel was able to proceed to Bergen under her own power, when the fire was finally extinguished. Repairs were executed quickly as she was back in service within a few weeks.

In November 2013 CLdN/Cobelfret launched a new ro-ro service between Rotterdam and Leixoes, Portugal. It replaced a service operated by the container ship *Arx* since the beginning of the year. Initially the vessel used was the *Adeline* but in March 2014 she was replaced by the *Catherine*. The *Arx* was switched to operate between Rotterdam and Avonmouth, with the hope that, in due course, the

Victorine *(J.J. Jager)*

Sirena Seaways *(Peter Therkildsen)*

route could be converted to a ro-ro service. However, in May 2014 the route was suspended and the *Arx* returned to the Leixoes route, doubling the frequency.

At the end of June, UPM Seaways, the shipping arm of Finnish paper company UPM-Kymmene wound up its ro-ro operations and transferred traffic to Finnlines. The charter of three of its vessels - the *Misana*, *Misida* and *Mistral* - was taken over by Finnlines. The arrangements whereby the vessels were part-chartered by Harwich Navyard based Mann Lines on their northbound journey ceased.

Cobelfret Ferries' laid up *Eglantine* left Tilbury Docks in mid-February 2013 and arrived at Jeddah in Saudi Arabia on 10th March. She was renamed the *Alnawa Express*.

In April 2014 DFDS Seaways announced that the long-standing Harwich-Esbjerg service, operated by the *Sirena Seaways* would cease at the end of September. This is the last passenger link between the UK and Scandinavia and is a victim of budget airlines and the increased costs that new emission regulations will lead to. It seems likely she will be moved to a Baltic route.

In January 2013, DFDS withdrew the *Selandia Seaways* from their Gothenburg - Tilbury service, reducing the service to a twice weekly run by the Rederi AB Transatlantic vessel *Transpulp*. The *Transpulp* had previous operated one trip per week to Tilbury and one to Zeebrugge.

EASTERN CHANNEL

TranEuropa Ferries' troubled Ramsgate - Ostend service received new hope in January 2013 when P&O's recently withdrawn *Pride of Calais* was chartered. Renamed the *Ostend Spirit* and repainted into TEF's red livery, she gave what appeared to be a much needed fillip to the route. Sadly, it was not to be and in April, in the face of mounting debts, the company went into administration and ceased trading. P&O quickly recovered their vessel and laid her up in Tilbury and all TEF's vessels were subsequently sold - the *Gardenia* and *Larkspur* to Oilchart International, a major creditor of the company, and the *Oleander*, on charter in the Mediterranean, to Russian interests. In April 2014 the *Gardenia*, renamed the *Ardenia*, left for a charter in Greek waters, followed by the *Larskspur*, renamed the *Larks*, the following month. The fate of the *Ostend Spirit* was even sadder since, in October 2014 she made a one-way trip to Alang, Turkey where she was broken up. She made a spectacular entry to the beach - a video of which has appeared on television and secured over one and half million hits on YouTube!

At Dover the main taking point was whether MyFerryLink, which started in January would be able to continue. The UK Office of Fair Trading ruled that, with the vessels owned by Eurotunnel and providing much assistance to the workers co-operative which nominally operated the service, the service gave the tunnel operator too large a share of the market, the fear being that MyFerryLink could force down fares to such an extent that other operators withdrew and left Eurotunnel with a monopoly on the short crossing. An appeal resulted in the OFT being asked to reconsider their authority in the matter, the argument being whether the company constituted a merger or a completely new operation. On 27th June, the Competition and Markets Authority (which had replaced the OFT), having already confirmed that they had the authority to rule on the issue, confirmed their original decision that the MyFerryLink service should cease within six months from a given date and that Eurotunnel should be banned from operating a Dover - Calais ferry service for ten years.

Meanwhile, P&O and DFDS Seaways continued much as before, the only major change being P&O's withdrawal of the *European Seaway* in April 2103 for lay up at Tilbury.

The Newhaven - Dieppe route continued to operate as a single ship operation during 2013, generally operated by the *Côte d'Albatre*, with the *Seven Sisters* held in reserve. However in March 2014 the latter vessel was transferred to the Portsmouth - Le Havre service, replacing the *Norman Voyager*. During 2013, the Syndicat Mixte de L'Activité Transmanche in Dieppe put the operation of the route out for tender, to run from January 2015. Only MyFerryLink bid, but this was not considered satisfactory and it was subsequently withdrawn. In June 2014 the French authorities renewed the existing arrangement with DFDS Seaways France for a further twelve months. However, the long term future of the route remains uncertain.

Berlioz (*Brian Maxted*)

Dieppe Seaways (*George Holland*)

Dover Seaways *(Brian Maxted)*

Spirit of France *(Matthew Punter)*

Etretat *(Andrew Cooke)*

Norman Atlantic *(Kevin Mitchel)*

WESTERN CHANNEL AND SOLENT

Cross channel ferry operations at Portsmouth were unchanged during 2013 but, as mentioned above, the *Seven Sisters* replaced the *Norman Voyager* in March 2014. The charter of the latter vessel was transferred to Brittany Ferries who, after a quick refit and rebranding, launched her onto a new 'budget' Portsmouth - Le Havre and Portsmouth - Santander service advertised as 'Economie'. She was renamed the *Etretat* and entered service at the end of the month.

Brittany Ferries reintroduced the *Barfleur* onto the Poole - Cherbourg passenger route in March 2013 and the freighter *Cotentin* was switched to a full time Poole - Santander and Poole - Bilbao roster. In October 2013 these routes closed and she was chartered to *Stena RoRo*, who renamed her the *Stena Baltica*. She was then sub-chartered to *Stena Line* and, in November, placed on the Karlskrona - Gdynia service.

In January 2014, Brittany Ferries announced the building of a new vessel at STX France, St Nazaire, France. Due to replace the *Pont-Aven* on England - Spain and Ireland - France sailings, she will be delivered in 2016 and be powered by LNG. The company announced proposals to convert the newer units in the fleet to LNG and to fit scrubbers to the older *Bretagne* and *Barfleur* to meet the new pollution regulations.

LD Lines re-entered the UK market in their own right in November 2014 with the launch of a new Poole - Santander service. A second Visentini vessel, the former *Scintu*, was charted and replaced the *Norman Asturias* on the St Nazaire - Gijon service. In January 2014 she was renamed the *Norman Atlantic* and Rosslare in Ireland was added to her roster. However, after a few days it was decided to make the Rosslare service summer only. The *Norman Asturias* took over the new Poole service and from January 2014 one of her two weekly trips to Spain was changed to operate Poole - St Nazaire - Gijon.

Condor Ferries returned to Weymouth in July 2013 after a gap of about 18 months, following repairs to the berth, which had become unsafe. There was however some concern that the next generation of fast used by the company ferries - possibly a trimaran built by Austal Ships of Australia - would be too big for the Dorset port.

Red Funnel Ferries 'raptor' class vessel *Red Falcon* received a major facelift during early 2104 and re-entered service in April. The other vessels will be treated in a similar way subject to the success of the refurbishment and availability of funding.

In November Gosport Ferry placed an order with Tehnomont of Pula in Croatia for a new ferry similar to the 2001 built *Sprit of Gosport* . Named the *Harbour Spirit*, she is likely to replace the *Gosport Queen* and *Portsmouth Queen*, both built in 1966.

IRISH SEA

Celtic Link, which operated between Rosslare and Cherbourg with the Visentini built *Celtic Horizon* was taken over by Stena Line in March 2014. The vessel was renamed the *Stena Horizon* at the end of the month.

Yet another Visentini vessel arrived in November 2013 in the form of the *Cartour Epsilon*. She was chartered to Irish Ferries and renamed the *Epsilon* in February 2014. She operates additional services between Dublin and Holyhead and a weekly service from Dublin to Cherbourg. She has also covered on the Rosslare - Cherbourg whilst the *Oscar Wilde* was covering on the Dublin - Holyhead route.

As previously mentioned, in January 2014 LD Lines inaugurated a new service from Rosslare to St Nazaire, using the *Norman Atlantic*.

Seatruck Ferries continued to own a fleet of 12 vessels but only needed five for its own services. However, most of the time the fleet were fully occupied through chartering out the vessel not required. Indeed from May 2013 until April 2014 a vessel was chartered in - DFDS Seaways' *Anglia Seaways*. She was originally deployed on the Heysham - Dublin route, the service she had operated when DFDS Seaways ran the route, but in September she moved to the Heysham - Warrenpoint service.

In January 2014, Stena Line, who continue to employ UK and Irish crews on their vessels, asked them accept pay freezes and longer hours of working to avoid large scale redundancies and replacement with

Severine *(John Bryant)*

foreign crews. Other operators in the area use a combination of UK and Irish officers and almost 100% east European and international crews. The demands were later relaxed.

In Aril 2014, the Isle of Man Steam packet company took the Seatruck ro-ro *Arrow*, a vessel they have often used in the past, on long term charter. Although not required at all times, the charter ensured that she was available at times she was needed - for example, during the TT Season and when one of the other ships was out of service for some reason. At other times she has been sub-chartered to other operators.

SCOTLAND

In October 2013, Western Ferries took delivery of two new vessels to replace their somewhat elderly ex Rotterdam ferries. Built by Cammell Laird at Birkenhead, the *Sound of Seil* and *Sound of Soay* were the first ferries to emerge from the yard for many years. Despite the yard's lack of experience, the new ships - an updated version of the vessels built by Fergusons, Port Glasgow in 2001 and 2003 - worked well and were soon in service. Such was the company's confidence in the new vessels that the old ships were disposed of within a few weeks of their replacements' arrival.

Bowing to local pressure, the Scottish government authorised Argyll Ferries to deploy Caledonian MacBrayne's *Coruisk* on the Gourock - Dunoon passenger service during the winter when the smaller vessels could not operate due to bad weather and to provide extra capacity during the commuter peak. In practice she was sometimes unable to operate herself during bad weather and passengers would be bussed via Western Ferries. In April 2014 she returned to her summer roster between Mallaig and Armadale.

Clydelink kept the *Cailin Oir* as Gourock - Kilcreggan back-up vessel through 2013 and the first part of 2014. She returned to Ireland in April 2014 for a summer charter. Meanwhile, the vessel which previous operator, Clyde Marine, had specially built for the route, the *Seabus*, was renamed the *Chieftain* and now operates as part of the company's excursion and charter fleet.

Caledonian MacBrayne's new hybrid duo, the *Hallaig* and *Lochinvar*, took rather longer to construct and commission than the new, more conventional, Western Ferries vessels. Launched in December 2012 at Ferguson's yard in Port Glasgow, the *Hallaig* was eventually delivered to its new owners in November 2013. She now operates between Sconser and Raasay. The *Lochivar* was launched in May 2013 and was delivered almost a year later. She now operates on the Tarbert - Portavadie service, replacing the *Isle of Cumbrae*. The innovative propulsion system - a combination of on board diesel engines and overnight shore supply feeding lithium batteries - probably partly accounted for the long gestation period.

Construction of the new vessel for the Ullapool - Stornoway service progressed rather more rapidly. Lunched at Flensburg on 21st March 2014, just seven weeks after her keel was laid, the 8478t vessel is expected to be delivered in July.

The chartered *Muirneag*, introduced in 2002 to provide additional freight capacity on the Ullapool - Stornoway route, left the company in October for a new careers in the Black Sea. She was replaced by the *Clipper Ranger* of Seatruck Ferries. Whilst the intention is that the charter will end when the *Loch Seaforth*, with her larger freight capacity is delivered, exactly when this will happen is unclear. The new vessel will be able to handle twice as many lorries as her predecessor and will operate three rather than two round trips per day, but overall there will be less capacity for unaccompanied trailers.

Bruce Watt, who operated the 1969 built *Western Isles* between Mallaig and Inverie on the Knoydart peninsular retired in September 2013. A new operator called Western Isles Cruises has taken over the vessel. The company faces competition from Knoydart Seabridge which operates three fast launches and a small vehicle ferry.

Serco operated NorthLink began a programme of rebranding over winter 2013/2014. The three passenger ships were painted into a new all white livery with a large picture of a Viking (with stereotypical but historically incorrect horned helmet) on the hull. The two chartered freighter continue to bear a black hull.

Stena Horizon (*Gordon Hislip*)

Eigg (*Brian Maxted*)

Calais Seaways *(John Hendy)*

SECTION 1 - GB AND IRELAND - MAJOR PASSENGER OPERATORS

BRITTANY FERRIES

THE COMPANY *Brittany Ferries* is the trading name of *BAI SA*, a French private sector company and the operating arm of the *Brittany Ferries Group*. The UK operations are run by *BAI (UK) Ltd*, a UK private sector company, wholly owned by the *Brittany Ferries Group*.

MANAGEMENT Group **Managing Director** Martine Jourdren, **Commercial Director, Passengers** Mike Bevens, **Commercial Director, Freight** Simon Wagstaff.

ADDRESS Millbay Docks, Plymouth, Devon PL1 3EW.

TELEPHONE Passenger - Administration *Plymouth* + 44 (0)871 244 0500, *Portsmouth* + 44 (0)871 244 0600, **Reservations** *All Services* + 44 (0)871 244 1400, **Freight** - Administration & Enquiries + 44 (0)871 244 0411, **Reservations** + 44 (0)871 244 0912.

FAX Freight - Administration & Reservations + 44 (0)871 244 0912.

INTERNET Passenger - Website www.brittanyferries.com (*English, French, Spanish, German*), Freight Website www.brittanyferriesfreight.co.uk (*English*)

ROUTES OPERATED Conventional Ferries *All year* Plymouth - Roscoff (6 hrs (day), 7 hrs - 9 hrs (night); *ARMORIQUE, PONT-AVEN*; up to 2 per day (Summer), 1 per day (Winter)), Poole - Cherbourg (4 hrs 15 mins; *BARFLEUR*; 1 per day), Portsmouth - St Malo (8 hrs 45 mins (day), 10 hrs 45 mins (night); *BRETAGNE*; 1 per day), Portsmouth - Caen (Ouistreham) (6 hrs (day), 6 hrs - 8 hrs (night); *NORMANDIE, MONT ST MICHEL*; 3 per day), Portsmouth - Le Havre (5 hrs 30 mins; *ETRETAT*; 5 per week), Portsmouth - Santander (Spain) (24 hrs; *ETRETAT, CAP FINISTERE, PONT-AVEN*; up to 3 per week, Portsmouth - Bilbao (Spain) (24/32 hrs; *CAP FINISTERE*; 2 per week, *Summer only* Plymouth - Santander (Spain) (19 hrs 30 mins; *PONT-AVEN*; 1 per week (April - October)), Cork - Roscoff (14 hrs; *PONT-AVEN*; 1 per week (March - November)). Fast Ferries *Summer only* Portsmouth – Cherbourg (3 hrs; *NORMANDIE EXPRESS*; 1 per day (April-September)), Portsmouth - Le Havre (3 hrs 45 mins; *NORMANDIE EXPRESS*; Thu-Sun (May - September); 1 per day).

1	ARMORIQUE	29468 t	09	23.0k	167.0m	1500P	470C	65L	BA2	FR	9364980
2	BARFLEUR	20133t	92	19.0k	158.0m	1212P	590C	112T	BA2	FR	9007130
3	BRETAGNE	24534t	89	19.5k	151.0m	1926P	580C	84T	BA	FR	8707329
4	CAP FINISTERE	32728t	01	28.0k	203.9m	1608P	1000C	140T	BA	FR	9198927
5	ETRETAT	26500t	08	23.5k	186.5	800P	185C	120L	A	FR	9420423
6	MONT ST MICHEL	35592t	02	21.2k	173.0m	2200P	880C	166T	BA2	FR	9238337
7	NORMANDIE	27541t	92	20.5k	161.0m	2120P	600C	126T	BA2	FR	9006253
8»	NORMANDIE EXPRESS	6581t	00	40.0k	97.2m	900P	260C	-	A	FR	8814134
9	PONT-AVEN	41748t	04	26.0k	184.3m	2400P	650C	85L	BA	FR	9268708

ARMORIQUE Built by STX Europe, Helsinki, Finland for *Brittany Ferries* to operate between Plymouth and Roscoff.

BARFLEUR Built as the BARFLEUR by Kvaerner Masa-Yards, Helsinki for the *Truckline* (freight division of *Brittany Ferries*) Poole - Cherbourg service to replace two passenger vessels and to inaugurate a year-round passenger service. In 1999 the *Truckline* branding was dropped for passenger services and she was repainted into full *Brittany Ferries* livery. In 2005 operated partly Cherbourg - Poole and partly Cherbourg - Portsmouth but in 2006 returned to operating mainly to Poole. In February 2010, she was laid up. The conventional car ferry service ended the following month. In February 2011 she resumed service on the Poole - Cherbourg route. In September 2011 she was withdrawn again. In April 2012 chartered to *DFDS Seaways* to operate between Dover and Calais and renamed the DEAL SEAWAYS. In November 2012 returned to *Brittany Ferries* and renamed the BARFLEUR. Resumed the Poole - Cherbourg service in March 2013, replacing the COTENTIN but offering a service for both freight and passengers.

Is there *any* better way to discover France or Spain?

For more information visit brittanyferries.com or call 0871 244 0404

Brittany Ferries

BRETAGNE Built by Chantiers de l'Atlantique, St Nazaire for the Plymouth - Santander and Cork - Roscoff services (with two sailings per week between Plymouth and Roscoff). In 1993 she was transferred to the Portsmouth - St Malo service. In 2004 also operated between Portsmouth and Cherbourg. In 2005 operated between Plymouth and Roscoff. In 2006 returned to the Portsmouth - St Malo route.

CAP FINISTERE Built as the SUPERFAST V by Howaldtswerke Deutsche Werft AG, Kiel, Germany for *Attica Enterprises* (now *Attica Group*) for use by *Superfast Ferries* of Greece. Initially operated between Patras and Ancona and in January 2007 switched to the Patras - Igoumenitsa - Bari route. In 2008 the route became Patras - Igoumenitsa - Ancona. In 2010 sold to *Brittany Ferries*, renamed the CAP FINISTERE and in March placed on the Portsmouth - Santander service, also operating some sailings between Portsmouth and Cherbourg. In 2011 began operating also between Portsmouth and Bilbao and only operated between Portsmouth and Cherbourg during the winter period.

ETRETAT Built as the NORMAN VOYAGER by CN Visentini, Porto Viro, Italy for *Epic Shipping* of the UK and chartered to *LD Lines*. Operated between Le Havre and Portsmouth and Le Havre and Rosslare. In September 2009 sub-chartered to *Celtic Link Ferries*. Initially operated between Cherbourg and Portsmouth and Cherbourg and Rosslare but the Portsmouth service was abandoned in November 2009. In October 2011 returned to *LD Lines* and placed on the St Nazaire - Gijon route. In November moved to the Portsmouth - Le Havre service and, following the establishment of the joint *LD Lines/DFDS* venture, the charter was transferred to *DFDS France*. In April 2012 sold to *Stena RoRo*; she continued to be chartered to *DFDS*. In March 2014 chartered to *Brittany Ferries* and placed on the new 'économie' services between Portsmouth and Le Havre and Portsmouth and Santander. Renamed the ETRETAT.

MONT ST MICHEL Built by Van der Giessen-de Noord, Krimpen aan den IJssel, Rotterdam for *Brittany Ferries*. Used on the Portsmouth - Caen route.

NORMANDIE Built by Kvaerner Masa-Yards, Turku, Finland for *Brittany Ferries*. Used on the Portsmouth - Caen route.

NORMANDIE EXPRESS Incat Evolution 10 catamaran built as the INCAT TASMANIA. In November 2000 chartered to *TranzRail* of New Zealand and renamed THE LYNX. Placed on the Wellington – Picton service. In July 2003 replaced by 1997-built Incat 86m craft INCAT 046, given the marketing name 'The Lynx' and laid up. In Spring 2005 chartered to *Brittany Ferries* to operate on their Cherbourg – Portsmouth and Caen – Portsmouth services and renamed the NORMANDIE EXPRESS. In 2007 purchased by *Brittany Ferries*. In 2015 operates to Cherbourg and Le Havre.

PONT-AVEN Built by Jos L Meyer Werft, Papenburg, Germany for *Brittany Ferries* to operate on the Plymouth - Roscoff, Plymouth - Santander and Cork - Roscoff routes.

Under Construction

10	NEWBUILDING	52500t	16	24.5k	210.0m	2474P	660C	60L	BA	FR	·

NEWBUILDING Under construction by STX France, St Nazaire, France. She will replace the PONT-AVEN on England - Spain and Ireland - France sailings. She will be powered by LNG.

CONDOR FERRIES

THE COMPANY *Condor Ferries Ltd* is a Channel Islands private sector company owned by the *Condor Group*, Guernsey which is owned by *Macquarie European Infrastructure*.

MANAGEMENT **Managing Director** Simon Edsall, **Sales and Marketing Director** Alicia Andrews, **Marketing Manager** Justin Amey, **Sales Manager** Jonathan Godson.

ADDRESS **Head Office** PO Box 10, New Jetty Offices, White Rock, St Peter Port, Guernsey GY1 3AF, **Sales and Marketing** Condor House, New Harbour Road South, Hamworthy, Poole BH15 4AJ.

TELEPHONE **Administration** *Guernsey* + 44 (0)1481 728620, *Poole* + 44 (0)1202 207207, **Passenger Reservations** + 44 (0)845 609 1024, **Freight Reservations** + 44 (0)1481 728521.

FAX **Administration** *Guernsey* + 44 (0)1481 728521, *Poole* + 44 (0)1202 685184, **Reservations** + 44(0)1305 760776.

Cap Finistere (*Brian Maxted*)

Mont St Michel (*George Holland*)

Condor Rapide *(Kevin Mitchell)*

Condor Express *(George Holland)*

INTERNET Email *Passenger* reservations@condorferries.co.uk **Freight** len.lepage@condorferries.co.uk **Website** www.condorferries.com *(English, French, German)*

ROUTES OPERATED *Conventional Passenger Ferry* Portsmouth to Guernsey (from 7 hrs) and Jersey (from 9 hrs) (*COMMODORE CLIPPER*; daily except Sun). *Fast Ferries* Poole - Guernsey (from 2 hrs 40 mins) and Jersey (from 4 hrs) (*CONDOR EXPRESS, CONDOR VITESSE, CONDOR RAPIDE*; April to October), Poole - St Malo (5 hrs 45 mins) (*CONDOR EXPRESS, CONDOR VITESSE*; CONDOR RAPIDE) May to September), Guernsey - Jersey (from 1 hr) and St Malo* (from 2 hrs), Jersey - Guernsey (from 1 hr) and St Malo (from 1 hr 20 mins) (*CONDOR EXPRESS, CONDOR RAPIDE, CONDOR VITESSE*;). *Some services connect in the Channel Islands. *Freight Ferry* Portsmouth - Guernsey - Jersey (10 hrs 30 min; *COMMODORE GOODWILL*; 1 per day), Guernsey - Jersey - St Malo (13 hrs; *COMMODORE GOODWILL*; 1 per week).

1	COMMODORE CLIPPER	14000t	99	18.0k	129.1m	500P	100C	92T	A	BS	9201750
2F	COMMODORE GOODWILL	11166t	96	17.3k	126.4m	12P	-	92T	A	BS	9117985
3»	CONDOR EXPRESS	5005t	96	39.0k	86.6m	741P	185C	-	A2	BS	9135896
4»	CONDOR RAPIDE	5007t	97	40.5k	86.6m	870P	200C	-	A	BS	9161560
5»	CONDOR VITESSE	5005t	97	40.0k	86.6m	741P	185C	-	A2	BS	9151008

COMMODORE CLIPPER Ro-pax vessel built by Van der Giessen-de Noord, Krimpen aan den IJssel, Rotterdam for *Commodore Ferries* to operate between Portsmouth and the Channel Islands. She replaced the ISLAND COMMODORE, a freight-only vessel. Her passenger capacity is normally restricted to 300 but is increased to 500 when the fast ferries are unable to operate.

COMMODORE GOODWILL Built by Koninklijke Scheldegroep BV, Vlissingen, The Netherlands for *Commodore Ferries*.

CONDOR EXPRESS Incat 86m catamaran built at Hobart, Tasmania, Australia. She was delivered in December 1996 and entered service in 1997.

CONDOR RAPIDE Incat 86m catamaran built at Hobart, Tasmania, Australia as the INCAT 045. Chartered to *Transport Tasmania* of Australia and operated between Melbourne (Victoria) and Devonport (Tasmania). In 1999 she was chartered to the *Royal Australian Navy*, renamed the HMAS JERVIS BAY and took part in moving Australian troops from Darwin to Dili (East Timor) as part of the United Nations operation. She operated over 75 trips between the two points carrying personnel and equipment for the United Nations Transitional Administration in East Timor (UNTAET). The charter ended in May 2001 and she was renamed the INCAT 045 and laid up. In Spring 2003 she was chartered to *Traghetti Isole Sarde (TRIS)* of Italy, renamed the WINNER and operated between Genoa and Palau (Sardinia). In Autumn 2003 the charter ended, she resumed the name INCAT 045 and was laid up at Portland, Dorset. In 2004 chartered to *SpeedFerries* and renamed the SPEED ONE. In May 2008 purchased by *SpeedFerries*. In November 2008 the services ceased and the company went into administration. She was laid up at Tilbury. In May she was sold at auction to *Epic Shipping* of the UK and renamed the SEA LEOPARD. In April 2010 sold to *Condor Ferries* and renamed the CONDOR RAPIDE. Entered service in May 2010.

CONDOR VITESSE Incat 86m catamaran built at Hobart. Built speculatively and launched as the INCAT 044. Moved to Europe in Summer 1997 and spent time in both the UK and Denmark but was not used. In 1998 she was chartered to *Condor Ferries* and renamed the CONDOR VITESSE. During Winter 1999/2000 she was chartered to *TranzRail* of New Zealand. Returned to UK in Spring 2000.

DAVID MACBRAYNE GROUP

THE COMPANY David MacBrayne Limited is a Scottish registered company, wholly owned by the Scottish Ministers. Its ferry operations are conducted through two subsidiary companies - Argyll Ferries Ltd and CalMac Ferries Ltd (trading as Caledonian MacBrayne). The majority of CalMac Ferries vessels are owned by Caledonian Maritime Assets Limited, a separate company which is also owned by the Scottish Ministers.

ARGYLL FERRIES

MANAGEMENT **Managing Director** Martin Dorchester, **Public Affairs Manager** David Cannon.

ADDRESS Ferry Terminal, Gourock PA19 1QP.

TELEPHONE **Administration** +44 (0)1475 650100, **Customer services** 0800 066 5000.

FAX **Administration** +44 (0)1475 650336,

INTERNET **Email** info@argyllferries.co.uk **Website** www.argyllferries.co.uk (English)

ROUTE OPERATED **All-year passenger-only ferry** Gourock - Dunoon (20 mins; ALI CAT, ARGYLL FLYER; CORUISK of Caledonian MacBrayne (winter only) 1 or 2 per hour.

1p	ALI CAT	74t	99	-	19.8m	250P	0C	0L	-	UK	
2p	ARGYLL FLYER	300t	01	19.5k	29.9m	227P	0C	0L	-	UK	9231016

ALI CAT Catamaran built for Solent & Wight Line Cruises of Ryde, Isle of Wight. She operated a passenger service from Cowes to Hamble and Warsash and cruises from Cowes. At times chartered to Wightlink to cover for the fast catamarans. In 2002 chartered to Red Funnel Ferries who had contracted with Caledonian MacBrayne to operate passenger-only services between Gourock and Dunoon in the morning and evening peaks. In June 2011 purchased by and operated by Argyll Ferries.

ARGYLL FLYER Built as the QUEEN OF ARAN II by OCEA, Les Sables d'Olonne, France for Inis Mór Ferries. In 2007 sold to Aran Island Ferries and renamed the BANRION CHONAMARA. In June 2011 sold to Argyll Ferries, renamed the ARGYLL FLYER and replaced the car ferry SATURN on the Gourock - Dunoon service.

CALEDONIAN MACBRAYNE

MANAGEMENT **Managing Director** Martin Dorchester, **Marketing and e.Commerce Manager** Cathy Craig, **Public Affairs Manager** David Cannon.

ADDRESS Ferry Terminal, Gourock PA19 1QP.

TELEPHONE **Administration** +44 (0)1475 650100, **Vehicle Reservations** +44 (0)800 066 5000.

FAX **Administration** +44 (0)1475 650336, **Vehicle Reservations** +44 (0)1475 635235.

INTERNET **Email** enquiries@calmac.co.uk **Website** www.calmac.co.uk (English)

ROUTES OPERATED **All-year vehicle ferries** (frequencies are for Summer – services are listed alphabetically, by mainland port or larger island port where service is between two islands), Ardmhor (Barra) - Eriskay (40 mins; LOCH ALAINN; up to 5 per day), Ardrossan - Brodick (Arran) (55 mins; CALEDONIAN ISLES, ISLE OF ARRAN; up to 6 per day), Colintraive - Rhubodach (Bute) (5 mins; LOCH DUNVEGAN; frequent service), Kennacraig - Port Askaig (Islay) (2 hrs 5 mins; FINLAGGAN, HEBRIDEAN ISLES; up to 4 per day), Kennacraig - Port Ellen (Islay) (2 hrs 20 mins; FINLAGGAN, HEBRIDEAN ISLES; service currently suspended due to harbour works), Largs - Cumbrae Slip (Cumbrae) (10 mins; LOCH RIDDON, LOCH SHIRA,; every 30 or 15 mins), Leverburgh (Harris) - Berneray (1 hr 10 mins; LOCH PORTAIN; 3-4 per day), Lochaline - Fishnish (Mull) (15 mins; LOCH FYNE; up to 14 per day), Mallaig - Armadale (Skye) (23 mins; CORUISK (Summer), LOCHNEVIS (Winter); up to 9 per day (2 in Winter)), Oban - Castlebay (Barra) (5 hrs (direct); CLANSMAN, LORD OF THE ISLES; 1 per day), Oban - Lochboisdale (South Uist) (5 hrs (if direct), 7 hrs (via Barra); CLANSMAN, LORD OF THE ISLES; 4 per week), Oban - Coll - Tiree (2 hrs 45 min to Coll, 3 hrs 50 min

Hebridean Isles and Clansman (*Stuart Mackilop*)

Finlaggan (*Brian Maxted*)

Lord of the Isles (*Brian Maxted*)

Hebrides (*Stuart Mackilop*)

to Tiree via Coll; *CLANSMAN, LORD OF THE ISLES*; 1 per day), Oban - Colonsay (2 hrs 15 mins; *CLANSMAN, LORD OF THE ISLES*; 5 per week), Oban - Craignure (Mull) (45 mins; *ISLE OF MULL*; up to 7 per day), Oban - Lismore (50 mins; *EIGG, LOCH STRIVEN*; up to 4 per day), Sconser (Skye) - Raasay (15 mins; *HALLAIG*; up to 11 per day), Tarbert (Loch Fyne) - Portavadie (25 mins; *LOCHINVAR*; up to 12 per day), Tayinloan - Gigha (20 mins; *LOCH RANZA*; up to 10 per day), Tobermory (Mull) - Kilchoan (35 mins; *LOCH LINNHE*; up to 7 per day), Uig (Skye) - Lochmaddy (North Uist) (1 hr 45 mins; *HEBRIDES*; 1 or 2 per day), Uig (Skye) - Tarbert (Harris) (1 hr 40 mins; *HEBRIDES*; 1 or 2 per day), Ullapool - Stornoway (Lewis) (2 hrs 45 mins; *LOCH SEAFORTH*; up to 3 per day), Wemyss Bay - Rothesay (Bute) (35 mins; *ARGYLE, BUTE*; hourly), **All-year passenger and restricted vehicle ferries** (frequencies are for Summer) Fionnphort (Mull) - Iona (5 mins; *LOCH BUIE*; frequent), Mallaig - Eigg - Muck - Rum - Canna - Mallaig (round trip 7 hrs (all islands); *LOCHNEVIS*; at least 1 sailing per day - most islands visited daily). **Note** Although these services are operated by vehicle ferries, special permission is required to take a vehicle and tourist cars are not normally conveyed, **Summer-only vehicle ferries** Ardrossan - Campbeltown (2 hrs 30 mins; *ISLE OF ARRAN*; 3 per week), Claonaig - Lochranza (Arran) (30 mins; *LOCH TARBERT*; up to 9 per day), Kennacraig - Port Askaig - Colonsay - Oban (3 hrs 35 mins; *HEBRIDEAN ISLES*; 1 per week), **Winter-only vehicle ferry** Tarbert (Loch Fyne) - Lochranza (Arran) (1 hr; *varies*; 1 per day).

#	Name		t	yr	kn	m	P	C	L	op	flag	no
1	ARGYLE	✓	2643t	07	14.0k	69.0m	450P	60C	-	BAS	UK	9365178
2	BUTE	✓	2612t	05	14.0k	69.0m	450P	60C	-	AS	UK	9319741
3	CALEDONIAN ISLES	✓	5221t	93	15.0k	94.3m	1000P	120C	10L	BA	UK	9051284
4	CLANSMAN	✓	5499t	98	16.5k	99.0m	638P	90C	6L	BA	UK	9158953
5	CORUISK		1599t	03	14.0k	65.0m	250P	40C	-	BA	UK	9274836
6	EIGG	✓	69t	75	8.0k	24.3m	75P	6C	-	B	UK	
7	FINLAGGAN		5626t	11	16.5k	89.9m	550P	88C	-	BA	UK	9482902
8	HALLAIG		499t	13	9.0k	43.5m	150P	23C	2L	BA	UK	9652832
9	HEBRIDEAN ISLES		3040t	85	15.0k	85.1m	494P	68C	10L	BAS	UK	8404812
10	HEBRIDES	✓	5506t	00	16.5k	99.0m	612P	110C	6L	BA	UK	9211975
11	ISLE OF ARRAN	✓	3296t	84	15.0k	85.0m	446P	68C	8L	BA	UK	8219554
12•	ISLE OF CUMBRAE	✓	201t	77	8.5k	37.7m	139P	18C	-	BA	UK	8219554
13	ISLE OF LEWIS	✓	6753t	95	18.0k	101.2m	680P	123C	10L	BA	UK	9085974
14	ISLE OF MULL	✓	4719t	88	15.0k	90.1m	962P	80C	20L	BA	UK	8608339
15	LOCH ALAINN		396t	98	10.0k	43.0m	150P	24C	-	BA	UK	9147722
16	LOCH BHRUSDA		246t	96	8.0k	35.4m	150P	18C	-	BA	UK	9129483
17	LOCH BUIE		295t	92	9.0k	35.5m	250P	9C	-	BA	UK	9031375
18	LOCH DUNVEGAN	✓	549t	91	9.0k	54.2m	200P	36C	-	BA	UK	9006409
19	LOCH FYNE	✓	549t	91	9.0k	54.2m	200P	36C	-	BA	UK	9006411
20	LOCH LINNHE	✓	206t	86	9.0k	35.5m	199P	12C	-	BA	UK	8512308
21	LOCH PORTAIN		950t	03	10.5k	50.0m	200P	32C	-	BA	UK	9274824
22	LOCH RANZA		206t	87	9.0k	35.7m	199P	12C	-	BA	UK	8519887
23	LOCH RIDDON		206t	86	9.0k	35.5m	199P	12C	-	BA	UK	8519875
24	LOCH SEAFORTH		8478t	14	19.2k	116.0m	700P	143C	20L	BA	UK	9665437
25	LOCH SHIRA		1024t	07	13.0k	43.0m	250P	24C	-	BA	UK	9376919
26	LOCH STRIVEN	✓	206t	86	9.0k	35.7m	199P	12C	-	BA	UK	8512293
27	LOCH TARBERT	✓	211t	92	9.0k	34.5m	149P	18C	-	BA	UK	9039389
28	LOCHINVAR	✓	523t	14	9.0k	43.5m	150P	23C	2L	BA	UK	9652844
29	LOCHNEVIS	✓	941t	00	13.0k	49.1m	190P	14C	-	A	UK	9209063
30	LORD OF THE ISLES	✓	3504t	89	16.0k	84.6m	506P	56C	16L	BAS	UK	8710869
31	RAASAY		69t	76	8.0k	24.3m	75P	6C	-	B	UK	
32•	SATURN		899t	78	13.0k	69.5m	381P	40C	-	AS	UK	7615490

Note In the following list, Gaelic names are shown in parenthesis.

ARGYLE *(EARRA-GHÀIDHEAL)*, BUTE *(EILEAN BHÒID)* Built by Stocznia Remontowa, Gdansk, Poland to operate on the Wemyss Bay - Rothesay route.

CALEDONIAN ISLES (EILEANAN CHALEDONIA) Built by Richards Shipyard, Lowestoft, UK for the Ardrossan - Brodick (Arran) service.

CLANSMAN (FEAR-CINNIDH) Built by Appledore Shipbuilders Ltd, Appledore, UK to replace the LORD OF THE ISLES on the Oban - Coll and Tiree and Oban - Castlebay and Lochboisdale services in the summer. She also serves as winter relief vessel on the Stornoway, Tarbert, Lochmaddy, Mull/Colonsay and Brodick routes.

CORUISK (COIR' UISG') Built by Appledore Shipbuilders Ltd, Appledore, UK to operate on the Mallaig - Armadale route during the summer. She operates on the Upper Clyde as a relief vessel during the winter. Between December 2013 and March 2014 operated for Argyle Ferries in lieu of the ALI CAT during peak periods and when that vessel could not sail due to adverse weather.

EIGG (EILEAN EIGE) Built by James Lamont & Co, Port Glasgow, UK. Since 1976 she has been employed mainly on the Oban - Lismore service. In 1996 she was transferred to the Tobermory (Mull) - Kilchoan route, very occasionally making sailings to the Small Isles (Canna, Eigg, Muck and Rum) for special cargoes. In 1999 her wheelhouse was raised to make it easier to see over taller lorries and she returned to the Oban - Lismore route. At present she continues to operate some sailings because of difficulties in operating the larger 'Loch class' vessels at the slipways at some states of the tide.

FINLAGGAN (FIONN LAGAN) Built by Stocznia Remontowa, Gdansk, Poland for the Kennacraig - Islay service.

HALLAIG (HALLAIG) Built by Ferguson Shipbuilders, Port Glasgow, UK to replace the LOCH STRIVEN on the Sconser - Raasay service. The vessel has both diesel and battery electric propulsion and can be 'plugged in' to a land supply on Raasay overnight.

HEBRIDEAN ISLES (EILEANAN INNSE GALL) Built by Cochrane Shipbuilders, Selby UK for the Uig - Tarbert/Lochmaddy service. She was used initially on the Ullapool - Stornoway and Oban - Craignure/Colonsay services pending installation of link-span facilities at Uig, Tarbert and Lochmaddy. She took up her regular role in May 1986. From May 1996 she no longer operated direct services in summer between Tarbert and Lochmaddy, this role being taken on by the new Harris - North Uist services of the LOCH BHRUSDA. In 2001 she was replaced by the HEBRIDES and transferred to the Islay service. In Autumn 2002 she operated between Scrabster and Stromness for NorthLink Orkney and Shetland Ferries before port modifications at Scrabster enabled the HAMNAVOE to enter service in Spring 2003. She then returned to the Islay service. She also relieved on the NorthLink Pentland Firth service between 2004 and 2007.

HEBRIDES (INNSE GALL) Built by Ferguson Shipbuilders Ltd, Port Glasgow, UK for the Uig - Tarbert and Uig - Lochmaddy services.

ISLE OF ARRAN (EILEAN ARAINN) Built by Ferguson Ailsa, Port Glasgow, UK for the Ardrossan - Brodick service. In 1993 transferred to the Kennacraig - Port Ellen/Port Askaig service, also undertaking the weekly Port Askaig - Colonsay - Oban summer service. From then until 1997/98 she also relieved on the Brodick, Coll/Tiree, Castlebay/Lochboisdale, Craignure and Tarbert/Lochmaddy routes in winter. In 2001 she was replaced by the HEBRIDEAN ISLES and became a reserve for the larger vessels. She has operated on the two-ship Islay service in summer since 2003; this service is now all-year-round. Following the delivery of the FINLAGGAN in May 2011 she became a spare vessel, and operates extra services between Ardrossan and Brodick and Ardrossan and Campbeltown during the peak summer period.

ISLE OF CUMBRAE (EILEAN CHUMRAIGH) Built by Ailsa Shipbuilding Ltd, Troon, UK for the Largs - Cumbrae Slip (Cumbrae) service. In 1986 she was replaced by the LOCH LINNHE and the LOCH STRIVEN and transferred to the Lochaline - Fishnish (Mull) service. She used to spend most of the winter as secondary vessel on the Kyle of Lochalsh - Kyleakin service; however, this ceased following the opening of the Skye Bridge in 1995. In 1997 she was transferred to the Colintraive - Rhubodach service. In Summer 1999 she was transferred to the Tarbert - Portavadie service. In May 2014 replaced by the new LOCHINVAR and laid up.

ISLE OF LEWIS (EILEAN LEÒDHAIS) Built by Ferguson Shipbuilders Ltd, Port Glasgow, UK for the Ullapool - Stornoway service.

Argyll Flyer (*Stuart Mackilop*)

Loch Tarbert (*Nick Widdows*)

Loch Dunvegan (*Stuart Mackilop*)

Isle of Mull (*Stuart Mackilop*)

ISLE OF MULL *(AN T-EILEAN MUILEACH)* Built by Appledore Ferguson, Port Glasgow, UK for the Oban - Craignure (Mull) service. She also operates some Oban - Colonsay sailings and until 1997/98 was the usual winter relief vessel on the Ullapool - Stornoway service. She has also deputised on the Oban - Castlebay/Lochboisdale and Oban - Coll/Tiree routes.

LOCH ALAINN *(LOCH ÀLAINN)* Built by Buckie Shipbuilders Ltd, Buckie, UK for the Lochaline - Fishnish service. Launched as the LOCH ALINE but renamed the LOCH ALAINN before entering service. After a brief period on the service for which she was built, she was transferred to the Colintraive - Rhubodach route. In 1998 she was transferred to the Largs - Cumbrae Slip service. In 2007 moved to the Ardmhor (Barra) - Eriskay service. She relieves the larger 'Loch' class vessels in the winter, with her own service covered by the LOCH BHRUSDA.

LOCH BHRUSDA *(LOCH BHRÙSTA)* Built by McTay Marine, Bromborough, Wirral, UK to inaugurate a new Otternish (North Uist) - Leverburgh (Harris) service. In 2001 the service became Berneray - Leverburgh. In 2003 she moved to the Eriskay - Barra service, previously operated by *Comhairle Nan Eilean Siar* vessels. In 2007 she became a spare vessel on the Clyde. Note 'Bhrusda' is pronounced "Vroosta".

LOCH BUIE *(LOCH BUIDHE)* Built by J W Miller & Sons Ltd, St Monans, Fife, UK for the Fionnphort (Mull) - Iona service to replace the MORVERN (see *Arranmore Island Ferry Services*) and obviate the need for a relief vessel in the summer. Due to height restrictions, loading arrangements for vehicles taller than private cars are stern-only. Only islanders' cars and service vehicles (eg mail vans, police) are carried; no tourist vehicles are conveyed.

LOCH DUNVEGAN *(LOCH DÙNBHEAGAN)* Built by Ferguson Shipbuilders Ltd, Port Glasgow, UK for the Kyle of Lochalsh - Kyleakin service. On the opening of the Skye Bridge in October 1995 she was withdrawn from service and offered for sale. In Autumn 1997, she returned to service on the Lochaline - Fishnish route. In 1998 she was due to be transferred to the Colintraive - Rhubodach route but this was delayed because of problems in providing terminal facilities. She operated on the Clyde and between Mallaig and Armadale during the early summer and spent the rest of that summer laid up. In 1999 she was transferred to the Colintraive - Rhubodach route.

LOCH FYNE *(LOCH FINE)* Built by Ferguson Shipbuilders Ltd, Port Glasgow, UK for the Kyle of Lochalsh - Kyleakin service (see the LOCH DUNVEGAN). In Autumn 1997, she also served on the Lochaline - Fishnish route and was transferred to this route as regular vessel in 1998.

LOCH LINNHE *(AN LINNE DHUBH)* Built by Richard Dunston (Hessle) Ltd, Hessle, UK. Until 1997 she was used mainly on the Largs - Cumbrae Slip (Cumbrae) service and until Winter 1994/95 she was usually used on the Lochaline - Fishnish service during the winter. Since then she has relieved on various routes in winter. In Summer 1998 she operated mainly on the Tarbert - Portavadie route. In 1999 she was transferred to the Tobermory - Kilchoan service in summer.

LOCH PORTAIN *(LOCH PORTAIN)* Built by McTay Marine, Bromborough, Wirral, UK (hull constructed in Poland) to replace the LOCH BHRUSDA on the Berneray - Leverburgh service.

LOCH RANZA *(LOCH RAONASA)* Built by Richard Dunston (Hessle) Ltd, Hessle, UK for the Claonaig - Lochranza (Arran) seasonal service and used a relief vessel in the winter. In 1992 she was replaced by the LOCH TARBERT and transferred to the Tayinloan - Gigha service.

LOCH RIDDON *(LOCH RAODAIN)* Built by Richard Dunston (Hessle) Ltd, Hessle, UK. Until 1997 she was used almost exclusively on the Colintraive - Rhubodach service. In 1997, she was transferred to the Largs - Cumbrae Slip service. In January 2014 she became regular vessel on the Oban - Lismore service. However, after problems with using the slipways, she became the second vessel on the Largs - Cumbrae Slip service.

LOCH SEAFORTH *(LOCH SHIPHOIRT)* Built by Flensburger Schiffbau-Gesellschaft, Flensburg, Germany for the Stornoway - Ullapool service, replacing the ISLE OF LEWIS and freight vessel MUIRNEAG.

LOCH SHIRA *(LOCH SIORA)* Built by Ferguson Shipbuilders, Port Glasgow, UK for the Largs – Cumbrae Slip route.

LOCH STRIVEN *(LOCH SROIGHEANN)* Built by Richard Dunston (Hessle) Ltd, Hessle, UK. Used mainly on the Largs - Cumbrae Slip service until 1997. In Winter 1995/96 and 1996/97 she was used on the

Tarbert - Portavadie and Claonaig - Lochranza routes. In 1997 she took over the Sconser - Raasay service. In winter 2014 replaced by the HALLAIG. In summer 2014 operating between Oban and Lismore.

LOCH TARBERT *(LOCH AN TAIRBEIRT)* Built by J W Miller & Sons Ltd, St Monans, Fife, UK for the Claonaig - Lochranza service. She was the winter relief vessel on the Largs - Cumbrae Slip route between 1994/95 and 2007/08.

LOCHINVAR *(LOCH AN BARR)* As the HALLAIG. Operates on the Tarbert - Portavadie route.

LOCHNEVIS *(LOCH NIBHEIS)* Built by Ailsa Shipbuilding, Troon, UK to replace the LOCHMOR on the Mallaig - Small Isles service and the winter Mallaig - Armadale service. Although a vehicle ferry, cars are not normally carried to the Small Isles; the ro-ro facility is used for the carriage of agricultural machinery and livestock and it is possible to convey a vehicle on the ferry from which goods can be unloaded directly onto local transport rather than transhipping at Mallaig.

LORD OF THE ISLES *(RIGH NAN EILEAN)* Built by Appledore Ferguson, Port Glasgow, UK to replace the CLAYMORE on the Oban - Castlebay and Lochboisdale services and also the COLUMBA (1420t, 1964) on the Oban - Coll and Tiree service. She took over the Mallaig - Armadale and Mallaig - Outer Isles services in July 1998 but returned to her previous routes during the winter period. In Spring 2003 the Mallaig – Armadale service was taken over by the PIONEER standing in for the new CORUISK and she operated services from Oban to South Uist and Barra. She now serves Colonsay, Coll, Tiree, Barra, Craignure and Lochboisdale from Oban.

RAASAY *(EILEAN RATHARSAIR)* Built by James Lamont & Co Ltd, Port Glasgow, UK for and used primarily on the Sconser (Skye) - Raasay service. In 1997 she was replaced by the LOCH STRIVEN, became a spare/relief vessel and inaugurated in October 2003 the winter service between Tobermory (Mull) and Kilchoan (Ardnamurchan).

SATURN *(SATHARN)* Built by Ailsa Shipbuilding, Troon for the Wemyss Bay - Rothesay services. Between 1986 and 2005 she usually rotated on this services and services from Gourock; until 2000 this, in summer, included Clyde cruising but this was not repeated in 2001. In the summers 2005 - 2010, she operated additional peak summer sailings between Ardrossan and Brodick with a maximum capacity of 250 passengers. In October 2010 she took over the Gourock - Dunoon service. In June 2011 replaced by *Argyll Ferries* passenger ferries. During Summer 2011 she operated additional sailings between Ardrossan and Brodick. In September returned to the Gourock - Dunoon route to provide additional capacity for the Cowal Games. She was then laid up.

DFDS SEAWAYS

THE COMPANY *DFDS Seaways* is a business unit within *DFDS A/S*, a Danish private sector company.

MANAGEMENT President and CEO DFDS A/S Niels Smedegaard, **Head of Shipping Division** Peder Gellert Pedersen, **Managing Director, DFDS Seaways PLC** Sean Potter, **Head of North Sea Business Area** Kell Robdrup, **Head of English Channel Business Area** Carsten Jensen, **Head of Passenger Business Area** Brian Thorsted Hansen.

ADDRESS A/S Sundkrogsgade 11 DK-2100 Copenhagen.

TELEPHONE Administration +45 3342 3342, **Passenger Reservations** 0871 522 9955, Freight Reservations see website.

FAX Freight Reservations see website.

INTERNET Websites *Passenger* www.dfdsseaways.co.uk *(Chinese, Danish, Dutch, English, German, Italian, Japanese, Norwegian, Polish, Swedish) Freight* freight.dfdsseaways.com *(English) Corporate* www.dfds.com *(English)*

ROUTES OPERATED *Passenger ferries* Harwich - Esbjerg (Denmark) (17 hrs; *SIRENA SEAWAYS*; 3 per week) (service ends September 2014), Newcastle (North Shields) - IJmuiden (near Amsterdam, The Netherlands) (15 hrs; *KING SEAWAYS, PRINCESS SEAWAYS*; daily). *Freight only ferries* Zeebrugge (Belgium) - Rosyth (Scotland) (20 hrs; *FINLANDIA SEAWAYS*; 3 per week), Esbjerg - Immingham (18 hrs; *JUTLANDIA SEAWAYS, ARK DANIA*, ARK GERMANIA*; 6 per week), Cuxhaven - Immingham

King Seaways (*Miles Cowsill*)

Princess Seaways (*Miles Cowsill*)

(19 hrs; *CLEMENTINE, CLIPPER POINT*; 4/5 per week), Gothenburg - Tilbury (37 hrs; *TRANSPULP*; 2 per week), Gothenburg - Immingham (26 hrs (direct), *45 hrs (via Brevik (Fri)); *BEGONIA SEAWAYS, FREESIA SEAWAYS, FICARIA SEAWAYS*; 7 per week), Brevik - Immingham (25 hrs (direct), 42 hrs (via Gothenburg); *BEGONIA SEAWAYS, FREESIA SEAWAYS, FICARIA SEAWAYS*; 2 per week), Gothenburg - Brevik (Norway) - Ghent (Belgium) (Gothenburg 32 hrs, Brevik 32 hrs; *MAGNOLIA SEAWAYS, PETUNIA SEAWAYS, PRIMULA SEAWAYS*; 5 per week), Vlaardingen - Immingham (14 hrs; *FIONIA SEAWAYS, HAFNIA SEAWAYS*; 6 per week), Vlaardingen - Felixstowe (7 hrs; *FLANDRIA SEAWAYS, SELANDIA SEAWAYS, SUECIA SEAWAYS*; 3 per day). Note Freight vessels are often moved between routes. *ARK DANIA to replace JUTLANDIA SEAWAYS in late summer 2014. JUTLANDIA SEAWAYS will probably replaces one of the chartered vessels on Cuxhaven - Immingham.

1F	ARK DANIA	25000t	14	20.0k	195.2m	12P	-	206T	A	DK	9609964
2F	ARK FUTURA	18725t	96	19.7k	183.3m	12P	-	164T	AS	DK	9129598
3F	ARK GERMANIA	25000t	14	20.0k	195.2m	12P	-	206T	A	DK	9609952
4F	BEGONIA SEAWAYS	37722t	04	22.5k	230.0m	12P	-	340T	AS	DK	9262089
5F	BRITANNIA SEAWAYS	24196t	00	21.1k	197.5m	12P	-	200T	AS	DK	9153032
6F	CLEMENTINE	23986t	97	17.8k	162.5m	24P	630C	157T	A	BE	9125384
7F	CLIPPER POINT	14759t	08	22.0k	142.0m	12P	-	120T	A	CY	9350666
8F	FICARIA SEAWAYS	37939t	04	22.5k	230.0m	12P	-	340T	AS	DK	9320568
9F	FINLANDIA SEAWAYS	11530t	00	20.0k	162.2m	12P	-	140T	A	LT	9198721
10F	FIONIA SEAWAYS	25609t	09	20.0k	184.8m	12P	-	250T	AS	UK	9395343
11F	FLANDRIA SEAWAYS	13073t	00	18.6k	142.5m	12P	-	114T	A	DK	9186637
12F	FREESIA SEAWAYS	37722t	04	22.5k	230.0m	12P	-	340T	AS	DK	9274848
13F	HAFNIA SEAWAYS	25609t	08	20.0k	184.8m	12P	-	250T	AS	UK	9357602
14F	JUTLANDIA SEAWAYS	25609t	10	20.0k	184.8m	12P	-	250T	AS	UK	9395355
15	KING SEAWAYS	31788t	87	20.0k	161.6m	2140P	600C	104T	BA	DK	8502406
16F	MAGNOLIA SEAWAYS	32289t	03	22.5k	199.8m	12P	-	280T	AS	DK	9259496
17F	PETUNIA SEAWAYS	32289t	04	22.5k	199.8m	12P	-	280T	AS	DK	9259501
18F	PRIMULA SEAWAYS	32289t	04	22.5k	199.8m	12P	-	280T	AS	DK	9259513
19	PRINCESS SEAWAYS	31356t	86	18.5k	161.0m	1600P	600C	100T	BA	DK	8502391
20F	SELANDIA SEAWAYS	24196t	98	21.0k	197.5m	12P	-	206T	A	DK	9157284
21	SIRENA SEAWAYS	22382t	03	22.0k	199.4m	596P	316C	154T	A	DK	9212163
22F	SUECIA SEAWAYS	24196t	99	21.0k	197.5m	12P	-	206T	AS	DK	9153020
23F	TRANSPULP	23128t	06	16.0k	190.7m	12P	-	200T	A	SE	9343261

ARK DANIA, ARK GERMANIA Built by P + S Werften GmbH, Stralsund, Germany. They are used for the German/Danish joint ARK Project providing NATO transport but are also available for *DFDS* use and charter when not required. They have a crane for loading containers on the weather deck. In December 2012 the order for these vessels was cancelled due to late delivery. Following negotiations with the shipyard it was agreed that they would be completed under a new contract which was signed in February 2013. Both vessels were delivered to DFDS in April 2014, the ARK GERMANIA almost complete, the ARK DANIA still incomplete. The latter vessel was towed to the Fayard shipyard, Odense, to be completed. The ARK GERMANIA entered service a few days after delivery, the ARK DANIA in summer 2014.

ARK FUTURA Built as the DANA FUTURA by C N Visentini di Visentini Francesco & C, Donada, Italy for *DFDS*. In 2001 she was renamed the *TOR FUTURA*. Initially operated mainly between Esbjerg and Harwich, but latterly operated mainly between Esbjerg and Immingham. In 2004 chartered to *Toll Shipping* of Australia. Later time-chartered to the *Danish MoD* for 5.5 years. However, when not required for military service she has been chartered to other operators such as *P&O Ferries, Cobelfret Ferries* and *Van Uden Ro-Ro* and used on *DFDS Tor Line* services. In 2006 sold to DFDS Lys Line Rederi A/S of Norway, a *DFDS* subsidiary and chartered back. In April 2011 renamed the ARK FUTURA.

BEGONIA SEAWAYS Built as the TOR BEGONIA by Flensburger Schiffbau-Gesellschaft, Flensburg, Germany for *DFDS Tor Line*. Operates on the Gothenburg - Immingham/Brevik route. In Summer 2009

Fionia Seaways *(Cees de Bijl)*

Selandia Seaways and Flandria Seaways *(Cees de Bijl)*

lengthened by 30m by MWB Motorenwerke Bremerhaven AG, Germany. In July 2012 renamed the BEGONIA SEAWAYS.

BRITANNIA SEAWAYS Built as the TOR BRITANNIA by Fincantieri-Cantieri Navali Italiani SpA, Ancona, Italy for *DFDS Tor Line*. Operated on the Gothenburg - Immingham route until 2004 when she was transferred to the Esbjerg - Immingham route. In January 2010 chartered to *Norfolkline* to operate between Vlaardingen and Felixstowe. In May 2011 renamed the BRITANNIA SEAWAYS.

CLEMENTINE Built by Kawasaki Heavy Industries, Sakaide, Japan for *Cobelfret*. Mainly used on the Zeebrugge - Immingham service. In 2007 moved to the Zeebrugge - Purfleet route. In March 2013 chartered to *RMR Shipping*. In July 2013 chartered to DFDS Seaways and placed on the Immingham - Cuxhaven service.

CLIPPER POINT Built by Astilleros de Huelva SA, Huelva, Spain for *Seatruck Ferries*. In May 2012 chartered to *DFDS Seaways* and placed on the Immingham-Cuxhaven route. In April 2013 chartered to the organisers of the 'SATA Rally Azores 2013' car rally to take cars from Portugal to the Azores. In May began operating for *DFDS Seaways* in the Baltic. In October transferred to the Immingham - Cuxhaven route.

FICARIA SEAWAYS Built as the TOR FICARIA by Flensburger Schiffbau-Gesellschaft, Flensburg, Germany for *DFDS Tor Line*. Operates on the Gothenburg - Immingham/Brevik service. In Summer 2009 lengthened by 30m by MWB Motorenwerke Bremerhaven AG, Germany. In July 2011 renamed the FICARIA SEAWAYS.

FINLANDIA SEAWAYS Launched as the FINNMAID but renamed the FINNREEL before delivery. Built by Jinling Shipyard, Nanjing, China for the *Macoma Shipping Group* and chartered to *Finnlines*. In 2008 sold to *DFDS Lisco* and in January 2009 delivered, chartered to *DFDS Tor Line* and renamed the TOR FINLANDIA. Operated on the Immingham - Rotterdam route until January 2011 when she was transferred to the Rosyth - Zeebrugge route. In May 2012 moved to the Cuxhaven - Immingham service but returned in July. In December 2012 renamed the FINLANDIA SEAWAYS. In October 2013 moved to the Kiel - St Petersburg service. In April 2014 returned to the Rosyth - Zeebrugge route.

FIONIA SEAWAYS Built as the TOR FIONIA by Jinling Shipyard, Nanjing, China for *Macoma Shipping Ltd* of the UK. Launched as the JINGLING 3. She was time-chartered to *DFDS Tor Line* for ten years (with an option on a further three). Delivered in May 2009 and initially replaced the TOR BEGONIA, TOR FICARIA and TOR FREESIA while they were being lengthened. In October 2011 renamed the FIONIA SEAWAYS.

FLANDRIA SEAWAYS Built as the MAERSK FLANDERS by Guangzhou Shipyard International, Guangzhou, China for *Norfolkline*. Used on the Scheveningen (from 2007 Vlaardingen) - Felixstowe service. In July 2010 renamed the FLANDRIA SEAWAYS.

FREESIA SEAWAYS Built as the TOR FREESIA by Flensburger Schiffbau-Gesellschaft, Flensburg, Germany for *DFDS Tor Line*. Operates on the Gothenburg - Immingham/Brevik service. In Summer 2009 lengthened by 30m by MWB Motorenwerke Bremerhaven AG, Germany. In August 2012 renamed the FREESIA SEAWAYS.

HAFNIA SEAWAYS Built as the TOR HAFNIA by Jinling Shipyard, Nanjing, China for *Macoma Shipping Ltd* of the UK and time-chartered to *DFDS Tor Line* for ten years. Until 2013, mainly operated on the Immingham - Esbjerg route. In March 2011 renamed the HAFNIA SEAWAYS. In February 2013 transferred to the Vlaardingen - Immingham route.

JUTLANDIA SEAWAYS Built as the TOR JUTLANDIA by Jinling Shipyard, Nanjing, China for *Macoma Shipping Ltd* of the UK and time-chartered to *DFDS Tor Line* for ten years. In July 2011 renamed the JUTLANDIA SEAWAYS. Currently operates on the Immingham - Esbjerg route. In late summer 2014 to be replaced by the ARK DANIA and moved to another route.

KING SEAWAYS Built as the NILS HOLGERSSON by Schichau Seebeckwerft AG, Bremerhaven, Germany for *Rederi AB Swedcarrier* of Sweden for their service between Trelleborg and Travemünde, joint with *TT-Line* of Germany (trading as *TT-Line*). In 1992 purchased by *Brittany Ferries* for entry into service in Spring 1993. After a major rebuild, she was renamed the VAL DE LOIRE and introduced onto the Plymouth - Roscoff, Plymouth - Santander and Cork - Roscoff routes. In 2004 transferred to the

Portsmouth - St Malo and Portsmouth – Cherbourg services. In 2005 operated mainly Portsmouth - St Malo. In 2006 sold to *DFDS*, renamed the KING OF SCANDINAVIA and placed on the Newcastle – IJmuiden route. In January 2011 renamed the KING SEAWAYS.

MAGNOLIA SEAWAYS Built as the TOR MAGNOLIA by Flensburger Schiffbau-Gesellschaft, Flensburg, Germany for *DFDS Tor Line*. In July 2011 renamed the MAGNOLIA SEAWAYS. Currently operates on the Gothenburg – Ghent route.

PETUNIA SEAWAYS Built as the TOR PETUNIA by Flensburger Schiffbau-Gesellschaft, Flensburg, Germany for *DFDS Tor Line*. In July 2011 renamed the PETUNIA SEAWAYS. Currently operates on the Gothenburg – Ghent route.

PRIMULA SEAWAYS Built as the TOR PRIMULA by Flensburger Schiffbau-Gesellschaft, Flensburg, Germany for *DFDS Tor Line*.. In July 2010 renamed the PRIMULA SEAWAYS. Currently operates on the Gothenburg – Ghent route.

PRINCESS SEAWAYS Built by Schichau Seebeckwerft AG, Bremerhaven, Germany as the PETER PAN for *TT-Line* for the service between Travemünde and Trelleborg. In 1992 sold to *TT Line* of Australia (no connection) for use on their service between Port Melbourne (Victoria) and Devonport (Tasmania) and renamed the SPIRIT OF TASMANIA. In 2002 sold to *Nordsjøferger K/S* of Norway and renamed the SPIR. After modification work she was, in 2003, renamed the FJORD NORWAY and chartered to *Fjord Line*. Placed on the Bergen - Egersund - Hanstholm route. In 2005 placed on the Bergen - Stavanger - Newcastle route, but operated once a week to Hanstholm. In October 2006 sold to *DFDS* and renamed the PRINCESS OF NORWAY, remaining on the Newcastle - Norway service but no longer serving Hanstholm. In May 2007 moved to the Newcastle - IJmuiden route. In February 2011 renamed the PRINCESS SEAWAYS.

SELANDIA SEAWAYS Built as the TOR SELANDIA by Fincantieri-Cantieri Navali Italiani SpA, Ancona, Italy for *DFDS Tor Line*. Operated on the Gothenburg - Immingham route until 2004 when she was moved to the Gothenburg – Ghent route. In 2005 she moved to the Gothenburg – Harwich route. In July the UK terminal moved to Tilbury. In August 2010 renamed the SELANDIA SEAWAYS. Currently operates on the Rotterdam - Felixstowe route.

SIRENA SEAWAYS Built as the GOLFO DEI DELFINI by Stocznia Szczecinska, Szczecin, Poland for *Lloyd Sardegna* of Italy for service between Italy and Sardinia. However, due to late delivery the order was cancelled. In 2002 purchased by *DFDS Seaways*, and, during Winter 2002/03, passenger accommodation was enlarged and refitted, increasing passenger capacity from 308 to 596. In June 2003, renamed the DANA SIRENA, she replaced unmodified sister vessel, the DANA GLORIA on the Esbjerg – Harwich service. In February 2013 she was renamed the SIRENA SEAWAYS. At the end of September 2014 the route will cease and she will move elsewhere.

SUECIA SEAWAYS Built as the TOR SUECIA by Fincantieri-Cantieri Navali Italiani SpA, Ancona, Italy for *DFDS Tor Line*. Operated on the Gothenburg - Immingham route until 2004 when she was transferred to the Esbjerg - Immingham route. Later transferred to the Danish flag. In March 2010 chartered to *Norfolkline* to operate between Vlaardingen and Felixstowe and continued on the route when it was taken over by *DFDS*. In June 2011 renamed the SUECIA SEAWAYS.

TRANSPULP Built by Aker Finnyards, Rauma, Finland for *Baltic Container Shipping* of the UK and chartered to *Rederi AB Transatlantic* of Sweden. Operated on service operated for Stora Enso Paper Group, mainly in the Baltic. In early 2011 transferred to the Gothenburg - Tilbury (once weekly) and Gothenburg - Zeebrugge (*CLdN* service) (once weekly) services. In January 2013 began operating twice weekly to Tilbury, replacing the SELANDIA SEAWAYS of *DFDS Seaways*.

DFDS SEAWAYS FRANCE

THE COMPANY *DFDS Seaways France* was inaugurated in March 2013 following the establishment of a *DFDS Seaways/LD Lines* joint venture in November 2012. It is 82% owned by *DFDS* and 12% by *LD Lines*. (see sections 6). The Newhaven - Dieppe route is branded as *Transmanche Ferries*, operating under a franchise awarded by *Syndicat Mixte de L'Activité Transmanche* in Dieppe.

MANAGEMENT **Director General** Jean-Claude Charlo.

Selandia Seaways (*Cees de Bijl*)

Ark Dania (*Peter Therkildsen*)

ADDRESS 18 rue Pasquier, Paris 75008, France.

TELEPHONE **Administration** +45 3342 3342, **Passenger Reservations** *Dover* 0871 574 7235, *Newhaven and Portsmouth* 0844 576 8836. **Freight Reservations** *Dover* +44 (0) 1304 874001, *Newhaven and Portsmouth* +33 2 32 145 205.

FAX **Freight Reservations** *Dover* +44 (0)1304 874040.

INTERNET **Website** www.dfds.com *(Chinese, Danish, Dutch, English, German, Italian, Japanese, Norwegian, Polish, Swedish)*

ROUTES OPERATED *(DFDS Seaways France)* Dover - Dunkerque (2 hrs; *DELFT SEAWAYS, DOVER SEAWAYS, DUNKERQUE SEAWAYS*, 12 per day), Dover - Calais (1 hr 30 mins; *CALAIS SEAWAYS, DIEPPE SEAWAYS*; 10 per day), Newhaven - Dieppe (4 hrs; *COTE D'ALBATRE*; 2 per day (ships continue to be branded *Transmanche Ferries*), Le Havre - Portsmouth (5 hrs 30 mins (day), 7 hrs 30 mins (night); *SEVEN SISTERS*; 1 per day, Marseilles – Tunis (currently freight only) (3 per week), Note the Marseilles – Tunis route is outside the scope of this book but is included for completeness.

1	CALAIS SEAWAYS	28833t	91	21.0k	163.6m	1850P	600C	100L	BA2	FR	8908466
2	COTE D'ALBATRE	18425t	06	22.0k	112.0m	600P	300C	62L	BA	FR	9320128
3	DELFT SEAWAYS	35923t	06	25.5k	187.0m	780P	200C	120L	BA2	UK	9293088
4	DIEPPE SEAWAYS	30285t	02	22.0k	203.3m	1200P	480C	110L	BA2	FR	9211511
5	DOVER SEAWAYS	35923t	06	25.8k	187.0m	780P	200C	120L	BA2	UK	9318345
6	DUNKERQUE SEAWAYS	35923t	05	25.8k	187.0m	780P	200C	120L	BA2	UK	9293076
7	SEVEN SISTERS	18425t	06	22.0k	112.0m	600P	300C	62L	BA	FR	9320130

CALAIS SEAWAYS Built as the PRINS FILIP by NV Boelwerf SA, Temse, Belgium for *Regie voor Maritiem Transport (RMT)* of Belgium for the Ostend - Dover service. Although completed in 1991, she did not enter service until May 1992. In 1994 the British port became Ramsgate. Withdrawn in 1997 and laid up for sale. In 1998 she was sold to *Stena RoRo* and renamed the STENA ROYAL. In November 1998 she was chartered to *P&O Ferries* to operate as a freight-only vessel on the Dover - Zeebrugge route. In Spring 1999 it was decided to charter the vessel on a long-term basis and she was repainted into *P&O Stena Line* (later *P&O Ferries*) colours and renamed the P&OSL AQUITAINE. In Autumn 1999 she was modified to make her suitable to operate between Dover and Calais and was transferred to that route, becoming a passenger vessel again. In 2002 renamed the PO AQUITAINE and in 2003 the PRIDE OF AQUITAINE. In September 2005 sold to *LD Lines* and renamed the NORMAN SPIRIT. In October, inaugurated a Le Havre - Portsmouth service, replacing that previously operated by *P&O Ferries*. In November 2009 moved to the Dover - Boulogne route. In March 2010 chartered to *TransEuropa Ferries*, placed on the Ostend - Ramsgate service (as part of a joint venture) and renamed the OSTEND SPIRIT. In May 2011 returned to the Portsmouth - Le Havre route and renamed the NORMAN SPIRIT. In November 2011 chartered to *DFDS Seaways* to add extra capacity to their Dover - Dunkerque route. In February 2012 transferred to the new Dover - Calais route, joint with *DFDS Seaways*. In March 2013 refurbished, repainted into *DFDS Seaways* colours and renamed the CALAIS SEAWAYS.

COTE D'ALBATRE Built by Astilleros Barreras SA, Vigo, Spain for *Transmanche Ferries* to operate between Newhaven and Dieppe. In February 2009 she was moved to the Boulogne - Dover and Dieppe - Dover routes. In September 2009 moved to the Le Havre - Portsmouth route. In April 2011 replaced by the NORMAN SPIRIT. Laid up most of the time except when required to replace the SEVEN SISTERS.

DELFT SEAWAYS, DOVER SEAWAYS, DUNKERQUE SEAWAYS Built as the MAERSK DELFT, DOVER SEAWAYS and MAERSK DUNKERQUE by Samsung Heavy Industries, Koje (Geoje) Island, South Korea for *Norfolkline* to operate between Dover and Dunkerque. In July and August 2010 renamed the DELFT SEAWAYS, DOVER SEAWAYS and DUNKERQUE SEAWAYS. In November 2012 the DOVER SEAWAYS was moved to the Dover - Calais route.

DIEPPE SEAWAYS Built as the SUPERFAST X by Howaldtswerke Deutsche Werft AG, Kiel, Germany for *Attica Enterprises* (now *Attica Group*) for use by *Superfast Ferries*. In May 2002 she and the SUPERFAST IX (see ATLANTIC VISION, *Tallink*, Section 6) began operating between Rosyth (Scotland) and Zeebrugge. In 2004 fitted with additional cabins and conference/seating areas. In 2007 sold to *Veolia Transportation* and renamed the JEAN NICOLI. Chartered to *CoTuNav* of Tunisia and operated between

Delft Seaways (*Brian Maxted*)

Dieppe Seaways (*John Bryant*)

France/Italy and Tunisia. Later chartered to *ANEK Lines* of Greece and operated on the Patras - Corfu - Igoumenitsa - Venice route. In July 2008 chartered to *SeaFrance* and renamed the SEAFRANCE MOLIERE. After modifications she was placed on the Dover - Calais route. In November 2011 laid up. In January 2012 offered for sale or charter. In July 2012 sold to *Scapino Shipping Ltd* of Monaco and renamed the MOLIERE. In October 2012 chartered to *DFDS/LD Lines* joint venture and, in November, renamed the DIEPPE SEAWAYS and introduced onto the Dover - Calais service. In May 2014 sold to *Stena Line North Sea Ltd*. Charter may end in October 2014.

SEVEN SISTERS Built by Astilleros Barreras SA, Vigo, Spain for *Transmanche Ferries* to operate between Newhaven and Dieppe. In recent years generally held as a reserve vessel. In March 2014 transferred to the Portsmouth - Le Havre service. She continues to carry *Transmanche Ferries* branding.

IRISH FERRIES

THE COMPANY *Irish Ferries* is an Irish Republic private sector company, part of the *Irish Continental Group*. It was originally mainly owned by the state-owned *Irish Shipping* and partly by *Lion Ferry AB* of Sweden. *Lion Ferry* participation ceased in 1977 and the company was sold into the private sector in 1987. Formerly state-owned *B&I Line* was taken over in 1991 and from 1995 all operations were marketed as *Irish Ferries*.

MANAGEMENT **Group Managing Director** Eamonn Rothwell, **Group Marketing Director** Tony Kelly.

ADDRESS PO Box 19, Ferryport, Alexandra Road, Dublin 1, Irish Republic.

TELEPHONE **Administration** +353 (0)1 607 5700, **Reservations** *Ireland* +353 (0)818300 400, *Rosslare Harbour* +353 (0)53 913 3158, *Holyhead* +44 (0)8717 300200, *Pembroke Dock* +44 (0)8717 300500, *National* 44 (0)8717 300400, *24 hour information* +353 (0)818300 400 (Ireland) or 44 (0)8717 300400 (UK).

FAX **Administration & Reservations** *Dublin* +353 (0)1 607 5660, *Rosslare* +353 (0)53 913 3544.

INTERNET **Email** info@irishferries.com **Website** www.irishferries.com *(English, French, German, Italian)*

ROUTES OPERATED **Conventional Ferries** Dublin - Holyhead (3 hrs 15 mins; *EPSILON*; *ULYSSES*; 2-4 per day), Rosslare - Pembroke Dock (4 hrs; *ISLE OF INISHMORE*; 4 per day), Dublin - Cherbourg (17-19 hrs; *EPSILON*; 1 per week), Rosslare - Cherbourg (France) (17 hrs 30 mins; *OSCAR WILDE*; 1 or 2 per week), Rosslare - Roscoff (France) (16 hrs; *OSCAR WILDE*; 1 or 2 per week). **Fast Ferry** Dublin - Holyhead (1 hr 49 min; *JONATHAN SWIFT*; 2 per day) marketed as 'DUBLINSwift'.

1	EPSILON	26375t	11	24.0k	177.5m	500P	500C	190T	BA	IT	9539054
2	ISLE OF INISHMORE	34031t	97	21.3k	182.5m	2200P	802C	152T	BA2	CY	9142605
3»	JONATHAN SWIFT	5989t	99	37.0k	86.6m	800P	200C	-	BA	CY	9188881
4	KAITAKI	22365t	95	19.0k	181.6m	1650P	600C	130T	BA	UK	9107942
5	OSCAR WILDE	31914t	87	22.0k	166.3m	1458P	580C	90T	BA	BS	8506311
6	ULYSSES	50938t	01	22.0k	209.0m	1875P	1342C	300T	BA2	CY	9214991

EPSILON Built as the CARTOUR EPSILON by CN Visentini, Porto Viro, Italy. Chartered to *Caronte & Tourist SPA* of Italy. In November 2013 chartered to *Irish Ferries*. In February 2014 renamed the EPSILON.

ISLE OF INISHMORE Built by Van der Giessen-de Noord, Krimpen aan den IJssel, Rotterdam for *Irish Ferries* to operate on the Holyhead - Dublin service. In 2001 replaced by the ULYSSES and moved to the Rosslare - Pembroke Dock route. She also relieves on the Dublin – Holyhead route when the ULYSSES receives her annual overhaul. In 2006 transferred to Cypriot registry.

JONATHAN SWIFT Austal Auto-Express 86 catamaran built by Austal Ships Pty, Fremantle, Australia for *Irish Ferries* for the Dublin - Holyhead route. In 2006 transferred to Cypriot registry.

KAITAKI Built as the ISLE OF INNISFREE by Van der Giessen-de Noord, Krimpen aan den IJssel, Rotterdam for *Irish Ferries* to operate on the Holyhead - Dublin route. In 1997 transferred to the Rosslare - Pembroke Dock service; for a short period, before modifications at Pembroke Dock were completed, she operated between Rosslare and Fishguard. In Spring 2001 she was replaced by the ISLE OF

Cartour Epsilon *(Gordon Hislip)*

Ulysses *(Gordon Hislip)*

INISHMORE and laid up. In July 2002 she was chartered to *P&O Portsmouth* for 5 years and renamed the PRIDE OF CHERBOURG. Entered service in October 2002. Withdrawn in October 2004. In January 2005, sub-chartered by *P&O* to *Stena RoRo*, renamed the STENA CHALLENGER and operated on the Karlskrona - Gdynia route. In June 2006 sub-chartered by *Stena RoRo* to *Toll Shipping* of New Zealand and renamed the CHALLENGER. In August 2006 she arrived in New Zealand and was placed on the Wellington - Picton route. In 2007 renamed the KAITAKI. In 2009 charter extended until 2013 and in 2013 charter extended until June 2017.

OSCAR WILDE Built as the KRONPRINS HARALD by Oy Wärtsilä AB, Turku, Finland for *Jahre Line* of Norway for the Oslo - Kiel service. In 1991 ownership was transferred to *Color Line*. In early 2007 sold to *Irish Ferries* for delivery in September 2007. Chartered back to *Color Line* until that date. When delivered, renamed the OSCAR WILDE and in November placed on the Rosslare - Roscoff/Cherbourg routes.

ULYSSES Built by Aker Finnyards, Rauma, Finland for *Irish Ferries* for the Dublin - Holyhead service. In 2006 transferred to Cypriot registry.

ISLE OF MAN STEAM PACKET COMPANY

THE COMPANY *The Isle of Man Steam Packet Company Limited* is an Isle of Man-registered company.

MANAGEMENT Chief Executive Officer Mark Woodward.

ADDRESS Imperial Buildings, Douglas, Isle of Man IM1 2BY.

TELEPHONE Administration + 44 (0)1624 645645, Reservations *From UK* 08722 992992, *From elsewhere* + 44 (0)1624 661661, Freight Bookings + 44 (0)1624 645620.

FAX Administration + 44 (0)1624 645609.

INTERNET Email iom.reservations@steam-packet.com Website www.steam-packet.com *(English)*

ROUTES OPERATED Conventional Ferries *All year* Douglas (Isle of Man) - Heysham (3 hrs 30 mins; *BEN-MY-CHREE*; up to 2 per day), *November-March* Douglas - Liverpool (Birkenhead) (4 hrs 15 mins; *BEN-MY-CHREE*; 2 per week). Fast Ferries *March-October* Douglas - Liverpool (2 hrs 40 mins; *MANANNAN*; up to 2 per day), Douglas - Belfast (2 hrs 55 mins; *MANANNAN*; up to 2 per week), Douglas - Dublin (2 hrs 55 mins; *MANANNAN*; up to 2 per week), Douglas - Heysham (2 hrs; *MANANNAN*; occasional), Freight Ferry Douglas - Heysham (3 hrs 30 mins; *ARROW*; as required)

1F	ARROW	7606t	98	17.0k	122.3m	12P	-	84T	A	IM	9119414
2	BEN-MY-CHREE	12747t	98	18.0k	124.9m	630P	275C	90T	A	IM	9170705
3»	MANANNAN	5743t	98	43.0k	96.0m	820P	200C	-	A	IM	9176072

ARROW Built as the VARBOLA by Astilleros de Huelva SA, Huelva, Spain for the *Estonian Shipping Company*. On completion, chartered to *Dart Line* and placed on the Dartford - Vlissingen route. In 1999 she was renamed the DART 6. At the end of August 1999, the charter was terminated and she was renamed the VARBOLA. She undertook a number of short-term charters, including *Merchant Ferries*. In 2000 long-term chartered to *Merchant Ferries* to operate between Heysham and Dublin. In 2003 the charter ended and she was chartered to *Dart Line* to replace the DART 9; she was placed initially on the Dartford - Vlissingen route but later transferred to the Dartford - Dunkerque route. Later sub-chartered to *NorseMerchant Ferries* and placed on the Heysham – Dublin route. In 2004 the charter transferred to *NorseMerchant Ferries*. In 2005 sold to *Elmira Shipping* of Greece and renamed the RR ARROW. In October 2007 sold to *Seatruck Ferries* but the charter to *Norfolkline* continued. Renamed the ARROW. In June 2009 returned to *Seatruck Ferries*. In April 2014 long term chartered to *IOMSP*. When not required she is sub-chartered to other operators.

BEN-MY-CHREE Built by Van der Giessen-de Noord, Krimpen aan den IJssel, Rotterdam for the *IOMSP Co* and operates between Douglas and Heysham. Additional passenger accommodation was added at her spring 2004 refit. In 2005 her passenger certificate was increased from 500 to 630. She operates some sailings between Douglas and Liverpool (Birkenhead) in the winter.

MANANNAN Incat 96m catamaran built at Hobart, Tasmania. Initially chartered to *Transport Tasmania* of Australia and operated between Port Melbourne (Victoria) and Georgetown (Tasmania). In 1999 chartered to *Fast Cat Ferries* of New Zealand and operated between Wellington (North Island) and Picton (South Island) under the marketing name 'Top Cat'. In 2000 she was laid up. In 2001 she was chartered to the *US Navy* and renamed the USS JOINT VENTURE (HSV-X1). In 2008 the charter was terminated and she was renamed the INCAT 050. Later purchased by *IOMSP*. Following conversion back to civilian use she was renamed the MANANNAN and entered service in May 2009.

LD LINES

THE COMPANY *LD Lines* is a French company, a subsidiary of *Louis Dreyfus Armateurs*.

MANAGEMENT **Managing Director** Christophe Santoni, **UK & Ireland/Passenger Manager** Gary Andrews.

ADDRESS 28 Quai Galliéni 92100 Suresnes.

TELEPHONE **Administration & Reservations UK** 0844 576 8836 (National UK numbers only) or 0800 917 1201, *France* 0825 304 304, *Ireland* 0818 332100 *Outside UK & France* +33 (0) 2 32 14 52 09, **Freight Reservations** *UK and IR* 0844 576 8837, *France and other countries* + 33 (0)2 32 14 52 05, *Spain* + 34 (0)918 272 988.

INTERNET **Email** Via website form **Website** www.ldlines.com *(English, French, Spanish)*

ROUTE OPERATED Poole - Santander (Spain) (26 hrs; *NORMAN ASTURIAS*; 1 per week), Poole - Gijon (Spain) (25hrs, *NORMAN ASTURIAS*; 1 per week), St-Nazaire (France) - Gijon (Spain) (14 hrs; *NORMAN ATLANTIC, NORMAN ASTURIAS*; 3 per week), Rosslare (Ireland) - St-Nazaire (France) (22 hrs; *NORMAN ATLANTIC*; 1 per week), Rosslare (Ireland) - Gijon (Spain) (39 to 48 hrs; *NORMAN ATLANTIC*; 1 per week).

| 1 | NORMAN ASTURIAS | 26500t | 07 | 24.0k | 186.5m | 1000P | 170C | 140L | BA | IT | 93497601 |
| 2 | NORMAN ATLANTIC | 26904t | 09 | 24.0k | 186.5m | 1000P | 170C | 140L | BA | IT | 9435466 |

NORMAN ASTURIAS Built by CN Visentini, Porto Viro, Italy. Whilst under construction, sold to *Stena RoRo* of Sweden and provisionally named the STENA AUSONIA. However, before delivery a charter was arranged with *Balearia* of Spain and she was delivered as the BORJA. Operated between Barcelona and Palma (Majorca). In February 2010 the charter ended and she was laid up at Rotterdam. In April 2010 chartered to *Ave Line* and renamed the BALTIC AMBER. In October 2010 chartered to *DFDS Seaways* to replace the fire-damaged LISCO GLORIA. In February 2011 chartered to *LD Lines* to operate between St Nazaire and Gijon. In June 2011 renamed the NORMAN ASTURIAS. In October 2011 the charter was ended but resumed the following month. In November 2013 transferred to a new Poole - Santander service. From January 2014 she was also used on Poole – Gijon and St Nazaire – Gijon route.

NORMAN ATLANTIC Built as the AKEMAN STREET by CN Visentini, Porto Viro, Italy. Chartered *T-Link Lines* of Italy and operated between Genoa (Italy) and Palermo (Sicily). In 2011 chartered to *Sarema* of Italy to operate between Sardinia and other islands and the Italian mainland. In June 2011 renamed the SCINTU. She continued on Italian Domestic trades for *GNV* then *Moby Lines* during 2013. In October 2013 chartered to *LD Lines* and replaced the NORMAN ASTURIAS on the St-Nazaire - Gijón service. In January 2014 renamed the NORMAN ATLANTIC and also used on new Rosslare – St Nazaire route once per week.

Louis Dreyfus Armateurs is also an 18% shareholder in English Channel and Mediterranean services operated and managed by *DFDS Seaways*.

MYFERRYLINK

THE COMPANY *MyFerryLink* is a French private sector company owned by *Groupe Eurotunnel SA* and operated by *SCOP* (Société coopérative et participative) *SeaFrance*, a co-operative formed primarily of former *SeaFrance* employees. Operations started in August 2012.

MANAGEMENT **Managing Director (UK)** Robin Wilkins.

Manannan (*FotoFlite*)

Norman Asturias (*George Holland*)

ADDRESS *France* 60 Boulevard de Turin, Tour de Lille, Euralille, 59777 Lille, France, **UK** Whitfield Court, Honeywood Close, Whitfield, Dover, Kent CT16 3PX.

TELEPHONE *Passenger reservations and information* 0844 2482 100 (from UK); 0811 654 765 (from Continental Europe), **Freight** + 33(0)3 21 46 80 40.

FAX **UK** - *Passenger* +44 (0)1304 828379, *Freight* + 33(0)3 21 46 80 39.

INTERNET Email clientservices@myferrylink.com (**Freight** freightsales@myferrylink.com) **Website** www.myferrylink.com *(English, French)*

ROUTES OPERATED *Passenger Ferries* Calais - Dover (1 hr 30 mins; *BERLIOZ, RODIN*; 8 per day), *Freight Ferry* Calais - Dover (1 hr 30 mins; *NORD PAS-DE-CALAIS*; 4 per day).

1	BERLIOZ	33940t	05	25.0k	186.0m	1900P	700C	120L	BA2 FR	9305843
2F+	NORD PAS-DE-CALAIS	7264t	87	21.5k	160.1m	100P	-	85L	BA2 FR	8512152
3	RODIN	33796t	01	25.0k	186.0m	1900P	700C	120L	BA2 FR	9232527

BERLIOZ Built as the SEAFRANCE BERLIOZ by Chantiers de l'Atlantique, St Nazaire for *SeaFrance*. Launched in March 2005. In November 2011 laid up. In June 2012 sold to *Eurotransmanche*, a *Groupe Eurotunnel* company. In July 2012 renamed the BERLIOZ. In August 2012 chartered to *MyFerryLink* and resumed operation between Calais and Dover.

NORD PAS-DE-CALAIS Built by Chantiers du Nord et de la Mediterranée, Dunkerque, France as the NORD PAS-DE-CALAIS at Dunkerque, France for *SNCF* for the Dunkerque (Ouest) - Dover train ferry service. Before being used on this service (which required the construction of a new berth at Dover (Western Docks)) in May 1988, she operated road freight services from Calais to Dover Eastern Docks. The train ferry service continued to operate following the opening of the Channel Tunnel in 1994, to convey road vehicles and dangerous loads which were banned from the Tunnel. However, it ceased in December 1995 and, after a refit, in February 1996 she was renamed the SEAFRANCE NORD PAS-DE-CALAIS and switched to the Calais - Dover service, primarily for road freight vehicles and drivers but also advertised as carrying up to 50 car passengers. Since the entry into service of a third multi-purpose ferry, she operated on a freight-only basis. In November 2011 laid up. In June 2012 sold to *Eurotransmanche*. In July renamed the NORD PAS-DE-CALAIS. In November 2012 chartered to *MyFerryLink* and resumed operation between Calais and Dover.

RODIN Built as the SEAFRANCE RODIN by Aker Finnyards, Rauma, Finland for *SeaFrance*. Launched in November 2001. In November 2011 laid up. In June 2012 sold to *Eurotransmanche*. In July 2012 renamed the RODIN. In August 2012 chartered to *MyFerryLink* and resumed operation between Calais and Dover.

NORTHLINK FERRIES

THE COMPANY *NorthLink Ferries* is a UK based company, wholly owned *Serco Group plc*. The service is operated on behalf of Scottish Ministers.

MANAGEMENT **Managing Director** Stuart Garrett, **Customer Service Director** Cheryl Fox.

ADDRESS Ferry Terminal, Ferry Road, Stromness, Orkney KW16 3BH.

TELEPHONE **Customer Services** +44 (0)845 6000 449, **Freight Reservations** +44 (0)845 6060 449.

FAX **Administration** +44 (0)1856 851795.

INTERNET Email info@northlinkferries.co.uk **Website** www.northlinkferries.co.uk *(English)* www.northlinkferries.co.uk/freight-timetables.html *(English)*

ROUTES OPERATED *Passenger Ferries* Scrabster - Stromness (Orkney) (1 hr 30 min; *HAMNAVOE*; up to 3 per day), Aberdeen - Lerwick (Shetland) (direct) (12 hrs; *HJALTLAND, HROSSEY*; 3 northbound/4 southbound per week), Aberdeen - Kirkwall, Hatston New Pier (Orkney) (5 hrs 45 mins) - Lerwick (14 hrs; *HJALTLAND, HROSSEY*; 4 northbound/3 southbound per week). *Freight Ferries* Aberdeen - Kirkwall (Orkney) (12 hrs; *HELLIAR, HILDASAY*; 4 per week), Aberdeen - Lerwick (Shetland) (*HELLIAR, HILDASAY*; 4 per week).

Rodin (*Brian Maxted*)

Nord Pas-de-Calais (*Brian Maxted*)

Hjaltland (*Willie Mackay*)

Graensay (*Miles Cowsill*)

1	HAMNAVOE	8780t	02	19.3k	112.0m	600P	95C	20L	BA	UK	9246061
2F	HELLIAR	7800t	98	17.0k	122.3m	12P	-	86T	A	IM	9119397
3F	HILDASAY	7606t	99	17.0k	122.3m	12P	-	84T	A	IM	9119426
4	HJALTLAND	11720t	02	24.0k	125.0m	600P	150C	30L	BA	UK	9244958
5	HROSSEY	11720t	02	24.0k	125.0m	600P	150C	30L	BA	UK	9244960

HAMNAVOE Built by Aker Finnyards, Rauma, Finland for *NorthLink Orkney and Shetland Ferries Ltd* to operate on the Scrabster - Stromness route. Did not enter service until Spring 2003 due to late completion of work at Scrabster to accommodate the ship. *Caledonian MacBrayne's* HEBRIDEAN ISLES covered between October 2002 and Spring 2003.

HELLIAR Built as the LEHOLA by Astilleros de Huelva SA, Huelva, Spain for the *Estonian Shipping Company*. Initially used on *ESCO* Baltic services. In 1998 chartered to *Czar Peter Line* to operate between Moerdijk (The Netherlands) and Kronstadt (Russia). In 1999 chartered to *Delom* of France to operate between Marseilles and Sete and Tunis. In 2000 she returned to *ESCO*, operating between Kiel and Tallinn. In 2003 chartered to *Scandlines AG* and transferred to subsidiary *Scandlines Estonia AS*. Operated Rostock - Helsinki – Muuga initially and later Rostock – Helsinki. Service finished at the end of 2004 and in 2005 she was chartered to *P&O Ferries* to operate between Hull and Rotterdam and Hull and Zeebrugge. In 2005 sold to *Elmira Shipping* of Greece. Later renamed the RR TRIUMPH. In 2006 transferred to *P&O Irish Sea* to operate between Liverpool and Dublin. In 2007 chartered to *Balearia* of Spain and operated from Barcelona. In December 2007 purchased by *Seatruck Ferries* and renamed the TRIUMPH. In Spring 2008 she was sub-chartered to *Condor Ferries* to cover for the refit period of the COMMODORE GOODWILL. In June 2008 placed on the Liverpool - Dublin route and in July renamed the CLIPPER RACER. In February 2009 replaced by the new CLIPPER PACE. In April 2009 again chartered to *Balearia*. In January 2011 chartered to *NorthLink Ferries* and renamed the HELLIAR.

HILDASAY Built as the LEILI by Astilleros de Huelva SA, Huelva, Spain for the *Estonian Shipping Company*. Used on Baltic services. In 2002 chartered to *Crowley Maritime* of the USA and renamed the PORT EVERGLADES EXPRESS. In 2004 resumed the name LEILI and chartered to *NorseMerchant Ferries* to operate between Birkenhead and Dublin. In July 2005 moved to the Heysham - Belfast route and at the same time sold to *Elmira Shipping* of Greece and renamed the RR SHIELD. In 2007 sold to *Attica Group* of Greece and renamed the SHIELD. In January 2008 sold to *Seatruck Ferries* but continued to be chartered to *Norfolkline*. In June 2009 returned to *Seatruck Ferries*. In January 2009 chartered to *NorthLink Orkney and Shetland Ferries* and renamed the HILDASAY.

HJALTLAND, HROSSEY Built by Aker Finnyards, Rauma, Finland for *NorthLink Orkney and Shetland Ferries* to operate on the Aberdeen - Kirkwall - Lerwick route when services started in 2002.

ORKNEY FERRIES

THE COMPANY *Orkney Ferries Ltd* (previously the *Orkney Islands Shipping Company*) is a British company, owned by *Orkney Islands Council*.

MANAGEMENT Operations Director Capt N H Mills, Ferry Services Manager D I Sawkins.

ADDRESS Shore Street, Kirkwall, Orkney KW15 1LG.

TELEPHONE Administration + 44 (0)1856 872044, Reservations + 44 (0)1856 872044.

FAX Administration & Reservations + 44 (0)1856 872921.

INTERNET Email info@orkneyferries.co.uk Website www.orkneyferries.co.uk *(English)*

ROUTES OPERATED Kirkwall (Mainland) to Eday (1 hr 15 mins), Rapness (Westray) (1 hr 25 mins), Sanday (1 hr 25 mins), Stronsay (1 hr 35 mins), Papa Westray (1 hr 50 mins), North Ronaldsay (2 hrs 30 mins) ('North Isles service') (timings are direct from Kirkwall - sailings via other islands take longer; *EARL SIGURD, EARL THORFINN, VARAGEN*; 1/2 per day except Papa Westray which is twice weekly and North Ronaldsay which is weekly), Pierowall (Westray) - Papa Westray (25 mins; *GOLDEN MARIANA*; up to six per day (Summer service - passenger-only)), Kirkwall - Shapinsay (25 mins; *SHAPINSAY*; 6 per day), Houton (Mainland) to Lyness (Hoy) (35 mins; *HOY HEAD*; 5 per day), and Flotta (35 mins; *HOY HEAD*; 4 per day) ('South Isles service') (timings are direct from Houton - sailings via other islands take longer), Tingwall (Mainland) to Rousay (20 mins; *EYNHALLOW*; 6 per day), Egilsay (30 mins; *EYNHALLOW*; 5 per day) and Wyre (20 mins; *EYNHALLOW*; 5 per day) (timings are direct from Tingwall - sailings via other islands take longer), Stromness (Mainland) to Moaness (Hoy) (25 mins; *GRAEMSAY*; 2/3 per day) and Graemsay (25 mins; *GRAEMSAY*; 2/3 per day) (passenger/cargo service - cars not normally conveyed).

1	EARL SIGURD	771t	90	12.5k	45.0m	190P	26C	•	BA	UK	8902711
2	EARL THORFINN	771t	90	12.5k	45.0m	190P	26C	•	BA	UK	8902723
3	EYNHALLOW	104t	87	10.5k	28.8m	95P	11C	•	BA	UK	8960880
4p	GOLDEN MARIANA	33t	73	9.5k	15.2m	40P	0C	•	•	UK	
5	GRAEMSAY	90t	96	10.0k	20.6m	73P	2C	•	C	UK	
6	HOY HEAD	358t	94	11.0k	53.5m	125P	24C	3L	BA	UK	9081722
7	SHAPINSAY	199t	89	10.0k	32.6m	91P	16C	•	BA	UK	8814184
8	THORSVOE	385t	91	10.6k	35.0m	122P	16C	•	BA	UK	9014743
9	VARAGEN	928t	88	14.5k	49.9m	144P	33C	5L	BA	UK	8818154

EARL SIGURD, EARL THORFINN Built by McTay Marine, Bromborough, Wirral, UK to inaugurate ro-ro working on the 'North Isles service'.

EYNHALLOW Built by David Abels Boat Builders, Bristol, UK to inaugurate ro-ro services from Tingwall (Mainland) to Rousay, Egilsay and Wyre. In 1991 she was lengthened by 5 metres, to increase car capacity.

GOLDEN MARIANA Built by Bideford Shipyard Ltd, Bideford, UK for *A J G England* of Padstow as a dual-purpose passenger and fishing vessel. In 1975 sold to *M MacKenzie* of Ullapool, then to *Pentland Ferries*, *Wide Firth Ferry* in 1982, and *Orkney Islands Council* in 1986. Passenger-only vessel. Generally operates summer-only feeder service between Pierowall (Westray) and Papa Westray.

GRAEMSAY Built by Ailsa Shipbuilding, Troon UK to operate between Stromness (Mainland), Moaness (Hoy) and Graemsay. Designed to offer an all-year-round service to these islands, primarily for passengers and cargo. Between October 2009 and January 2010 lengthened by 4.4 metres.

HOY HEAD Built by Appledore Shipbuilders Ltd, Appledore, UK to replace the THORSVOE on the 'South Isles service'. During winter 2012/13 extended by 14 metres at Cammell Laird Shiprepairers & Shipbuilders, Birkenhead, England.

SHAPINSAY Built by Yorkshire Drydock Ltd, Hull, UK for the service from Kirkwall (Mainland) to Shapinsay. In April 2011 lengthened by 6 metres at the Macduff Shipyards, Macduff, Scotland to increase car capacity from 12 to 16 and re-engined.

THORSVOE Built by Campbeltown Shipyard, Campbeltown, UK for the 'South Isles service'. In 1994 replaced by the new HOY HEAD and became the main reserve vessel for the fleet.

VARAGEN Built by Cochrane Shipbuilders, Selby, UK for *Orkney Ferries*, a private company established to start a new route between Gills Bay (Caithness, Scotland) and Burwick (South Ronaldsay, Orkney). However, due to problems with the terminals it was not possible to maintain regular services. In 1991, the company was taken over by *Orkney Islands Shipping Company* and the VARAGEN became part of their fleet, sharing the 'North Isles service' with the EARL SIGURD and the EARL THORFINN and replacing the freight vessel ISLANDER (494t, 1969).

P&O FERRIES

THE COMPANY *P&O Ferries Holdings Ltd* is a private sector company, a subsidiary of *Dubai World*, owned by the Government of Dubai. In Autumn 2002 *P&O North Sea Ferries*, P&O Irish Sea, P&O Portsmouth and *P&O Stena Line* (*Stena Line* involvement having ceased) were merged into a single operation.

MANAGEMENT **Chief Executive Officer** Helen Deeble, **Fleet Director** John Garner, **Communications Director** Chris Laming, **Freight Director** Ronald Daelman, **Human Resources Director** Lesley Cotton, **Ports Director** Sue Mackenzie, **Commercial Director** Janette Bell, **Company Secretary** Susan Kitchin.

Thorsvoe *(Miles Cowsill)*

Pride of Rotterdam *(Miles Cowsill)*

ADDRESSES *Head Office and Dover Services* Channel House, Channel View Road, Dover, Kent CT17 9TJ, *Hull* King George Dock, Hedon Road, Hull HU9 5QA, *Larne* P&O Irish Sea, Larne Harbour, Larne, Co Antrim BT40 1AW *Rotterdam* Beneluxhaven, Rotterdam (Europoort), Postbus 1123, 3180 Rozenburg, Netherlands, *Zeebrugge* Leopold II Dam 13, Havendam, 8380 Zeebrugge, Belgium.

TELEPHONE Administration *UK* + 44 (0)1304 863000, **Passenger Reservations** *UK* 08716 64 64 64, *France* + 33 (0)825 12 01 56, *Belgium* + 32 (0)70 70 77 71, *The Netherlands* + 31 (0)20 20 08333, *Spain* + 34 (0)902 02 04 61, *Luxembourg* + 34 (0)20 80 82 94. **Freight Reservations** *UK* 0870 6000 868, *Irish Republic* + 353 (0)1 855 0522.

FAX Passenger Reservations *UK East and South Coast* + 44 (0)1304 863464, *West Coast* 44 (0)2828 872195, *The Netherlands* + 31 (0)118 1225 5215, *Belgium* + 32 (0)50 54 71 12, **Freight Reservations** *Cairnryan* + 44 (0)1581 200282, *Larne* + 44 (0)28 2827 2477..

INTERNET Email customer.services@poferries.com Website www.poferries.com *(English, French, Dutch, German)* www.poirishsea.com *(English)* www.poferriesfreight.com *(English, French, German)*

ROUTES OPERATED Passenger - conventional ferries Dover - Calais (1 hr 15 mins - 1 hr 30 mins; *PRIDE OF BURGUNDY, PRIDE OF CANTERBURY, PRIDE OF KENT, SPIRIT OF BRITAIN, SPIRIT OF FRANCE*; up to 25 per day), Hull - Zeebrugge (Belgium) (from 12 hrs 30 mins; *PRIDE OF BRUGES, PRIDE OF YORK*; 1 per day), Hull - Rotterdam (Beneluxhaven, Europoort) (The Netherlands) (from 10 hrs; *PRIDE OF HULL, PRIDE OF ROTTERDAM*; 1 per day), Cairnryan - Larne (1 hr 45 min; *EUROPEAN CAUSEWAY, EUROPEAN HIGHLANDER*; 7 per day), Liverpool - Dublin (8 hrs; *EUROPEAN ENDEAVOUR, NORBANK, NORBAY*; up to 3 per day (some sailings are freight only). **Fast Ferry** (March-October) Cairnryan - Larne (1 hr; *EXPRESS*; 1 per day), Troon - Larne (1 hr 49 min; *EXPRESS* 2 per day). **Freight-only** Tilbury - Zeebrugge (8 hrs; *NORSKY, NORSTREAM* ; 10 per week), Middlesbrough (Teesport) - Rotterdam (Beneluxhaven, Europoort) (16 hrs; *WILHELMINE* ; 3 per week), Middlesbrough (Teesport) - Zeebrugge (15 hrs 30 mins; *BORE SONG*; 3 per week).

1	BORE SONG	25235t	11	18.5k	195.0m	12P	-	210T	A2	FI	9443566
2	EUROPEAN CAUSEWAY	20646t	00	22.7k	159.5m	410P	315C	84T	BA2	BS	9208394
3	EUROPEAN ENDEAVOUR	22152t	00	22.5k	180.0m	366P	-	120L	BA2	UK	9181106
4	EUROPEAN HIGHLANDER	21128t	02	22.6k	162.7m	410P	315C	84T	BA2	BS	9244116
5F+•	EUROPEAN SEAWAY	22986t	91	21.0k	179.7m	200P	-	120L	BA2	UK	9007283
6»	EXPRESS	5902t	98	43.0k	91.3m	868P	195C	-	A	BS	9176046
7	NORBANK	17464t	93	22.5k	166.7m	114P	-	125T	A	NL	9056583
8	NORBAY	17464t	92	21.5k	166.7m	114P	-	125T	A	BM	9056595
9F	NORSKY	19992t	99	20.0k	180.0m	12P	-	194T	A	NL	9186182
10F	NORSTREAM	19992t	99	20.0k	180.0m	12P	-	194T	A	NL	9186194
11	PRIDE OF BRUGES	31598t	87	18.5k	179.0m	1050P	310C	185T	A	NL	8503797
12	PRIDE OF BURGUNDY	28138t	92	21.0k	179.7m	1420P	465C	120L	BA2	UK	9015254
13	PRIDE OF CANTERBURY	30635t	91	21.0k	179.7m	2000P	537C	120L	BA2	UK	9007295
14	PRIDE OF HULL	59925t	01	22.0k	215.4m	1360P	205C	263T	AS	BS	9208629
15	PRIDE OF KENT	30635t	92	21.0k	179.7m	2000P	537C	120L	BA2	UK	9015266
16	PRIDE OF ROTTERDAM	59925t	00	22.0k	215.4m	1360P	205C	263T	AS	NL	9208617
17	PRIDE OF YORK	31785t	87	18.5k	179.0m	1050P	310C	185T	A	BS	8501957
18	SPIRIT OF BRITAIN	47592t	11	22.0k-	212.0m	2000P	194C	180L	BA2	UK	9524231
19	SPIRIT OF FRANCE	47592t	12	22.0k-	212.0m	2000P	194C	180L	BA2	UK	9533816
20F	WILHELMINE	21020t	12	15.8k	150.0m	12P	-	170T	A	LU	9539080

BORE SONG Built by Flensburger Schiffbau-Gesellschaft, Flensburg, Germany for *Bore Shipowners (Rettig Group Bore)* of Finland. In July 2011 chartered to *Mann Lines* to cover for the ESTRADEN'S refit. In September 2011 chartered to *P&O Ferries* and placed on the Middlesbrough - Zeebrugge route.

EUROPEAN CAUSEWAY Built by Mitsubishi Heavy Industries, Shimonoseki, Japan for *P&O Irish Sea* for the Cairnryan - Larne service.

EUROPEAN ENDEAVOUR Built as the MIDNIGHT MERCHANT by Astilleros Españoles SA, Seville, Spain for *Cenargo* (then owners of *NorseMerchant Ferries*). On delivery, chartered to *Norfolkline* to operate

Norsky *(J.J. Jager)*

Pride of Bruges *(J.J. Jager)*

Spirit of France *(John Hendy)*

as second vessel on the Dover - Dunkerque (Ouest) service. In 2002 modified to allow two-deck loading. In 2006 chartered to *Acciona Trasmediterranea* of Spain and renamed the EL GRECO. Used on Mediterranean and Canary Island services. In 2007 sold to *P&O Ferries* and renamed the EUROPEAN ENDEAVOUR. Operated on the Dover - Calais route and as a re-fit relief vessel on Irish Sea routes. In May 2010 laid up. In February 2011 moved to the Liverpool - Dublin route.

EUROPEAN HIGHLANDER Built by Mitsubishi Heavy Industries, Shimonoseki, Japan for *P&O Irish Sea* for the Cairnryan - Larne service.

EUROPEAN SEAWAY Built by Schichau Seebeckwerft AG, Bremerhaven, Germany for *P&O European Ferries* for the Dover - Zeebrugge freight service. In 2000 a regular twice-daily freight-only Dover-Calais service was established, using this vessel which continued to operate to Zeebrugge at night. In 2001 car passengers (not foot or coach passengers) began to be conveyed on the Dover - Zeebrugge service. In 2003 the Zeebrugge service ended and she operated only between Dover and Calais in a freight-only mode. In 2004 withdrawn and laid up. In January 2005 returned to the Dover – Calais route. In July 2012 chartered to

GLID, a joint venture between Centrica Renewable Energy Limited and EIG, for use by technicians working on the North Sea Lynn and Inner Dowsing wind farm array four miles off Skegness. In October 2012 returned to the Dover - Calais service. In April 2013 laid up at Tilbury.

EXPRESS Incat 91m catamaran built at Hobart, Tasmania, Australia for *Buquebus* of Argentina as the CATALONIA 1 and used by *Buquebus España* on their service between Barcelona (Spain) and Mallorca. In April 2000 chartered to *P&O Portsmouth* and renamed the PORTSMOUTH EXPRESS. During Winter 2000/01 she operated for *Buquebus* between Buenos Aires (Argentina) and Piriapolis (Uruguay) and was renamed the CATALONIA. Returned to *P&O Portsmouth* in Spring 2001 and was renamed the PORTSMOUTH EXPRESS. Returned to *Buquebus* in Autumn 2001 and then returned to *P&O Portsmouth* in Spring 2002. Laid up in Europe during Winter 2002/03 and renamed the CATALONIA. She returned to *P&O Ferries* in Spring 2003 trading under the marketing name 'Express'. In November she was renamed the EXPRESS. In 2004 she operated as the 'Cherbourg Express'. In 2005 transferred to *P&O Irish Sea* and operated on the Larne - Cairnryan/Troon service.

NORBANK Built by Van der Giessen-de Noord, Krimpen aan den IJssel, Rotterdam, The Netherlands for *North Sea Ferries* for the Hull - Rotterdam service. She was originally built for and chartered to *Nedlloyd* but the charter was taken over by *P&O* in 1996 and she was bought by *P&O* in 2003. She retains Dutch crew and registry. In May 2001 moved to the Felixstowe - Europoort route. In January 2002 transferred to *P&O Irish Sea* and operated on the Liverpool – Dublin route.

NORBAY Built by Van der Giessen-de Noord, Krimpen aan den IJssel, Rotterdam, The Netherlands for *North Sea Ferries* for the Hull - Rotterdam service. Owned by *P&O*. In January 2002 transferred to *P&O Irish Sea* and operated on the Liverpool – Dublin route.

NORSKY, NORSTREAM Built by Aker Finnyards, Rauma, Finland for *Bore Line* of Finland and chartered to *P&O North Sea Ferries*. They generally operated on the Teesport - Zeebrugge service. In September 2011, the NORSTREAM was moved to the Tilbury - Zeebrugge route. In January 2013, the NORSKY was also moved to the Tilbury - Zeebrugge route.

PRIDE OF BRUGES Built as the NORSUN by NKK, Tsurumi, Japan for the Hull - Rotterdam service of *North Sea Ferries*. She was owned by *Nedlloyd* and was sold to *P&O* in 1996 but retains Dutch crew and registry. In May 2001 replaced by the PRIDE OF ROTTERDAM and in July 2001, after a major refurbishment, she was transferred to the Hull - Zeebrugge service, replacing the NORSTAR (26919t, 1974). In 2003 renamed the PRIDE OF BRUGES.

PRIDE OF BURGUNDY Built by Schichau Seebeckwerft AG, Bremerhaven, Germany for *P&O European Ferries* for the Dover - Calais service. When construction started she was due to be a sister vessel to the EUROPEAN SEAWAY (see Section 3) called the EUROPEAN CAUSEWAY and operate on the Zeebrugge freight route. However, it was decided that she should be completed as a passenger/freight vessel (the design allowed for conversion) and she was launched as the PRIDE OF BURGUNDY. In 1998, transferred to *P&O Stena Line* and renamed the P&OSL BURGUNDY. In 2002 renamed the PO BURGUNDY and in 2003 renamed the PRIDE OF BURGUNDY. In 2004 she operated mainly in freight-only mode. In 2005 returned to full passenger service.

Pride of Canterbury (*Miles Cowsill*)

European Highlander (*Gordon Hislip*)

PRIDE OF CANTERBURY Built as the EUROPEAN PATHWAY by Schichau Seebeckwerft AG, Bremerhaven, Germany for *P&O European Ferries* for the Dover - Zeebrugge freight service. In 1998 transferred to *P&O Stena Line*. In 2001 car/foot passengers were again conveyed on the route. In 2002/03 rebuilt as a full passenger vessel and renamed the PRIDE OF CANTERBURY; now operates between Dover and Calais.

PRIDE OF HULL Built by Fincantieri-Cantieri Navali Italiani SpA, Venice, Italy for *P&O North Sea Ferries* to replace (with the PRIDE OF ROTTERDAM) the NORSEA and NORSUN plus the freight vessels NORBAY and NORBANK on the Hull - Rotterdam service.

PRIDE OF KENT Built as the EUROPEAN HIGHWAY by Schichau Seebeckwerft AG, Bremerhaven, Germany for *P&O European Ferries* for the Dover - Zeebrugge freight service. In 1998 transferred to *P&O Stena Line*. In Summer 1999 she operated full-time between Dover and Calais. She returned to the Dover - Zeebrugge route in the autumn when the P&OSL AQUITAINE was transferred to the Dover - Calais service. In 2001 car/foot passengers were again conveyed on the route. In 2002/03 rebuilt as a full passenger vessel and renamed the PRIDE OF KENT; now operates between Dover and Calais.

PRIDE OF ROTTERDAM Built by Fincantieri-Cantieri Navali Italiani SpA, Venice, Italy. Keel laid as the PRIDE OF HULL but launched as the PRIDE OF ROTTERDAM. Owned by Dutch interests until 2006 when she was sold to *P&O Ferries*. Further details as the PRIDE OF HULL.

PRIDE OF YORK Built as the NORSEA by Govan Shipbuilders Ltd, Glasgow, UK for the Hull - Rotterdam service of *North Sea Ferries* (jointly owned by *P&O* and *The Royal Nedlloyd Group* of The Netherlands until 1996). In December 2001 she was replaced by the new PRIDE OF HULL and, after a two-month refurbishment, in 2002 transferred to the Hull - Zeebrugge service, replacing the NORLAND (26290t, 1974). In 2003 renamed the PRIDE OF YORK.

SPIRIT OF BRITAIN, SPIRIT OF FRANCE Built by STX Europe, Rauma, Finland for the Dover - Calais service. Car capacity relates to dedicated car deck only; additional cars can be accommodated on the freight decks as necessary.

WILHELMINE Built by the Kyokuyo Shipyard, Shimonoseki, Japan for *CLdN*. After completion, a additional deck and sponsons were retro-fitted at the Chengxi Shipyard, Jiangyin, China. Initially used on the Zeebrugge - Purfleet service. In January 2013 chartered to *P&O Ferries* to operate between Tilbury and Zeebrugge. After three weeks moved to the Middlesbrough - Rotterdam service.

PENTLAND FERRIES

THE COMPANY *Pentland Ferries* is a UK private sector company.

MANAGEMENT Managing Director Andrew Banks, **Designated Person Ashore** Kathryn Banks.

ADDRESS Pier Road, St Margaret's Hope, South Ronaldsay, Orkney KW17 2SW.

TELEPHONE Administration & Reservations + 44 (0)1856 831226.

FAX Administration & Reservations + 44 (0)1856 831697.

INTERNET Email sales@pentlandferries.co.uk Website www.pentlandferries.co.uk *(English)*

ROUTE OPERATED Gills Bay (Caithness) - St Margaret's Hope (South Ronaldsay, Orkney) (1 hour; *PENTALINA*; up to 4 per day).

1	PENTALINA	2382t	08	17.1k	59.0m	345P	70C	9L	A	UK 9437969

PENTALINA Built by FBMA Marine, Cebu, Philippines for *Pentland Ferries*.

Wilhelmine (J.J.Jager)

Red Falcon (Andrew Cooke)

Red Osprey *(Andrew Cooke)*

Red Jet 5 *(Andrew Cooke)*

RED FUNNEL FERRIES

THE COMPANY Red Funnel Ferries is the trading name of the *Southampton, Isle of Wight and South of England Royal Mail Steam Packet Company Limited*, a British private sector company. The company was acquired by *JP Morgan International Capital Corporation* in 2000; it was purchased by the management in 2004 and in 2007 it was sold to *Infracapital Partners LP* – the infrastructure fund of the *Prudential Group*.

MANAGEMENT **Managing Director** Tom Docherty, **Commercial Director** Colin Hetherington.

ADDRESS 12 Bugle Street, Southampton SO14 2JY.

TELEPHONE **Administration** *UK* 0844 844 2699, **Passenger Reservations** *UK* 0844 844 9988, *Elsewhere* +44 (0) 845 155 2442, **Freight Reservations** *UK* 0844 844 2666.

FAX **Administration & Reservations** *UK* 0844 844 2698.

INTERNET **Email** post@redfunnel.co.uk **Website** www.redfunnel.co.uk *(English)*

ROUTES OPERATED **Conventional Ferries** Southampton - East Cowes (55 mins; *RED EAGLE, RED FALCON, RED OSPREY*; hourly). **Fast Passenger Ferries** Southampton - West Cowes (22 mins; *RED JET 3, RED JET 4, RED JET 5*; every hour or half hour).

1	RED EAGLE	3953t	96	13.0k	93.2m	895P	200C	18L	BA	UK	9117337
2	RED FALCON	3953t	94	13.0k	93.2m	895P	200C	18L	BA	UK	9064047
3»p	RED JET 3	213t	98	33.0k	32.9m	190P	0C	0L	-	UK	9182758
4»p	RED JET 4	342t	03	35.0k	39.8m	277P	0C	0L	-	UK	9295854
5»p	RED JET 5	209t	99	35.0k	35.0m	177P	0L	0L	-	UK	8954415
6	RED OSPREY	3953t	94	13.0k	93.2m	895P	200C	18L	BA	UK	9064059

RED EAGLE Built by Ferguson Shipbuilders, Port Glasgow, UK for the Southampton - East Cowes service. During Winter 2004/05 stretched by 10 metres and height raised by 3 metres at Gdansk, Poland.

RED FALCON Built by Ferguson Shipbuilders, Port Glasgow, UK for the Southampton - East Cowes service. In 2004 stretched by 10 metres and height raised by 3 metres at Gdansk, Poland. In spring 2014 she received a £2m upgrade (including extended accomodation).

RED JET 3 FBM Marine catamaran built at Cowes, UK for the Southampton - West Cowes service.

RED JET 4 North West Bay Ships Pty Ltd catamaran built in Hobart, Tasmania, Australia for the Southampton - West Cowes service.

RED JET 5 Built by Pequot River Shipworks, New London, Connecticut, USA to FBM Marine design as the BO HENGY for *Bahamas Fast Ferries* of The Bahamas. In May 2009 sold to *Red Funnel Ferries* and renamed the RED JET 5.

RED OSPREY Built by Ferguson Shipbuilders, Port Glasgow, UK for the Southampton - East Cowes service. In 2003 stretched by 10 metres and height raised by 3 metres at Gdansk, Poland.

SHETLAND ISLANDS COUNCIL

THE COMPANY *Shetland Islands Council* is a British local government authority.

MANAGEMENT **Ferry Services Manager** Ken Duerden, Acting **Marine Superintendent** Kevin Main.

ADDRESS Port Administration Building, Sella Ness, Mossbank, Shetland ZE2 9QR.

TELEPHONE **Administration** +44 (0)1806 244234, 244266, **Reservations** *Yell Sound & Bluemull* +44 (0)1595 745804, *Fair Isle* +44 (0)1595 760222, *Whalsay* +44(0)1806 566259, *Skerries* +44 (0)1806 515266, *Papa Stour* +44 (0)1595 745804.

VOICEBANK *Bluemull Sound* +44 (0)1595 743971, *Bressay* +44 (0)1595 743974, *Fair Isle* +44 (0)1595 743978, *Papa Stour* +44 (0)1595 743977, *Skerries* +44 (0)1595 743975, *Whalsay* +44 (0)1595 743973, *Yell Sound* +44 (0)1595 743972.

FAX +44 (0)1806 244232.

INTERNET Email ferries@sic.shetland.gov.uk Website: www.shetland.gov.uk/ferries *(English)*

ROUTES OPERATED Yell Sound Service Toft (Mainland) - Ulsta (Yell) (20 mins; *DAGALIEN, DAGGRI*; up to 26 per day), **Bluemull Sound Service** (Gutcher (Yell) - Belmont (Unst) (10 mins; *BIGGA, FIVLA, GEIRA*; up to 28 per day), Gutcher – Hamars Ness (Fetlar) (25 mins; *BIGGA, FIVLA, GEIRA*; up to 8 per day), **Bressay** Lerwick (Mainland) - Maryfield (Bressay) (5 mins; *LEIRNA*; up to 23 per day), **Whalsay** Laxo/Vidlin (Mainland) - Symbister (Whalsay) (30-45 mins; *HENDRA, LINGA*; up to 18 per day), **Skerries** Vidlin (Mainland) – Out Skerries (1 hr 30 mins; *FILLA*; up to 10 per week), Out Skerries – Lerwick (3 hours; *FILLA*; 2 per week), **Fair Isle** (Grutness (Mainland) - Fair Isle (3 hrs; *GOOD SHEPHERD IV*; 2 per week), **Papa Stour** West Burrafirth (Mainland) – Papa Stour (40 mins; *SNOLDA*; up to 7 per week).

1	BIGGA	274t	91	11.0k	33.5m	96P	21C	4L	BA	UK	9000821
2	DAGALIEN	1861t	04	12.0k	61m	145P	30C	4L	BA	UK	9291626
3	DAGGRI	1861t	04	12.0k	61m	145P	30C	4L	BA	UK	9291614
4	FILLA	356t	03	12.0k	35.5m	30P	10C	2L	BA	UK	9269192
5	FIVLA	230t	85	11.0k	29.9m	95P	15C	4L	BA	UK	8410237
6	GEIRA	226t	88	10.8k	29.9m	95P	15C	4L	BA	UK	8712489
7	GOOD SHEPHERD IV	76t	86	10.0k	18.3m	12P	1C	0L	C	UK	
8	HENDRA	248	82	11.0k	33.8m	100P	18C	4L	BA	UK	8200254
9	LEIRNA	420t	92	9.0k	35.1m	100P	20C	4L	BA	UK	9050199
10	LINGA	658t	01	11.0k	35.8m	100P	16C	2L	BA	UK	9242170
11	SNOLDA	130t	83	9.0k	24.4m	12P	6C	1L	A	UK	8302090
12	THORA	147t	75	8.5k	25.3m	93P	10C	2L	BA	UK	7347354

BIGGA Built by JW Miller & Sons Ltd, St Monans, Fife, UK. Used on the Toft - Ulsta service. In 2005 moved to the Bluemull Sound service.

DAGALIEN, DAGGRI Built by Stocznia Polnócna, Gdansk, Poland to replace the BIGGA and HENDRA on Toft - Ulsta service.

FILLA Built by Stocznia Polnócna, Gdansk, Poland for the Lerwick /Vidlin - Out Skerries service. She looks like an oil rig supply vessel and is capable of transporting fresh water for replenishing the tanks on the Skerries in case of drought.

FIVLA Built by Ailsa Shipbuilding, Troon, UK. Now a spare vessel, though often used on the Bluemull service.

GEIRA Built by Richard Dunston (Hessle), Hessle, UK. Formerly used on the Laxo - Symbister route. Replaced by the HENDRA in 2005 and moved to the Bluemull Sound service.

GOOD SHEPHERD IV Built by JW Miller & Sons Ltd, St Monans, Fife, UK. Used on the service between Grutness (Mainland) and Fair Isle. Vehicles conveyed by special arrangement and generally consist of agricultural vehicles. She is pulled up on the marine slip on Fair Isle at the conclusion of each voyage.

HENDRA Built by McTay Marine, Bromborough, Wirral, UK for the Laxo - Symbister service. In 2002 transferred to the Toft - Ulsta service. In 2004 replaced by new vessels DAGGRI and DAGALIEN and moved to the Bluemull Sound service. In May 2005 returned to the Laxo - Symbister service as second vessel.

LEIRNA Built by Ferguson Shipbuilders, Port Glasgow, UK. Used on the Lerwick - Maryfield (Bressay) service.

LINGA Built by Stocznia Polnócna, Gdansk, Poland. Used on the Laxo - Symbister service.

SNOLDA Built as the FILLA by Sigbjorn Iversen, Flekkefjord, Norway. Used on the Lerwick (Mainland) - Out Skerries and Vidlin (Mainland) - Out Skerries services. At other times she operated freight and

Bigga *(Miles Cowsill)*

Dagalien *(Miles Cowsill)*

charter services around the Shetland Archipelago. She resembles a miniature oil rig supply vessel. Passenger capacity was originally 20 from 1st April to 31st October inclusive but is now 12 all year. In 2003 renamed the SNOLDA; replaced by the new FILLA and, in 2004, transferred to the West Burrafirth - Papa Stour route.

THORA Built by Tórshavnor Skipasmidja, Tórshavn, Faroe Islands. After a period as a spare vessel, in 1998 she took over the Laxo - Symbister service from the withdrawn KJELLA (158t, 1957). Withdrawn again in 2001 and became a spare vessel.

STENA LINE

THE COMPANY *Stena Line Limited* is incorporated in Great Britain and registered in England and Wales. *Stena Line BV* is a Dutch company. The ultimate parent undertaking is *Stena AB* of Sweden.

MANAGEMENT Area Director, North Sea Pim de Lange, Area Director, Irish Sea Michael McGrath.

ADDRESS *UK* 1 Suffolk Way, Sevenoaks, Kent TN13 1YL, *The Netherlands* PO Box 2, 3150 AA, Hook of Holland, The Netherlands.

TELEPHONE Administration *UK* +44 (0)1732 585858, *The Netherlands* +31 (0)174 389333, Reservations *UK* 08075 707070 (from UK only), *The Netherlands* +31 (0)174 315811.

FAX Administration & Reservations *UK* +44 (0)1407 606811, *The Netherlands* +31 (0)174 387045, Telex 31272.

INTERNET Email info@stenaline.com **Website** www.stenaline.com (*English, Danish, Dutch, German, Norwegian, Polish, Swedish*)

ROUTES OPERATED Conventional Ferries Cairnryan - Belfast (2 hrs 15 mins; *STENA SUPERFAST VII, STENA SUPERFAST VII*; up to 6 per day, Port of Liverpool (Twelve Quays River Terminal, Birkenhead) - Belfast (8 hrs; *STENA HIBERNIA (freight only), STENA LAGAN, STENA MERSEY*; 1 per day (Mon), 2/3 per day (Sun, Tue-Sat)), Holyhead - Dublin (3 hrs 15 mins; *STENA ADVENTURER, STENA NORDICA*; 4 per day), Fishguard - Rosslare (3 hrs 30 mins; *STENA EUROPE*; 2 per day), Rosslare - Cherbourg (20 hrs; *STENA HORIZON*; 3 per week), Harwich - Hook of Holland (The Netherlands) (7 hrs 30 mins; *STENA BRITANNICA, STENA HOLLANDICA*; 2 per day), **Fast Ferry** Holyhead - Dún Laoghaire (2 hrs; *STENA EXPLORER (April - September only)*; 1 per day), **Freight Ferries** Heysham - Belfast (7 hrs; *STENA PERFORMER, STENA PRECISION*; 2 per day), Harwich - Rotterdam (8 hrs; *CAPUCINE, SEVERINE*; 11 per week), Killingholme - Hook of Holland (11 hrs; *STENA TRANSIT, STENA TRANSPORTER*; 1 per day).

1F	CAPUCINE	16342t	11	16.0k	150.0m	12P	-	140T	A	UK 9539066
2F	SEVERINE	16342t	12	16.0k	150.0m	12P	-	140T	A	NL 9539078
3	STENA ADVENTURER	43532t	03	22.0k	210.8m	1500P	-	210L	BA2	UK 9235529
4	STENA BRITANNICA	63600t	10	22.0k	240.0m	1200P	-	300T	BA2	UK 9419175
5	STENA EUROPE	24828t	81	20.5k	149.0m	2076P	456C	60T	BA	UK 7901760
6»	STENA EXPLORER	19638t	96	40.0k	126.6m	1500P	375C	50L	A	UK 9080194
7F	STENA HIBERNIA	13017t	96	18.6k	142.5m	12P	-	114T	A	NL 9121637
8	STENA HOLLANDICA	63600t	10	22.5k	240.0m	1200P	-	300T	BA2	NL 9419163
9	STENA HORIZON	26500t	06	23.5k	186.5m	1000P	200C	120L	A	IT 9332559
10	STENA LAGAN	27510t	05	23.5k	186.5m	980P	160C	135T	A	UK 9329849
11	STENA MERSEY	27510t	05	23.5k	186.5m	980P	160C	135T	A	UK 9329851
12	STENA NORDICA	24206t	01	25.7k	169.8m	405P	375C	122T	BA2	UK 9215505
13F	STENA PERFORMER	19722t	12	21.0k	142.0m	12P	-	151T	A	IM 9506227
14F	STENA PRECISION	19722t	12	21.0k	142.0m	12P	-	151T	A	IM 9506239
15	STENA SUPERFAST VII	30285t	01	26.6k	203.3m	717P	695C	110L	BA2	UK 9198941
16	STENA SUPERFAST VIII	30285t	01	26.6k	203.3m	717P	695C	110L	BA2	UK 9198953
17F+	STENA TRANSIT	34700t	11	22.2k	212.0m	300P	-	290T	A2	NL 9469388
18F+	STENA TRANSPORTER	34700t	11	22.2k	212.0m	300P	-	290T	A2	NL 9469376

Stena Nordica *(Gordon Hislip)*

Stena Adventurer *(Miles Cowsill)*

CAPUCINE, SEVERINE Built by the Kyokuyo Shipyard, Shimonoseki, Japan for *CLdN*. Initially operated on their Ipswich - Rotterdam service. This service was suspended in August 2012. In September, they were chartered to *Stena Line* and placed on the Harwich - Rotterdam service.

STENA ADVENTURER Ro-pax vessel built by Hyundai Heavy Industries, Ulsan, South Korea, for *Stena RoRo* and chartered to *Stena Line* to operate between Holyhead and Dublin.

STENA BRITANNICA Built by Waden Yards in Wismar and Warnemünde, Germany, for *Stena Rederi* (bow sections constructed at Warnemünde and stern and final assembly at Wismar). Replaced the 2003 built STENA BRITANNICA on the Harwich - Hook of Holland service.

STENA EUROPE Built as the KRONPRINSESSAN VICTORIA by Götaverken Arendal AB, Gothenburg, Sweden for *Göteborg-Frederikshavn Linjen* of Sweden (trading as *Sessan Linjen*) for their Gothenburg - Frederikshavn service. Shortly after delivery, the company was taken over by *Stena Line* and services were marketed as *Stena-Sessan Line* for a period. In 1982 she was converted to an overnight ferry by changing one vehicle deck into two additional decks of cabins and she was switched to the Gothenburg - Kiel route (with, during the summer, daytime runs from Gothenburg to Frederikshavn and Kiel to Korsør (Denmark)). In 1989 she was transferred to the Oslo - Frederikshavn route and renamed the STENA SAGA. In 1994, transferred to *Stena Line BV*, renamed the STENA EUROPE and operated between Hook of Holland and Harwich. She was withdrawn in June 1997, transferred to the *Lion Ferry* (a *Stena Line* subsidiary) Karlskrona - Gdynia service and renamed the LION EUROPE. In 1998 she was transferred back to *Stena Line* (remaining on the same route) and renamed the STENA EUROPE. In early 2002 the cabins installed in 1982 were removed and other modifications made and she was transferred to the Fishguard - Rosslare route.

STENA EXPLORER Finnyards HSS1500 built at Rauma, Finland for *Stena RoRo* and chartered to *Stena Line*. Operates on the Holyhead - Dún Laoghaire route.

STENA HIBERNIA Built as the MAERSK IMPORTER by Miho Shipyard, Shimizu, Japan for *Norfolkline*. Used on the Scheveningen (from 2007 Vlaardingen) - Felixstowe service. In October 2009 moved to the Heysham-Belfast service. In July 2010 renamed the HIBERNIA SEAWAYS. In July 2011 renamed the STENA HIBERNIA. In September 2012 transferred to *Stena RoRo*. In November chartered to *Stena Line* and placed on the Birkenhead - Belfast service.

STENA HOLLANDICA Built by Nordic Yards in Wismar and Warnemünde, Germany, for *Stena Rederi* (bow sections constructed at Warnemünde and stern and final assembly at Wismar) to replace the previous STENA HOLLANDICA on the Harwich - Hook of Holland service. Entered service May 2010.

STENA HORIZON Built as the CARTOUR BETA by CN Visentini, Porto Viro, Italy for Levantina Trasporti of Italy. Chartered to *Caronte & Tourist* of Italy and operated between Messina and Salerno (Sicily). In October 2011 chartered to *Celtic Link Ferries*, renamed the CELTIC HORIZON and placed on the Rosslare - Cherbourg route. In March 2014 service and charter taken over by *Stena Line*. Renamed the STENA HORIZON.

STENA LAGAN, STENA MERSEY Built as the LAGAN VIKING and MERSEY VIKING by CN Visentini, Donada, Italy for *Levantina Trasporti* of Italy. Chartered to *NorseMerchant Ferries* and placed on the Birkenhead - Belfast route. In 2008 sold to *Norfolkline*, then resold to *Epic Shipping* and chartered back. In August 2010, following *Norfolkline's* purchase by *DFDS Seaways*, they were renamed the LAGAN SEAWAYS and MERSEY SEAWAYS respectively. Between January and July 2011 they were operated by *Stena Line Irish Sea Ferries*, a 'stand-alone' company pending consideration of the take-over by the UK and Irish competition authorities. In July 2011 the take-over was confirmed and in August 2011 they were renamed the STENA LAGAN and STENA MERSEY. In April 2012 they sold to *Stena RoRo*; they continue to be chartered to *Stena Line*.

STENA NORDICA Built as the EUROPEAN AMBASSADOR by Mitsubishi Heavy Industries, Shimonoseki, Japan for *P&O Irish Sea* for the Liverpool - Dublin service. Service transferred to Mostyn in November 2001. Also operated between Dublin and Cherbourg once a week. In 2004 the Mostyn route closed and she was sold to *Stena RoRo*. Chartered to *Stena Line* to operate between Karlskrona and Gdynia and renamed the STENA NORDICA. In 2008 transferred to the Holyhead - Dublin service. In 2009 transferred to UK registry.

Stena Superfast VII *(Miles Cowsill)*

Stena Superfast VIII *(Miles Cowsill)*

STENA PERFORMER Built as the SEATRUCK PERFORMANCE by Flensburger Schiffbau-Gesellschaft, Flensburg, Germany for *Seatruck Ferries*. In September 2012 chartered to *Stena Line* to operate between Heysham and Belfast and renamed the STENA PERFORMER.

STENA PRECISION Built as the SEATRUCK PRECISION by Flensburger Schiffbau-Gesellschaft, Flensburg, Germany for *Seatruck Ferries*. In September 2012 chartered to *Stena Line* to operate between Heysham and Belfast and renamed the STENA PRECISION.

STENA SUPERFAST VII, STENA SUPERFAST VIII Built as the SUPERFAST VII and SUPERFAST VIII by Howaldtswerke Deutsche Werft AG, Kiel, Germany for *Attica Enterprises* (now *Attica Group*) for use by *Superfast Ferries* between Rostock and Hanko. In 2006 sold to *Tallink*. The Finnish terminal was transferred to Helsinki and daily return trips between Helsinki and Tallinn were introduced. These ceased in September 2008. The operation was ceased for the winter season in December 2009 and 2010. Service resumed at the end of April 2010 and 2011. In August 2011 chartered to *Stena Line* for three years (with an option to extend by one year) and renamed the STENA SUPERFAST VII, STENA SUPERFAST VIII. In November 2011, after a major refit, they were placed on a service between Cairnryan and Belfast (replacing the Stranraer - Belfast service).

STENA TRANSIT, STENA TRANSPORTER Built by Samsung Heavy Industries, Koje, South Korea. Used on the Hook of Holland - Killingholme service.

Note The DIEPPE SEAWAYS (*DFDS Seaways France*) was purchased by *Stena Line North Sea Ltd* in May 2014. When the charter to *DFDS* ends in October 2014 she is likely to move to the Holyhead - Dublin route and be renamed.

WESTERN FERRIES

THE COMPANY *Western Ferries (Clyde) Ltd* is a British private sector company.

MANAGEMENT **Managing Director** Gordon Ross.

ADDRESS Hunter's Quay, Dunoon, Argyll PA23 8HJ.

TELEPHONE **Administration** + 44 (0)1369 704452, **Reservations** Not applicable.

FAX **Administration** + 44 (0)1369 706020, **Reservations** Not applicable.

INTERNET **Email** enquiries@western-ferries.co.uk **Website** www.western-ferries.co.uk (*English*)

ROUTE OPERATED McInroy's Point (Gourock) - Hunter's Quay (Dunoon) (20 mins; *SOUND OF SCARBA, SOUND OF SEIL, SOUND OF SHUNA, SOUND OF SOAY*; every 20 mins (15 mins in peaks)).

1	SOUND OF SCARBA	489t	01	11.0k	49.95m	220P	40C	4/5L	BA	UK	9237424
2	SOUND OF SEIL	497t	13	11.0k	49.95m	220P	54C	4/5L	BA	UK	9665217
3	SOUND OF SHUNA	489t	03	11.0k	49.95m	220P	40C	4/5L	BA	UK	9289441
4	SOUND OF SOAY	497t	13	11.0k	49.95m	220P	54C	4/5L	BA	UK	9665229

SOUND OF SCARBA, SOUND OF SHUNA Built by Ferguson Shipbuilders, Port Glasgow, UK for *Western Ferries*.

SOUND OF SEIL, SOUND OF SOAY Built by Cammell Laird Shiprepairers & Shipbuilders, Birkenhead, UK for *Western Ferries*.

SOUND OF SEIL, SOUND OF SOAY Under construction by Cammell Laird Shiprepairers & Shipbuilders, Birkenhead, UK to replace the SOUND OF SANDA and SOUND OF SCALPAY.

Stena Performer *(Gordon Hislip)*

Stena Hollandica *(John Bryant)*

Sound of Soay (*Stuart Mackilop*)

Wight Light (*Brian Maxted*)

WIGHTLINK

THE COMPANY *Wightlink* is a British private sector company, owned by the *Macquarie Group* of Australia. The routes and vessels were previously part of *Sealink (British Rail)* but were excluded from the purchase of most of the *Sealink* operations by *Stena Line AB* in 1990. They remained in *Sea Containers'* ownership until purchased by *CINVen* Ltd, a venture capital company in 1995. The company was the subject of a management buy-out financed by the *Royal Bank of Scotland* in 2001 and was sold to the *Macquarie Group* in 2005.

MANAGEMENT Chief Executive Russell Kew, **Marketing Manager** Kerry Jackson, **Commercial Director** Clive Tilley.

ADDRESS Gunwharf Road, Portsmouth PO1 2LA.

TELEPHONE Administration and Reservations 0871 376 1000 (from UK only), + 44 (0)23 9285 5230 (from overseas).

FAX Administration & Reservations + 44 (0)23 9285 5257.

INTERNET Email bookings@wightlink.co.uk **Website** www.wightlink.co.uk *(English, Dutch, French, German)*

ROUTES OPERATED Conventional Ferries Lymington - Yarmouth (Isle of Wight) (approx 35 mins; *WIGHT LIGHT, WIGHT SKY, WIGHT SUN*; every 40 or 60 mins), Portsmouth - Fishbourne (Isle of Wight) (approx 35 mins; *ST. CECILIA, ST. CLARE, ST. FAITH, ST. HELEN*; half-hourly or hourly depending on time of day). **Fast Passenger Ferries** Portsmouth - Ryde (Isle of Wight) (passenger-only) (under 20 mins; *WIGHT RYDER I, WIGHT RYDER II*; 2 per hour).

1	ST. CECILIA	2968t	86	12.0k	77.0m	771P	142C	12L	BA	UK	8518546
2	ST. CLARE	5359t	01	13.0k	86.0m	878P	186C	-	BA	UK	9236949
3	ST. FAITH	3009t	89	12.5k	77.0m	771P	142C	12L	BA	UK	8907228
4	ST. HELEN	2983t	83	12.0k	77.0m	771P	142C	12L	BA	UK	8120569
5	WIGHT LIGHT	1500t	08	11.0k	62.4m	360P	65C	-	BA	UK	9446972
6»p	WIGHT RYDER I	520t	09	20.0k	40.9m	260P	0C	-	-	UK	9512537
7»p	WIGHT RYDER II	520t	09	20.0k	40.9m	260P	0C	-	-	UK	9512549
8	WIGHT SKY	1500t	08	11.0k	62.4m	360P	65C	-	BA	UK	9446984
9	WIGHT SUN	1500t	09	11.0k	62.4m	360P	65C	-	BA	UK	9490416

ST. CECILIA, ST FAITH Built by Cochrane Shipbuilders, Selby, UK for *Sealink British Ferries* for the Portsmouth - Fishbourne service.

ST. CLARE Built by Stocznia Remontowa, Gdansk, Poland for the Portsmouth - Fishbourne service. She is a double-ended ferry with a central bridge.

ST. HELEN Built by Henry Robb Caledon Yard, Leith, UK (part of British Shipbuilders Ltd) for *Sealink UK Ltd* for the Portsmouth - Fishbourne service.

WIGHT LIGHT, WIGHT SKY, WIGHT SUN Built by Brodogradilište Kraljevica, Croatia for the Lymington - Yarmouth route.

WIGHT RYDER I, WIGHT RYDER II Catamarans built by FBMA Marine, Balamban, Cebu, Philippines. Operate on the Portsmouth - Ryde service.

Eilean Dhiura *(Brian Maxted)*

SECTION 2 - MINOR FERRY OPERATORS

ARGYLL AND BUTE COUNCIL

THE COMPANY Argyll and Bute Council is a British local government authority.

MANAGEMENT Executive Director of Development and Infrastructure Pippa Milne, Head of Economic Development and Strategic Transportation Fergus Murray, Operations Manager Martin Gorringe.

ADDRESS Whitegates Offices, Whitegates Road, Lochgilphead, Argyll PA31 8SY.

TELEPHONE Administration + 44 (0)1546 604673.

FAX Administration + 44 (0)1546 604738.

INTERNET Email martin.gorringe@argyll-bute.gov.uk Website www.argyll-bute.gov.uk/transport-and-streets/ferry-travel

ROUTES OPERATED Vehicle ferries Seil - Luing (5 mins; BELNAHUA; approx half-hourly), Port Askaig (Islay) - Feolin (Jura) (5 mins; EILEAN DHIURA; approx half-hourly). Passenger-only ferries Port Appin – Lismore (10 mins; THE LISMORE; approx hourly), Ellenabeich – Easdale (5 mins; EASDALE; approx quarter-hourly).

1	BELNAHUA	35t	72	8.0k	17.1m	40P	5C	1L	BA	UK
2p	EASDALE	-	93	6.5k	6.4m	11P	0C	0L	-	UK
3	EILEAN DHIURA	86t	98	9.0k	25.6m	50P	13C	1L	BA	UK
4p	THE LISMORE	12t	88	8.0k	9.7m	20P	0C	0L	-	UK

BELNAHUA Built by Campbeltown Shipyard, Campbeltown, UK for Argyll County Council for the Seil - Luing service. In 1975, following local government reorganisation, transferred to Strathclyde Regional Council. In 1996, transferred to Argyll and Bute Council.

EASDALE Built for Strathclyde Regional Council for the Ellenabeich - Easdale passenger-only service. In 1996, following local government reorganisation, transferred to Argyll and Bute Council.

EILEAN DHIURA Built by McTay Marine, Bromborough, Wirral, UK for Argyll and Bute Council to replace the Western Ferries (Argyll) SOUND OF GIGHA on the Islay - Jura route. ASP Ship Management manage and operate this vessel on behalf of Argyll and Bute Council.

THE LISMORE Built for Strathclyde Regional Council for the Port Appin – Lismore passenger-only service. In 1996, following local government reorganisation, transferred to Argyll and Bute Council.

ARRANMORE FAST FERRIES

THE COMPANY Arranmore Fast Ferries is the trading name of Arranmore Charters is an Irish Republic private sector company.

MANAGEMENT Managing Director Seamus Boyle.

ADDRESS Leabgarrow, Arranmore, County Donegal, Irish Republic.

TELEPHONE Administration & Reservations + 353 (0)87 3171810.

INTERNET Email: seamusboyle4@eircom.net Website www.arranmorefastferry.com (English)

ROUTE OPERATED Summer only Car Ferry Burtonport (County Donegal) - Leabgarrow (Arranmore Island) (15 mins; MORVERN; up to 5 per day). All Year Fast Ferry Burtonport - Leabgarrow (5 mins; REALT NA MAIDNE; up to 3 per day).

1	GIRL GRAY	-	96	14.0k	13.1m	12P	0C	-	-	IR
2	MORVERN	64t	73	8.0k	23.8m	12P	6C	-	B	IR
3	REALT NA MAIDNE	-	07	30.0k	11.0m	12P	0C	-	-	IR
4	RENFREW ROSE	65t	84	-	21.9m	12P	2C	-	B	IR

Foyle Venture *(Nick Widdows)*

Portaferry II *(Nick Widdows)*

SECTION 2 – Minor Ferry Operators

5	YOKER SWAN	65t	84	-	21.9m	12P	2C	-	B	IR

GIRL GRAY AquaStar 43' built by Aqua-Star Ltd, St Sampsons, Guernsey for *Southern Marine Services* of Brighton and used as a charter boat out of Brighton Marina. Later sold to *Arranmore Charters*. Normally used for fishing trips but used as a back-up for the ferries as required.

MORVERN Built by James Lamont & Co Ltd, Port Glasgow, UK for *Caledonian MacBrayne*. After service on a number of routes she was, after 1979, the main vessel on the Fionnphort (Mull) - Iona service. In 1992 she was replaced by the LOCH BUIE and became a spare vessel. In 1995 sold to *Arranmore Island Ferry Services*. In 2001 sold to *Bere Island Ferries*. In February 2010 refurbished by Bere Island Boatyard and sold to *Arranmore Charters*.

REALT NA MAIDNE Stormforce 11 RIB (Rigid Inflatable Boat) built by Redbay Boats Ltd, Cushendall, Co Antrim. As well as the fast ferry service, she is also used on fishing, sight-seeing, photography or other ocean expeditions.

RENFREW ROSE, YOKER SWAN Built by MacCrindle Shipbuilding Ltd, Ardrossan for *Strathclyde PTE* (later *Strathclyde Partnership for Transport*). Operated passenger only between Renfrew and Yoker. In March 2010 laid up. In June 2012 sold to *Arranmore Fast Ferries* for use as passenger/car ferries.

ARRANMORE ISLAND FERRY SERVICES

THE COMPANY *Arranmore Island Ferry Services (Bád Farrantoireacht Árainn Mhór)* is an Irish Republic company, supported by *Roinn na Gaeltachta (The Gaeltacht Authority)*, a semi-state-owned body responsible for tourism and development in the Irish-speaking areas of The Irish Republic.

MANAGEMENT **Managing Director** Dominic Sweeney.

ADDRESS Cara na nOilean, Burtonport Pier, Letterkenny, Co. Donegal Irish Republic.

TELEPHONE **Administration & Reservations** +353 (0)7495 20532, +353 (0)7495 42233,

INTERNET **Email** arranmoreferry@gmail.com **Website** www.arranmoreferry.com *(English)*

ROUTE OPERATED Burtonport (County Donegal) - Leabgarrow (Arranmore Island) (15 mins; COLL, RHUM; up to 10 per day (Summer), 8 per day (Winter)).

1	COLL	69t	74	8.0k	25.3m	96P	6C	-	B	IR
2	RHUM	69t	73	8.0k	25.3m	96P	6C	-	B	IR

COLL Built by James Lamont & Co Ltd, Port Glasgow, UK for *Caledonian MacBrayne*. For several years she was employed mainly in a relief capacity. In 1986 she took over the Tobermory (Mull) - Kilchoan service from a passenger-only vessel; the conveyance of vehicles was not inaugurated until 1991. In 1996 she was transferred to the Oban - Lismore route. In 1998 she was sold to *Arranmore Island Ferry Services*.

RHUM Built by James Lamont & Co Ltd, Port Glasgow, UK for *Caledonian MacBrayne*. Until 1987, she was used primarily on the Claonaig - Lochranza (Arran) service. After that time she served on various routes. In 1994 she inaugurated a new service between Tarbert (Loch Fyne) and Portavadie. In 1997 she operated between Kyles Scalpay and Scalpay until the opening of the new bridge on 16th December 1997. In 1998 she was sold to *Arranmore Island Ferry Services*.

BERE ISLAND FERRIES

THE COMPANY *Bere Island Ferries Ltd* is an Irish Republic private sector company.

MANAGEMENT **Operator** Colum Harrington.

ADDRESS Ferry Lodge, West End, Bere Island, Beara, County Cork, Irish Republic.

TELEPHONE **Administration** +353 (0)27 75009, **Reservations** Not applicable, **Mobile** +353 (0)86 2423140.

FAX **Administration** +353 (0)27 75000, **Reservations** Not applicable.

INTERNET Email biferry@eircom.net Website www.bereislandferries.com (English)

1F	KIRSTY M	109t	66	10.5k	23.7m	0P	-	1L	B	IR
2	OILEAN NA H-OIGE	69t	80	7.0k	18.6m	75P	4C	-	B	IR
3	SANCTA MARIA	67t	83	7.0k	18.6m	75P	4C	-	B	IR

KIRSTY M Landing craft (Klasse 521) built as the LCM 12 SPROTTE by Rheinwerft Walsum, Walsum, Germany for the German Navy. In 1993 withdrawn and sold to a German firm and converted to a civilian ferry. She was later sold to *Mainstream Salmon Farm (Aquascot Seafarms Ltd)*, Orkney, renamed the KIRSTY M and used as a work boat. In December 2009 sold to *Bere Island Ferries* and converted back to ferry operation. She is used in a freight-only mode and doesn't have a licence to carry passengers.

OILEAN NA H-OIGE Built as the EILEAN NA H-OIGE by Lewis Offshore Ltd, Stornoway, UK for *Western Isles Islands Council* (from 1st April 1996 the *Western Isles Council* and from 1st January 1998 *Comhairle Nan Eilean Siar*) for their Ludaig (South Uist) - Eriskay service. From 2000 operated from a temporary slipway at the Eriskay causeway. This route ceased in July 2001 following the full opening of the causeway and she was laid up. In 2002 she was moved to the Eriskay - Barra service. In 2003 replaced by the LOCH BHRUSDA of *Caledonian MacBrayne* and laid up. Later sold to *Bere Island Ferries* and renamed the OILEAN NA H-OIGE (same name - "The Island of Youth" - in Irish rather than Scots Gaelic).

SANCTA MARIA Built as the EILEAN BHEARNARAIGH by George Brown & Company, Greenock, UK for *Western Isles Islands Council* for their Otternish (North Uist) - Berneray service. From 1996 until 1999 she was operated by *Caledonian MacBrayne* in conjunction with the LOCH BHRUSDA on the service between Otternish and Berneray and during the winter she was laid up. Following the opening of a causeway between North Uist and Berneray in early 1999, the ferry service ceased and she became reserve vessel for the Eriskay route. This route ceased in July 2001 following the opening of a causeway and she was laid up. In 2002 operated between Eriskay and Barra as reserve vessel. In 2003 sold to *Transalpine Redemptorists Inc*, a community of monks who live on Papa Stronsay, Orkney. Used for conveying supplies to the island - not a public service. In 2008 sold to *Bere Island Ferries*. Entered service in May 2009.

BK MARINE

THE COMPANY *BK Marine* is a UK company.

MANAGEMENT Managing Director Gordon Williamson.

ADDRESS Herrislea House Hotel, Veensgarth, Tingwall, Shetland ZE2 9SB.

TELEPHONE Administration & Reservations + 44 (0)1595840208, Sailing information voice bank + 44 (0)1595 743976.

INTERNET Website www.bkmarine.co.uk (English)

ROUTE OPERATED *All year* Foula - Walls (Mainland) (2 hours; *NEW ADVANCE*; 2 per week (Winter), 3 per week (Summer)), *Summer only* Foula - Scalloway (3 hrs 30 mins; *NEW ADVANCE*; alternate Thursdays).

1	NEW ADVANCE	25t	96	8.7k	9.8m	12P	1C	0L	C	UK

NEW ADVANCE Built by Richardson's, Stromness, Orkney, UK for *Shetland Islands Council* for the Foula service. Although built at Penryn, Cornwall, she was completed at Stromness. She has a Cygnus Marine GM38 hull and is based on the island where she can be lifted out of the water. Vehicle capacity is to take residents' vehicles to the island - not for tourist vehicles. In 2004 it was announced that the vessel and service would be transferred to the *Foula Community*. However, it was then found that under EU rules the route needed to be offered for competitive tender. In July 2006 the contract was awarded to *Atlantic Ferries Ltd* who began operations in October 2006. In August 2011 replaced by *BK Marine*.

SECTION 2 – Minor Ferry Operators

Glenachulish *(John Hendy)*

Corran *(Brian Maxted*

CLARE ISLAND FERRY COMPANY

THE COMPANY *Clare Island Ferry Company* is owned and operated by the O'Grady family, natives of Clare Island, Irish Republic, who have been operating the Clare Island Mail Boat Ferry service since 1880.

MANAGEMENT Managing Director Chris O'Grady.

ADDRESS Clare Island Ferry Co Ltd, Clare Island, Co Mayo, Republic Of Ireland.

TELEPHONE/FAX *May-September* +353 (0)98 23737 *Winter* +353 (0)98 25212, +353 (0)86 8515003.

INTERNET Email clareislandferry@anu.ie **Website** www.clareislandferry.com *(English)*

ROUTE OPERATED Roonagh (Co Mayo) - Clare Island (15 mins; *CLEW BAY QUEEN, PIRATE QUEEN*; *Winter* 1 to 2 trips per day, *Summer* up to 5 per day, Roonagh - Inishturk (50 mins; *CLEW BAY QUEEN, PIRATE QUEEN*; *Winter* 1 per day *Summer* up to 2 per day. Tourist vehicles are not normally carried.

1	CLEW BAY QUEEN	64t	72	10.0k	23.8m	96P	6C	-	B	IR
2p	PIRATE QUEEN	73t	96	10.5k	20.1m	96P	0C	-	-	IR

CLEW BAY QUEEN Built as the KILBRANNAN by James Lamont & Co Ltd, Port Glasgow, UK for *Caledonian MacBrayne*. Used on a variety of routes until 1977, she was then transferred to the Scalpay (Harris) - Kyles Scalpay service. In 1990 she was replaced by the CANNA and, in turn, replaced the CANNA in her reserve/relief role. In 1992 sold to *Arranmore Island Ferry Services* and renamed the ÁRAINN MHÓR. She was subsequently sold to *Údarás na Gaeltachta* and leased back to *Arranmore Island Ferry Services*. In 2008 she was sold to *Clare Island Ferry Company* and renamed the CLEW BAY QUEEN. She operates a passenger and heavy freight service to both Clare Island and Inishturk all year round. In winter passenger capacity is reduced to 47 with 3 crew. Fitted with crane for loading and unloading cargo.

PIRATE QUEEN Built by Arklow Marine Services in 1996 for *Clare Island Ferry Company*. She operates a daily passenger and light cargo service to Clare Island and Inishturk all year round. In winter passenger capacity is reduced to 47 with 3 crew. Fitted with crane for loading and unloading cargo.

CROMARTY FERRY COMPANY

THE COMPANY The *Cromarty Ferry Company* operate under contract to *The Highland Council*.

MANAGEMENT Managing Director Tom Henderson.

ADDRESS Udale Farm, Poyntzfield By Dingwall, Ross-Shire IV7 8LY.

TELEPHONE +44 (0)1381 610269, **Mobile** +44 (0)7717 207875.

FAX +44 (0)1381 610408.

INTERNET Email via website **Website** www.cromarty-ferry.co.uk *(English)*

ROUTE OPERATED *June-October* Cromarty - Nigg (Ross-shire) (10 mins; *CROMARTY QUEEN*; half-hourly - 0800 to 1800 ex Cromarty (19.00 in July and August)).

1	CROMARTY QUEEN	68t	10	9.0k	17.3m	50P	4C	-	B	UK

CROMARTY QUEEN Built by Southampton Marine Services for *Cromarty Ferry Company*.

CROSS RIVER FERRIES

THE COMPANY *Cross River Ferries Ltd* is an Irish Republic company, part of the *Doyle Shipping Group*.

MANAGEMENT Operations Manager Eoin O'Sullivan.

ADDRESS Westlands House, Rushbrooke, Cobh, County Cork, Irish Republic.

TELEPHONE Administration +353 (0)21 42 02 900 **Reservations** Not applicable.

FAX Administration + 353 (0)21 481 2645, **Reservations** Not applicable.

INTERNET Website www.scottcobh.ie/pages/ferry.html (*English*)

ROUTE OPERATED Carrigaloe (near Cobh, on Great Island) - Glenbrook (Co Cork) (4 mins; *CARRIGALOE, GLENBROOK*; frequent service 07.00 - 00.15 (one or two vessels used according to demand)).

1	**CARRIGALOE**	225t	70	8.0k	49.1m	200P	27C	-	BA	IR	7028386
2	**GLENBROOK**	225t	71	8.0k	49.1m	200P	27C	-	BA	IR	7101607

CARRIGALOE Built as the KYLEAKIN by Newport Shipbuilding and Engineering Company, Newport (Gwent), UK for the *Caledonian Steam Packet Company* (later *Caledonian MacBrayne*) for the Kyle of Lochalsh - Kyleakin service. In 1991 sold to *Marine Transport Services Ltd* and renamed the CARRIGALOE. She entered service in March 1993. In Summer 2002 chartered to the *Lough Foyle Ferry Company*, returning in Spring 2003.

GLENBROOK Built as the LOCHALSH by Newport Shipbuilding and Engineering Company, Newport (Gwent), UK for the *Caledonian Steam Packet Company* (later *Caledonian MacBrayne*) for the Kyle of Lochalsh - Kyleakin service. In 1991 sold to *Marine Transport Services Ltd* and renamed the GLENBROOK. She entered service in March 1993.

THE HIGHLAND COUNCIL

THE COMPANY *The Highland Council* (previously *Highland Regional Council*) is a British local government authority.

MANAGEMENT Area Transport, Environment & Community Works Services Manager James Cameron Kemp, **Ferry Foremen** Allan McCowan and Donald Dixon.

ADDRESS *Area Office* Lochybridge Depot, Carr's Corner Industrial Estate, Fort William PH33 6TQ, *Ferry Office* Ferry Cottage, Ardgour, Fort William PH33 7AA.

TELEPHONE Administration *Area Office* + 44 (0)1397 709000, *Corran* + 44 (0)1855 841243, *Camusnagaul* – Now run by private operator *Highland Ferries* by vessel CAILIN AN AISEAG.

INTERNET Email tecs@highland.gov.uk **Website** www.highland.gov.uk/yourenvironment/roadsandtransport/publictransport/ferries.htm (*English*)

ROUTES OPERATED Vehicle Ferries Corran - Ardgour (5 mins; *CORRAN, MAID OF GLENCOUL*; half-hourly), **Passenger-only Ferry** Fort William - Camusnagaul (10 mins; *CAILIN AN AISEAG*; frequent).

1p	**CAILIN AN AISEAG**	-	80	7.5k	9.8m	26P	0C	0L	-	UK	
2	**CORRAN**	351t	01	10.0k	42.0m	150P	30C	2L	BA	UK	9225990
3	**MAID OF GLENCOUL**	166t	75	8.0k	32.0m	116P	16C	1L	BA	UK	7521613

CAILIN AN AISEAG Built by Buckie Shipbuilders Ltd, Buckie, UK for *Highland Regional Council* and used on the Fort William - Camusnagaul passenger-only service. In 2006 the service transferred to *Geoff Ward* under contract with a different vessel. In 2013 resumed service under new operator *Highland Ferries*.

CORRAN Built by George Prior Engineering Ltd, Hull, UK for *The Highland Council* to replace the MAID OF GLENCOUL as main vessel.

MAID OF GLENCOUL Built by William McCrindle Ltd, Shipbuilders, Ardrossan, UK for *Highland Regional Council* for the service between Kylesku and Kylestrome. In 1984 the ferry service was replaced by a bridge and she was transferred to the Corran - Ardgour service. In April 1996, ownership transferred to *The Highland Council*. In 2001 she became the reserve vessel.

ISLES OF SCILLY STEAMSHIP COMPANY

THE COMPANY *Isles of Scilly Steamship Company* is a British private sector company.

MANAGEMENT **Chief Executive** Robert Goldsmith, **Marketing Manager** Sharon Sandercock.

ADDRESS *Scilly* PO Box 10, Hugh Town, St Mary's, Isles of Scilly TR21 0LJ, *Penzance* Steamship House, Quay Street, Penzance, Cornwall, TR18 4BZ.

TELEPHONE **Administration & Reservations** +44 (0)845 710 5555.

FAX **Administration & Reservations** +44 (0)1736 334228.

INTERNET **Email** sales@islesofscilly-travel.co.uk **Website** www.islesofscilly-travel.co.uk(*English*)

ROUTES OPERATED *Passenger services:* Penzance - St Mary's (Isles of Scilly) (2 hrs 40 mins; *SCILLONIAN III*; 1 per day), St Mary's - Tresco/St Martin's/St Agnes/Bryher; *LYONESSE LADY, SWIFT LADY (inter-island boats)*; irregular), *Freight service*: GRY MARITHA; Freight from Penzance Monday, Wednesday and Fridays (weather dependant, all year round).

1F	GRY MARITHA	590t	81	10.5k	40.3m	6P	5C	1L	C	UK	8008462
2	LYONESSE LADY	40t	91	9.0k	15.5m	4P	1C	0L	AC	UK	
3	SCILLONIAN III	1346t	77	15.5k	67.7m	432P	5C	-	C	UK	7527796
4F	SWIFT LADY	-	04	30.0k	8.4m	0P	0C	0L	-	UK	

GRY MARITHA Built by Moen Slip AS, Kolvereid, Norway for *Gjofor* of Norway. In design she is a coaster rather than a ferry. In 1990 she was sold to the *Isles of Scilly Steamship Company*. She operates a freight and passenger service all year (conveying most goods to and from the Islands). During the winter she provides the only sea service to the islands, the SCILLONIAN III being laid up.

LYONESSE LADY Built Lochaber Marine Ltd of Corpach, Fort William, Scotland, for inter-island ferry work.

SCILLONIAN III Built by Appledore Shipbuilders Ltd, Appledore, UK for the Penzance - St Mary's service. She operates from late March to November and is laid up in the winter. She is the last major conventional passenger/cargo ferry built for UK waters and probably Western Europe. Extensively refurbished during Winter 1998/99 and 2012/13. She can carry cars in her hold and on deck, as well as general cargo/perishables, boats, trailer tents and passenger luggage.

SWIFT LADY Stormforce 8.4 RIB (Rigid Inflatable Boat) built by Redbay Boats of Cushendall, Co Antrim, Northern Ireland for inter-island ferry work conveying mail and as back-up to the LYONESSE LADY.

KERRERA FERRY

THE COMPANY *Kerrera Ferry Ltd* is a UK company.

MANAGEMENT **Managing Director** Duncan MacEachen.

ADDRESS The Ferry, Isle of Kerrera, by Oban PA34 4SX.

TELEPHONE **Administration** +44 (0)1631 563665.

INTERNET **Email** kerreraferry@hotmail.com **Website** www.kerrera-ferry.co.uk *(English)*

ROUTE OPERATED Gallanach (Argyll) - Kerrera (5 mins; *GYLEN LADY*; on demand 10.30 - 12.30 and 14.00 - 18.00, Easter - October, other times by arrangement).

1	GYLEN LADY	9t	99	8.0k	10.0m	12P	1C	-	B	UK

GYLEN LADY Built by Corpach Boatyard, Corpach, UK to inaugurate a vehicle ferry service to the Isle of Kerrera, replacing an open passenger boat.

SECTION 2 – Minor Ferry Operators

KNOYDART SEABRIDGE

THE COMPANY Knoydart Seabridge is a British company.

MANAGEMENT Operator Jon Sellars.

ADDRESS Knoydart Seabridge, Knoydart, Mallaig PH41 4PL.

TELEPHONE Administration & Reservations +44 (0)1687 462 916.

INTERNET Email jon@sandaig.com Website www.knoydartferry.com (English)

ROUTE OPERATED Mallaig - Inverie (Knoydart). The MERI 3 can take one car but only residents' vehicles are permitted.

1	MERI 3	11t	85	10.0k	12.0m	12P	1C	-	B	UK	
2p	THE ODYSSEY	6t	06	35.0k	10.5m	12P	-	-	-	UK	
3p	VANGUARD	12t	06	16.0k	13.0m	12P	-	-	-	UK	
4p	VENTURER	12t	06	16.0k	13.0m	12P	-	-	-	UK	

MERI 3 Built by Lohi Boats, Finland. She is a miniature beach landing draft.

THE ODYSSEY ProCharter 3 built by ProCharter, Wadebridge, Cornwall.

VANGUARD, VENTURER Interceptor 41 built by Safehaven Marine, Cobh, Republic of Ireland.

LOUGH FOYLE FERRY COMPANY

THE COMPANY Lough Foyle Ferry Company Ltd is an Irish Republic Company.

MANAGEMENT Managing Director Jim McClenaghan.

ADDRESS The Pier, Greencastle, Co Donegal, Irish Republic.

TELEPHONE Administration +353 (0)74 93 81901.

FAX Administration +353 (0)74 93 81903.

INTERNET Email info@loughfoyleferry.com Website www.loughfoyleferry.com (English)

ROUTES OPERATED Lough Foyle Service Greencastle (Inishowen, Co Donegal, Irish Republic) - Magilligan (Co Londonderry, Northern Ireland) (10 mins; FOYLE VENTURE; about every 20 mins), Lough Swilly Service (Summer only) Buncrana (Inishowen, Co Donegal) - Rathmullan (Co Donegal) (20 mins; FOYLE RAMBLER; hourly).

1	FOYLE RAMBLER	122t	72	10.0k	35.0m	100P	20C	-	BA	IR	8985531
2	FOYLE VENTURE	324t	78	10.0k	47.9m	300P	44C	-	BA	IR	7800033

FOYLE VENTURE Built as the SHANNON WILLOW by Scott & Sons (Bowling) Ltd, Bowling, Glasgow, UK for Shannon Ferry Ltd. In 2000 replaced by the SHANNON BREEZE and laid up for sale. In 2003 sold to the Lough Foyle Ferry Company Ltd and renamed the FOYLE VENTURE.

FOYLE RAMBLER Built as the STEDINGEN by Abeking & Rasmussen, Lemwerder, Germany for Schnellastfähre Berne-Farge GmbH (later Fähren Bremen-Stedingen GmbH) to operate across the River Weser (Vegesack - Lemwerder and Berne - Farge). In 2004 sold to the Lough Foyle Ferry Company Ltd and renamed the FOYLE RAMBLER.

MURPHY'S FERRY SERVICE

THE COMPANY Murphy's Ferry Service is privately operated.

MANAGEMENT Operator Carol Murphy.

ADDRESS Anchorage, Lawrence Cove, Bere Island, Co Cork, Irish Republic.

TELEPHONE Administration +353 (0)27 75014 Mobile +353 (0)87 2386095.

SECTION 2 – Minor Ferry Operators

Bramble Bush Bay *(Kevin Mitchel)*

Dartmouth Higher Ferry *(Nick Widdows)*

FAX Administration + 353 (0)27 75014.

INTERNET Email info@murphysferry.com Website www.murphysferry.com *(English)*

ROUTE OPERATED Castletownbere (Pontoon - 3 miles to east of town centre) - Bere Island (Lawrence Cove, near Rerrin) (20 mins; *IKOM K*; up to 8 per day).

1	IKOM K	55t	99	10.0k	16.0m	60P	4C	1L	B	IR

IKOM K Built by Arklow Marine Services, Arklow, Irish Republic for *Murphy's Ferry Service*.

PASSAGE EAST FERRY

THE COMPANY *Passage East Ferry Company Ltd* is an Irish Republic private sector company.

MANAGEMENT **Manager** Gary O Hanlon, **Company Secretary** Derek Donnelly.

ADDRESS Barrack Street, Passage East, Co Waterford, Irish Republic.

TELEPHONE **Administration** + 353 (0)51 382480, **Reservations** Not applicable.

FAX **Administration** + 353 (0)51 382598, **Reservations** Not applicable.

INTERNET Email passageferry@yahoo.ie Website www.passageferry.ie *(English)*

ROUTE OPERATED Passage East (County Waterford) - Ballyhack (County Wexford) (7 mins; *FBD TINTERN*; frequent service).

1	FBD TINTERN	236t	71	9.0k	54.8m	130P	30C	-	BA	IR

FBD TINTERN Built as the STADT LINZ by Schiffswerft Oberwinter, Oberwinter/Rhein, Germany for *Rheinfähre Linz - Remagen GmbH* of Germany and operated on the Rhine between Linz and Remagen. In 1990 renamed the ST JOHANNES. In 1997 sold to *Fähren Bremen-Stedingen GmbH*, renamed the VEGESACK and operated across the Weser between Lemwerder and Vegesack. In 2003 she became a reserve vessel and in 2004 was renamed the STEDINGEN (the name previously carried by the ferry sold to *Lough Foyle Ferry Company*). Later sold to *Schraven BV* of The Netherlands and refurbished. In Autumn 2005 sold to *Passage East Ferry* and renamed the FBD TINTERN.

RATHLIN ISLAND FERRY

THE COMPANY *Rathlin Island Ferry Ltd* is a UK private sector company owned by Ciarán and Mary O'Driscoll of County Cork, Irish Republic.

MANAGEMENT **Managing Director** Ciarán O'Driscoll.

ADDRESS Ballycastle Ferry Terminal, 18 Bayview Road, Ballycastle, County Antrim BT54 6BT.

TELEPHONE **Administration & Reservations** + 44 (0)28 2076 9299.

INTERNET Email info@rathlinballycastleferry.com Website www.rathlinballycastleferry.com *(English)*

ROUTE OPERATED **Vehicle Ferry** Ballycastle - Rathlin Island (45 min; *CANNA*; up to 4 per day). **Passenger-only Fast Ferry** (20 min; *RATHLIN EXPRESS*; up to 5 per day). The service is operated on behalf of the *Northern Ireland Department of Regional Development.*

1	CANNA	69t	76	8.0k	24.3m	140P	6C	1L	B	UK
2»p	RATHLIN EXPRESS	31t	09	18.0k	17.7m	98P	0C	0L	-	UK
3»p	ST SORNEY	12t	99	17.0k	12.2m	38P	0C	0L	-	IR

CANNA Built by James Lamont & Co Ltd, Port Glasgow, UK for *Caledonian MacBrayne*. She was the regular vessel on the Lochaline - Fishnish (Mull) service. In 1986 she was replaced by the ISLE OF CUMBRAE and until 1990 she served in a relief capacity in the north, often assisting on the Iona service. In 1990 she was placed on the Kyles Scalpay (Harris) - Scalpay service (replaced by a bridge in Autumn 1997). In Spring 1997 *Caledonian MacBrayne* was contracted to operate the Ballycastle - Rathlin Island route and she was transferred to this service. In June 2008 she was chartered by *Caledonian Maritime Assets Limited* to *Rathlin Island Ferry Ltd* who took over the operation of the service.

RATHLIN EXPRESS Built by Arklow Marine Services, Arklow, Irish Republic for *Rathlin Island Ferry Ltd.*

ST SORNEY A Lochin 40 cruiser built by Ryan & Roberts, Limerick, Ireland. In 2008 placed on the Ballycastle - Rathlin Island service. Now reserve vessel.

SHANNON FERRY

THE COMPANY *Shannon Ferry Group Ltd* is an Irish Republic private company owned by eighteen shareholders on both sides of the Shannon Estuary.

MANAGEMENT **Managing Director** Eugene Maher.

ADDRESS Ferry Terminal, Killimer, County Clare, Irish Republic.

TELEPHONE **Administration** + 353 (0)65 9053124, **Reservations** Phone bookings not available; Online booking available.

FAX **Administration** + 353 (0)65 9053125, **Reservations** Fax bookings not available; Online booking available.

INTERNET **Email** enquiries@shannonferries.com **Website** www.shannonferries.com *(English)*

ROUTE OPERATED Killimer (County Clare) - Tarbert (County Kerry) (20 mins; *SHANNON BREEZE, SHANNON DOLPHIN*; hourly (half-hourly during May, June, July, August and September)).

| 1 | SHANNON BREEZE | 611t | 00 | 10.0k | 80.8m | 350P | 60C | - | BA | IR | 9224910 |
| 2 | SHANNON DOLPHIN | 501t | 95 | 10.0k | 71.9m | 350P | 52C | - | BA | IR | 9114933 |

SHANNON BREEZE, SHANNON DOLPHIN Built by Appledore Shipbuilders, Appledore, UK for *Shannon Ferry Group Ltd.*

SKYE FERRY

THE COMPANY The *Skye Ferry* is owned by the *Isle of Skye Ferry Community Interest Company*, a company limited by guarantee.

ADDRESS 6 Coulindune, Glenelg, Kyle, Ross-shire, IV40 8JU.

TELEPHONE **Administration & Reservations** + 44 (0)1599 522236.

INTERNET **Email** info@skyeferry.com **Website** www.skyeferry.com *(English)*

ROUTE OPERATED *Easter - October only* Glenelg - Kylerhea (Skye) (10 mins; *GLENACHULISH*; frequent service).

| 1 | GLENACHULISH | 44t | 69 | 9.0k | 20.0m | 12P | 6C | - | BSt | UK |

GLENACHULISH Built by Ailsa Shipbuilding Company, Troon, UK for the *Ballachulish Ferry Company* for the service between North Ballachulish and South Ballachulish, across the mouth of Loch Leven. In 1975 the ferry was replaced by a bridge and she was sold to *Highland Regional Council* and used on a relief basis on the North Kessock - South Kessock and Kylesku - Kylestrome routes. In 1983 she was sold to *Murdo MacKenzie*, who had operated the Glenelg - Skye route as ferryman since 1959. The vessel was eventually bought by *Roddy MacLeod* and the service resumed in September 1990. The *Isle of Skye Ferry Community Interest Company* reached agreement with *Mr MacLeod* that he would operate the ferry in 2006. In 2007 she was sold to the Company. During winter 2012 she was chartered to *The Highland Council* to operate between North and South Strome following a road closure due to a rock fall. She is the last turntable ferry in operation.

STRANGFORD LOUGH FERRY SERVICE

THE COMPANY The *Strangford Lough Ferry Service* is operated by the *DRD (Department for Regional Development)*, a Northern Ireland Government Department (formerly operated by *Department of the Environment (Northern Ireland)*).

MANAGEMENT **Ferry Manager** Seamus Fitzsimons.

ADDRESS Strangford Lough Ferry Service, The Slip, Strangford, Co Down BT30 7NE.

TELEPHONE **Administration** + 44 (0)28 4488 1637, **Reservations** Not applicable.

FAX **Administration** + 44 (0)28 4488 1044, **Reservations** Not applicable.

INTERNET **Website** www.nidirect.gov.uk/strangford-ferry-timetable *(English)*

ROUTE OPERATED Strangford - Portaferry (County Down) (10 mins; *PORTAFERRY II, STRANGFORD FERRY*; half-hourly).

1	PORTAFERRY II	312t	01	12.0k	38.2m	260P	28C	-	BA	UK	9237436
2	STRANGFORD FERRY	186t	69	10.0k	32.9m	263P	20C	-	BA	UK	6926311

PORTAFERRY II Built by McTay Marine, Bromborough, Wirral, UK for *DRD (Northern Ireland)*.

STRANGFORD FERRY Built by Verolme Dockyard Ltd, Cork, Irish Republic for *Down County Council*. Subsequently transferred to the *DOE (Northern Ireland)* and then the *DRD (Northern Ireland)*. Following delivery of the PORTAFERRY II, she became reserve ferry.

C TOMS & SON LTD

THE COMPANY *C Toms & Son Ltd* is a British private sector company.

MANAGEMENT **Managing Director** Allen Toms.

ADDRESS East Street, Polruan, Fowey, Cornwall PL23 1PB.

TELEPHONE **Administration** + 44 (0)1726 870232.

FAX **Administration** + 44 (0)1726 870318.

INTERNET **Email** enquiries@ctomsandson.co.uk **Website** www.ctomsandson.co.uk *(English)*

ROUTE OPERATED *Car Ferry* Fowey - Bodinnick (Cornwall) (5 mins; *GELLAN, JENACK*; frequent), *Passenger Ferry* Fowey - Polruan (Cornwall) (5 mins; *KALEY, LADY DIANA, LADY JEAN, TAMSIN, THREE COUSINS*; frequent).

1	GELLAN	50t	03	4.5k	36.0m	50P	10C	-	BA	UK
2	JENACK	60t	00	4.5k	36.0m	50P	15C	-	BA	UK
3P	KALEY	7.6t	03	-	9.5m	48P	0C	-	-	UK
4P	LADY DI	-	81	-	8.2m	36P	0C	-	-	UK
5P	LADY JEAN	-	-	-	-	12P	0C	-	-	UK
6P	THREE COUSINS	-	14	-	-	12P	0C	-	-	UK

GELLAN, JENACK Built by C Toms & Sons Ltd, Fowey, UK.

KALEY, LADY DIANA, LADY JEAN, THREE COUSINS Built by C Toms & Sons Ltd, Fowey, UK.

VALENTIA ISLAND FERRIES

THE COMPANY *Valentia Island Ferries Ltd* is an Irish Republic private sector company.

MANAGEMENT **Manager** Richard Foran.

ADDRESS Valentia Island, County Kerry, Irish Republic.

TELEPHONE **Administration** + 353 (0)66 76141, **Reservations** Not applicable.

FAX Administration + 353 (0)66 76377, **Reservations** Not applicable.

INTERNET **Email** reforan@indigo.ie **Website** www.gokerry.ie/valentia-island-car-ferry *(English)*

ROUTE OPERATED Reenard (Co Kerry) - Knightstown (Valentia Island) (5 minutes; *GOD MET ONS III*; frequent service, 1st April - 30th September).

1	GOD MET ONS III	95t	63	-	43.0m	95P	18C	-	BA	IR	

GOD MET ONS III Built by BV Scheepswerven Vh HH Bodewes, Millingen, The Netherlands for *FMHE Res* of The Netherlands for a service across the River Maas between Cuijk and Middelaar. In 1987 a new bridge was opened and the service ceased. She was latterly used on contract work in the Elbe and then laid up. In 1996 acquired by *Valentia Island Ferries* and inaugurated a car ferry service to the island. **Note** This island never had a car ferry service before. A bridge was opened at the south end of the island in 1970; before that a passenger/cargo service operated between Reenard Point and Knightstown.

WOOLWICH FREE FERRY

THE COMPANY The *Woolwich Free Ferry* is operated by *Briggs Marine*, a British private sector company on behalf of *Transport for London*.

MANAGEMENT Ferry Manager Jeremy Mccarthy.

ADDRESS New Ferry Approach, Woolwich, London SE18 6DX.

TELEPHONE Administration + 44 (0)20 8853 9400, **Reservations** Not applicable.

FAX Administration + 44 (0)20 8316 6096, **Reservations** Not applicable.

INTERNET Website www.tfl.gov.uk/modes/river/woolwich-free-ferry *(English)*

ROUTE OPERATED Woolwich - North Woolwich (free ferry) (5 mins; *ERNEST BEVIN, JAMES NEWMAN, JOHN BURNS*; every 10 mins (weekdays - two ferries in operation), every 15 mins (weekends - one ferry in operation)). **Note** One ferry is always in reserve/under maintenance.

1	ERNEST BEVIN	1194t	63	8.0k	56.7m	310P	32C	6L	BA	UK	5426998
2	JAMES NEWMAN	1194t	63	8.0k	56.7m	310P	32C	6L	BA	UK	5411905
3	JOHN BURNS	1194t	63	8.0k	56.7m	310P	32C	6L	BA	UK	5416010

ERNEST BEVIN, JAMES NEWMAN, JOHN BURNS Built by Robb Caledon Shipbuilders Ltd, Dundee, UK for the *London County Council* who operated the service when the vessels were new. In 1965 ownership was transferred to the *Greater London Council*. Following the abolition of the *GLC* in April 1986, ownership was transferred to the *Department of Transport* and in 2001 to *Transport for London*. The *London Borough of Greenwich* operated the service on their behalf. In 2008 the operation of the service was transferred to Serco. An alternative loading is 6 x 18m articulated lorries and 14 cars; lorries of this length are too high for the nearby northbound Blackwall Tunnel.

Seatruck Pace *(FotoFlite)*

SECTION 3 - GB & IRELAND - FREIGHT ONLY FERRIES

CLDN/COBELFRET FERRIES

THE COMPANIES Compagnie Luxembourgouise de Navigation SA (CLdN) is a Luxemburg company. Cobelfret Ferries NV is a Belgian private sector company, a subsidiary of Cobelfret NV of Antwerp. The two companies operate as a single network with a single fleet.

MANAGEMENT C.RO Agencies NV (Zeebrugge) Tom De Wannemacker, CLdN Ro-Ro SA (Luxembourg) Caroline Dubois, Cobelfret Waterways SA (Vlissingen) Geert Bogaerts, CLdN ro-ro Agencies Ltd (UK) Martin Thompson.

ADDRESSES Belgium Sneeuwbeslaan 14, B-2610 Antwerp, Belgium, C.RO Ports Zeebrugge NV, Britannia Quay, 8380 Zeebrugge, Belgium, Luxembourg CLdN ro-ro SA, 3-7 rue Schiller, 2519 Luxembourg, Luxembourg, UK - Purfleet CCLdN ro-ro Agencies Ltd, London Road, Purfleet, Essex RM19 1RP, UK – Dartford (currently unused) C.RO Ports Dartford Ltd, Clipper Boulevard, Crossways, Dartford, Kent DA2 6QB, UK - Killingholme C.RO Ports Killingholme Ltd, Clough Lane, North Killingholme, Immingham DN40 3JS, UK, The Netherlands - Rotterdam C.RO Ports Nederland BV, Merseyweg 70, Port no: 5230 Rotterdam, Botlek, The Netherlands – Vlissingen C.RO Ports Nederland BV, CdMR Terminal, 4389 PA Ritthem, Harbour No. 1125, Vlissingen Oost.

TELEPHONE Administration & Reservations Belgium + 32 (0)3 829 9100, Luxembourg + 352 (0)26 44 66 1, UK (Purfleet, Ipswich & Killingholme) + 44 (0)1708 865522, The Netherlands + 31 (0)118 480005.

FAX Administration & Reservations Belgium + 32 (0)3 829 45 07, UK (Purfleet & Killingholme) + 44 (0)1708 866418, Luxembourg + 352(0)26 44 66 299, The Netherlands- + 31 118480009.

INTERNET Website www.cldn.com www.cobelfret.com (English)

ROUTES OPERATED Cobelfret Ferries Services Zeebrugge - Purfleet (9 hrs; ADELINE, CELANDINE, MAZARINE CLASS, VALENTINE, VICTORINE; 2/3 per day), Zeebrugge - Killingholme (13 hrs; PAULINE, YASMINE; 6 per week), CLdN Services Rotterdam - Purfleet (14 hrs 30 mins; MAZARINE CLASS); 6 per week), Rotterdam - Killingholme (14 hrs; OPALINE CLASS and MAZARINE CLASS; 6 per week), Zeebrugge - Esbjerg (24hrs; ADELINE, CELANDINE, VALENTINE, VICTORINE; 1 per week), Zeebrugge - Dublin (36 hrs; MAZARINE CLASS and OPALINE CLASS; 2 per week), Rotterdam - Dublin (38 hrs;), MAZARINE CLASS and OPALINE CLASS; 2 per week), Rotterdam - Leixoes (Portugal) (69-79 hrs; CATHERINE; 1 per week), Zeebrugge - Gothenburg (32-33 hrs; SCHIEBORG, SLINGEBORG, SPAARNEBORG; 5 per week). MAZARINE CLASS = MAZARINE, PALATINE, PEREGRINE and VESPERTINE; OPALINE CLASS = AMANDINE and OPALINE.

Note: The Zeebrugge - Gothenburg service is operated by CLdN and Wagenborg for the Stora-Enso paper and board group, for the conveyance of their products. CLdN act as handling agents at Zeebrugge and Gothenburg and market the surplus capacity on the vessels, which is available for general ro-ro traffic. Although this route is strictly outside the scope of this book it is included for the sake of completeness.

Contract Services for Ford Motor Company Vlissingen - Dagenham (11 hrs; CYMBELINE, MELUSINE, UNDINE; 2 per day).

1	ADELINE	21020t	12	15.8k	150.0m	12P	-	170T	A	LU	9539092
2	AMANDINE	33960t	11	18.5k	195.4m	12P	-	270T	A	LU	9424869
3	CATHERINE	21287t	02	18.0k	182.2m	12P	-	200T	A2	BE	9209453
4	CELANDINE	23987t	00	17.9k	162.5m	12P	630C	157T	A	BE	9183984
5	CELESTINE	23986t	96	17.8k	162.5m	24P	630C	157T	A	BE	9125372
6	CYMBELINE	11866t	92	17.0k	147.4m	8P	350C	100T	A2	LU	9007764
7	HATCHE	29004t	09	21.5k	193.0m	12P	-	249T	A	LU	9457165
8	LONGSTONE	23235t	03	21.0k	193.0m	12P	-	180T	A	AU	9234082
9	MAZARINE	25593t	09	18.5k	195.4m	12P	-	180T	A	LU	9376696
10	MELUSINE	23987t	99	17.8k	162.5m	12P	630C	157T	A	BE	9166637
11	OPALINE	33960t	10	18.5k	195.4m	12P	-	270T	A	MT	9424869

Adeline *(J.J.Jager)*

Cymbeline *(J.J.Jager)*

12	PALATINE	25593t	09	18.5k	195.4m	12P	-	180T	A	LU	9376701
13	PAQIZE	29429t	10	21.5k	193.0m	12P	-	249T	A	LU	9457206
14	PAULINE	49166t	06	21.7k	200.0m	12P	656C	258T	A	LU	9324473
15	PEREGRINE	25235t	10	18.5k	195.4m	12P	-	180T	A	MT	9376725
16	QEZBAN	29004t	10	21.5k	193.0m	12P	-	249T	A	LU	9457189
17	SCHIEBORG	21005t	00	18.0k	183.4m	12P	-	180T	A	NL	9188233
18	SLINGEBORG	21005t	00	18.0k	183.4m	12P	-	180T	A	NL	9188245
19	SPAARNEBORG	21005t	00	18.0k	183.4m	12P	-	180T	A	NL	9188221
20	UNDINE	11854t	91	15.0k	147.4m	8P	350C	100T	A2	LU	9006112
21	VALENTINE	23987t	99	18.0k	162.5m	12P	630C	157T	A	BE	9166625
22	VESPERTINE	25235t	10	18.5k	195.4m	12P	-	180T	A	LU	9376713
23	VICTORINE	23987t	00	17.8k	162.5m	12P	630C	157T	A	BE	9184029
24	WILLIAMSBORG	23235t	03	17.1k	193.0m	12P	-	180T	A	MT	9234094
25	YASMINE	49166t	07	21.7k	200.0m	12P	656C	258T	A	LU	9337353

ADELINE Built by the Kyokuyo Shipyard, Shimonoseki, Japan. After competition, a additional deck and sponsons were retro-fitted at the Chengxi Shipyard, Jiangyin, China. In November 2012 chartered to RMR Shipping to operate between Western Europe and West Africa. In January 2013 sub-chartered to Castor Shipping of Bulgaria. In March undertook another trip to West Africa and then returned to the Zeebrugge - Purfleet route in April. In November inaugurated a new ro-ro service from Rotterdam to Leixoes (Portugal). In March 2014 returned to the Zeebrugge -Purfleet route.

AMANDINE Built by Flensburger Schiffbau-Gesellschaft, Flensburg, Germany. Operates mainly between Rotterdam and Killingholme and Rotterdam/Zeebrugge and Dublin.

CATHERINE Built as the ROMIRA by Zhonghua Shipyard, Zhonghua, China for Dag Engström Rederi of Sweden. For six months engaged on a number of short-term charters, including Cobelfret Ferries who used her on both the Rotterdam - Immingham and Zeebrugge - Purfleet routes. In September 2002 purchased by Cobelfret Ferries and, in November 2002, renamed the CATHERINE and placed on the Rotterdam - Immingham service. In Spring 2003 chartered to the US Defense Department to convey materials to the Persian Gulf. Returned in late summer and operated thereafter on the Rotterdam - Immingham service. In January 2009 chartered to CoTuNav of Tunisia. In February 2010 returned to Cobelfret service and operated on the Rotterdam - Purfleet service. In March 2010 again chartered to CoTuNav. In March 2011 chartered to RMR Shipping to operate between Western Europe and Antwerp, Eemshaven, Harwich and Dublin to Lagos (Nigeria). In May 2011 returned to Cobelfret Ferries and used on the Zeebrugge - Gothenburg service until January 2013 when she began operating on the Purfleet route during the week and the Gothenburg route at weekend (one round trip). From April 2013 operated full-time on the Purfleet service. In March 2014 transferred to the Rotterdam - Leixoes route.

CELANDINE, VALENTINE, VICTORINE Built by Kawasaki Heavy Industries, Sakaide, Japan for Cobelfret. The CELANDINE was originally to be called the CATHERINE and the VICTORINE the CELANDINE. The names were changed before delivery. Generally used on the Zeebrugge - Purfleet route. In May 2011 the CELANDINE was chartered to RMR Shipping.

CELESTINE Built by Kawasaki Heavy Industries, Sakaide, Japan as the CELESTINE. In 1996 chartered to the British MoD and renamed the SEA CRUSADER. She was originally expected to return to Cobelfret Ferries in early 2003 and resume the name CELESTINE; however, the charter was extended because of the Iraq war. Returned in September 2003 and placed on the Zeebrugge - Immingham service. In November 2006 moved to the Zeebrugge - Purfleet route. In November 2008 moved to the Ostend - Dartford service. In April 2009 the route became Ostend - Purfleet. In April 2010 chartered to RMR Shipping.

CYMBELINE, UNDINE Built by Dalian Shipyard, Dalian, China for Cobelfret Ferries. Currently mainly used on the Dagenham - Vlissingen route. They were occasionally used on a weekend Southampton - Vlissingen service but this ceased in 2012 following the closure of the Southampton Ford Transit factory.

HATCHE Built as the MAAS VIKING by Odense Staalskibsværft A/S, Odense, Denmark for Epic Shipping of the UK and chartered to Norfolkline. Charter taken over by DFDS Seaways. Operated between Vlaardingen and Killingholme. In September 2012 sold to CLdN of Luxembourg and renamed the KENT.

At the end of the month the charter was ended. Operated from Rotterdam to Purfleet and Killingholme. In January 2013 renamed the HATCHE and chartered to *Ekol Lojistik* of Turkey to operate between Trieste in Italy and Haydarpasa (Istanbul) in Turkey.

LONGSTONE Built by Flensburger Schiffbau-Gesellschaft, Flensburg, Germany for *AWSR Shipping*. Chartered to *Transfennica* and operated between Hanko (Finland) and Lübeck (Germany). In January 2009 chartered to *Finnlines* and placed on the Helsinki - Aarhus route. In January 2012 chartered to *North Sea RoRo*. In March 2013 the operation ceased and the charter was taken over by *DFDS Seaways* and she was placed on the Immingham - Cuxhaven route. In May took over the Zeebrugge - Rosyth route. In October 2013 sold to *C Bulk NV* of Belgium, an associated company of *CLdN/Cobelfret Ferries*. In April 2014 charter ended and she was chartered to an Australian operator.

MAZARINE, PALATINE, PEREGRINE, VESPERTINE Built by Flensburger Schiffbau-Gesellschaft, Flensburg, Germany.

MELUSINE Built by Kawasaki Heavy Industries, Sakaide, Japan for *Cobelfret*. Similar to the CLEMENTINE. Currently used on Zeebrugge - Purfleet or Rotterdam - Purfleet.

OPALINE Built by Flensburger Schiffbau-Gesellschaft, Flensburg, Germany. Operates mainly between Rotterdam and Killingholme and Rotterdam and Dublin.

PAQIZE Built as the MERCIA by Odense Staalskibsværft A/S, Odense, Denmark for *Epic Shipping* of the UK and chartered to *UN RoRo* of Turkey. Operated between Istanbul (Turkey) and Toulon (France). In February 2011 transferred to the Istanbul - Constanza (Romania) route. In May 2012 laid up in Greece. In September 2012 sold to *CLdN* of Luxembourg. In January 2013 renamed the PAQIZE and chartered to *Ekol Lojistik* of Turkey to operate between Trieste in Italy and Haydarpasa (Istanbul) in Turkey.

PAULINE, YASMINE Built by Flensburger Schiffbau-Gesellschaft, Flensburg, Germany to operate on the Zeebrugge - Killingholme route.

QEZBAN Built as the WESSEX by Odense Staalskibsværft A/S, Odense, Denmark for *Epic Shipping* of the UK and chartered to *UN RoRo* of Turkey. Operated between Istanbul (Turkey) and Toulon (France). In February 2011 chartered to *LD Lines* to operate between Marseilles and Tunis. In March 2011 returned to *UN RoRo*. In March 2012 laid up in Greece. In September 2012 sold to *CLdN* of Luxembourg. In January 2013 renamed the QEZBAN and chartered to *Ekol Lojistik* of Turkey to operate between Trieste in Italy and Haydarpasa (Istanbul) in Turkey.

SCHIEBORG, SLINGEBORG, Built by Flender Werft AG, Lübeck, Germany for *Wagenborg* of The Netherlands and time-chartered to *Stora-Enso* to operate between Zeebrugge and Gothenburg.

SPAARNEBORG Built by Flender Werft AG, Lübeck, Germany for *Wagenborg* of The Netherlands and time-chartered to *Stora-Enso* to operate between Zeebrugge and Gothenburg. She also operated between Tilbury and Gothenburg during 2010. In August 2011 chartered to the *Canadian MoD* to operate between Montreal and Cyprus in connection with the Libyan 'no fly zone'. On return in November she was laid up in Zeebrugge and in January 2012 moved to Gothenburg. In August 2012 chartered to *LD Lines* to operate between Marseilles and Tunis. In March 2013 returned to the Zeebrugge - Gothenburg route.

WILLIAMSBORG Built as the BEACHY HEAD by Flensburger Schiffbau-Gesellschaft, Flensburg, Germany for *AWSR Shipping*. On delivery, chartered to *Transfennica* and operated between Hanko (Finland) and Lübeck (Germany). In July 2006 chartered to *Stora Enso* and placed on the Kotka - Gothenburg route. In late August transferred to the Antwerp - Gothenburg service. In 2007 chartered to *Transfennica*. In January 2009 chartered to *Finnlines* and normally used on the Helsinki - Aarhus route. In January 2012 chartered to *North Sea RoRo*. In March 2013 the service ceased and she was chartered to *DFDS Seaways*. In April 2014 sold to *C Bulk NV* of Belgium, an associated company of *CLdN/Cobelfret Ferries* and renamed the WILLIAMSBORG. In July she was chartered to *Nordana Line A/S* of Denmark operating from Mediterranean ports to the USA and Latin America.

CLdN also own the CLEMENTINE, on charter to *DFDS Seaways*, the CAPUCINE and SEVERINE, on charter to *Stena Line* and the WILHELMINE, on charter to *P&O Ferries*.

FINNLINES

THE COMPANY *Finnlines PLC* is a Finnish private sector company. Services to the UK are marketed by *Finnlines UK Ltd*, a British private sector company. From 1st January 2001, *Finncarriers* was merged into the parent company, trading as *Finnlines Cargo Service*.

MANAGEMENT *Finnlines* President & CEO Uwe Bakosch, Vice-President Simo Airas.

ADDRESS *Finland* PO Box 197, 00181 Helsinki, Finland, **UK** Finnlines UK Ltd, Finhumber House, Queen Elizabeth Dock, Hedon Road, HULL HU9 5PB.

TELEPHONE Administration & Reservations *Finland* +358 (0)10 343 50, **UK** +44 (0)1482 377 655.

FAX Administration *Finland* +358 (0)10 343 5200, **UK** +44 (0)1482 787 229.

INTERNET Email *Finland* info.fi@finnlines.com **UK** info.uk@finnlines.com **Website** www.finnlines.com *(English, Finnish, German, Polish, Swedish)*

ROUTES OPERATED Irregular service from St Petersburg, Helsinki, Rauma and Kotka to Hull, Immingham, Amsterdam, Antwerp and Bilbao. For details see website. In view of the fact that ships are liable to be transferred between routes, the following is a list of all *Finnlines Cargo Service* ro-ro vessels, including those which currently do not serve the UK. Ro-pax vessels on Baltic services are listed in Section 6.

1	BALTICA	21224t	90	19.0k	157.7m	0P	-	163T	A	MT	8813154
2	FINNBREEZE	28002t	11	20.0k	184.8m	12P	600C	200T	A	FI	9468889
3	FINNHAWK	11530t	01	20.0k	162.2m	12P	-	140T	A	FI	9207895
4	FINNKRAFT	11530t	00	20.0k	162.2m	12P	-	140T	A	FI	9207883
5	FINNMILL	25732t	02	20.0k	184.8m	12P	-	190T	A	FI	9212656
6	FINNPULP	25732t	02	20.0k	184.8m	12P	-	190T	A	FI	9212644
7	FINNSEA	28002t	11	21.0k	184.8m	12P	600C	200T	A	FI	9468891
8	FINNSKY	28002t	12	21.0k	184.8m	12P	600C	200T	A	LU	9468906
9	FINNSUN	28002t	12	21.0k	184.8m	12P	600C	200T	A	LU	9468918
10	FINNTIDE	28002t	12	21.0k	184.8m	12P	600C	200T	A	LU	9468920
11	FINNWAVE	28002t	12	21.0k	184.8m	12P	600C	200T	A	FI	9468932
12	MISANA	14100t	07	20.0k	163.9m	12P	-	150T	A	FI	9348936
13	MISIDA	14100t	07	20.0k	163.9m	12P	-	150T	A	FI	9348948

BALTICA Built by Hyundai Heavy Industries, Ulsan, South Korea as the AHLERS BALTIC for *Ahlers Line* and chartered to *Finncarriers*. In 1995 acquired by *Poseidon Schiffahrt AG* of Germany and renamed the TRANSBALTICA. She continued to be chartered to *Finncarriers* and was acquired by them when they purchased *Poseidon Schiffahrt AG* (now *Finnlines Deutschland AG*) in 1997. In 2003 sold to Norwegian interests and chartered back; She was renamed the BALTICA. In recent years she operated on the Helsinki - St Petersburg - Hamina - Helsinki - Zeebrugge - Tilbury – Amsterdam - Antwerp - service with the MERCHANT. During 2007 she operated Helsinki - Turku - Antwerp on a one-week cycle. In January 2008 moved to Baltic services. In April 2011 chartered to *Power Line* to operate between Helsinki and Travemünde. In January 2013 returned to *Finnlines*.

FINNBREEZE, FINNSEA, FINNSKY, FINNSUN, FINNTIDE, FINNWAVE Built by Jinling Shipyard, Nanjing, China for *Finnlines*.

FINNHAWK Built by Jinling Shipyard, Nanjing, China for the *Macoma Shipping Group* and chartered to *Finnlines*. In April 2008 purchased by *Finnlines*. Currently operates used on service between Finland and The Netherlands, Belgium, the UK and Spain.

FINNKRAFT Built by Jinling Shipyard, Nanjing, China for the *Macoma Shipping Group* and chartered to *Finncarriers*. In April 2008 purchased by *Finnlines*. Currently operates on services between Finland and Germany.

Catherine (Doug Shaw)

Finnbreeze (FotoFlite)

FINNMILL, FINNPULP Built by Jinling Shipyard, Nanjing, China for the *Macoma Shipping Group* and chartered to *Finnlines*. In 2008 purchased by *Finnlines*. During Winter 2008/09 extra ramps were added at STX Europe Helsinki shipyard to enable ro-ro traffic to be conveyed on the weather deck.

MISANA, MISIDA Built by J J Sietas, Hamburg, Germany for *Godby Shipping AB* of Finland and time-chartered to *UPM-Kymmene* of Finland to operate between Finland, Spain and Portugal. In July 2013 charter taken over by *Finnlines*.

FORELAND SHIPPING

THE COMPANY *Foreland Shipping Limited* (formerly *AWSR Shipping Limited*) is a UK private sector company. The principal shareholder in *Foreland Shipping* is now *Hadley Shipping Group*; *Bibby Group* and *James Fisher plc* having sold their shares to *Hadley Shipping*.

MANAGEMENT Chairman Peter Morton, **Managing Director** Paul Trudgeon.

ADDRESS 117-119 Houndsditch, London EC3A 7BT.

TELEPHONE + 44 (0)20 7480 4140.

FAX + 44 (0)20 7280 8790.

INTERNET Website www.foreland-shipping.co.uk *(English)*

ROUTES OPERATED No routes are operated. Ships are for charter to the *UK Ministry of Defence* for their 'Strategic Sealift Capability'.

1	ANVIL POINT	23235t	03	17.1k	193.0m	12P	-	180T	A	UK	9248540
2	EDDYSTONE	23235t	02	17.1k	193.0m	12P	-	180T	A	UK	9234070
3	HARTLAND POINT	23235t	03	17.1k	193.0m	12P	-	180T	A	UK	9248538
4	HURST POINT	23235t	02	17.1k	193.0m	12P	-	180T	A	UK	9234068

ANVIL POINT, HARTLAND POINT Built by Harland & Wolff, Belfast, UK for *AWSR Shipping*.

EDDYSTONE, HURST POINT Built by Flensburger Schiffbau-Gesellschaft, Flensburg, Germany for *AWSR Shipping*.

MANN LINES

THE COMPANY *Mann Lines* are owned by *Mann & Son (London) Ltd* of Great Britain. They replaced in 2001 *ArgoMann Ferry Service*, a joint venture between *Argo Reederei* of Germany and *Mann & Son*.

MANAGEMENT Managing Director Bill Binks, **Commercial Manager** David Brooks.

ADDRESS Mann & Son (London) Ltd, The Naval House, Kings Quay Street, Harwich CO12 3JJ..

TELEPHONE Administration & Reservations *UK* + 44 (0)1255 245200, *Germany* + 49 (0)421 1638500, *Finland* + 358 (0)2 275 0000, *Estonia* + 372 (0)679 1450.

FAX Administration & Reservations *UK* + 44 (0)1255 245219, *Germany* + 49 (0)421 1638520, *Finland* + 358 (0)2 253 5905, *Estonia* + 372 (0)679 1455.

INTERNET Email enquiry@manngroup.co.uk Website www.mannlines.com *(English, Finnish, Estonian, German, Russian)*

ROUTES OPERATED *Circuit 1* Harwich (Navyard) - Cuxhaven - Paldiski - Turku - Bremerhaven (Germany) – Harwich *(ESTRADEN*; weekly).

| 1 | ESTRADEN | 18205t | 99 | 19.0k | 162.7m | 12P | 130C | 170T | A | FI | 9181077 |

ESTRADEN Built as the ESTRADEN by Aker Finnyards, Rauma, Finland for *Rederi Ab Engship* (later *Bore Shipowners*) of Finland and chartered to *ArgoMann*. Later in 1999 renamed the AMAZON. In 2001 the charter was taken over by *Mann Lines* and later in the year she resumed the name ESTRADEN. In 2006 *Rederi AB Engship* was taken over by *Rettig Group Bore* and she remained on charter to Mann Lines.

SCA TRANSFOREST

THE COMPANY *SCA Transforest* is a Swedish company.

MANAGEMENT Managing Director (UK) Hugo Heij.

ADDRESS *Sweden* Box 805, 851 23, Sundsvall, Sweden, *UK* Interforest Terminal London Ltd, 44 Berth, Tilbury Dock, Essex RM18 7HR.

TELEPHONE Administration & Reservations *Sweden* +46 (0)60 19 35 00, *UK* +44 (0)1375 488501.

FAX Administration & Reservations *Sweden* +46 (0)60-19 35 65, *UK* +44 (0)1375 488503.

INTERNET Email *Sweden* info@transforest.sca.com *UK* interforest.london@sca.com

Website www.sca.com/transforest *(English)*

ROUTE OPERATED Umeå - Sundsvall - Tilbury - Rotterdam (Eemhaven) - Helsingborg - Umeå (8/9 day round trip; *OBBOLA, ORTVIKEN, ÖSTRAND*; 1 per week), Umeå - Sundsvall - Tilbury - Rotterdam (Eemhaven) - Oxelösund - Umeå (8/9 day round trip; *OBBOLA, ORTVIKEN, ÖSTRAND*; 1 per week).

1	OBBOLA	20168t	96	16.0k	170.6m	0P	-	-	A	SE	9087350
2	ORTVIKEN	20154t	97	16.0k	170.4m	0P	-	-	A	SE	9087374
3	ÖSTRAND	20171t	96	16.0k	170.6m	0P	-	-	A	SE	9087362

OBBOLA, ORTVIKEN, ÖSTRAND Built by Astilleros Españoles, Seville, Spain for *Gorthon Lines* and chartered to *SCA Transforest*. They are designed for the handling of forest products in non-wheeled 'cassettes' but can also accommodate ro-ro trailers; however, no trailer capacity is quoted. The ORTVIKEN was lengthened during Autumn 2000 and the OBBOLA and ÖSTRAND were lengthened during 2001. In June 2001 purchased by *SCA Transforest*.

SEA-CARGO

THE COMPANY *Sea-Cargo AS* of Norway is a joint venture between *Nor-Cargo AS* (a Norwegian company owned by *Posten Norge*, the Norwegian Postal Service.) and *SeaTrans DS* of Norway.

MANAGEMENT Managing Director Ole Saevild, Director Sales and Marketing Erik A Paulsen, General Manager (UK) Mark Brighton.

ADDRESS *Norway* Sea-Cargo AS, PO Box 353, Nesttun, 5853 Bergen, Norway, *Immingham* Sea-Cargo UK, West Riverside Road, Immingham Dock, Immingham DN40 2NT, *Aberdeen* Sea-Cargo Aberdeen Ltd, Matthews Quay, Aberdeen Harbour, Aberdeen, AB11 5PG.

TELEPHONE Administration & Bookings *Bergen* +47 55 10 84 84, *Immingham* +44 (0)1469 577119, *Aberdeen* +44 (0)1224 596481.

FAX Administration & Reservations *Bergen* +47 85 02 82 16, *Immingham* 44 (0)1469 577708, *Aberdeen* +44 (0)1224 582360.

INTERNET Email mail@sea-cargo.no Website www.sea-cargo.no *(English)*

ROUTES OPERATED *Sea-Cargo* operate a network of services from West Norway to Amsterdam, Aberdeen, Immingham and Esbjerg. The schedule varies from week to week and is shown on the company website. The BALTIC BRIGHT and NORRLAND are generally used on the twice-weekly Immingham - Tanager, Haugesund, Bergen and Odda service and the SEA-CARGO EXPRESS on the weekly Aberdeen - Tanager, Haugesund, Bergen, Florø, Aalesund, Kristiansund, Trondheim and Molde service.

1 ·	BALTIC BRIGHT	9708t	96	15.0k	134.4m	12P	-	65T	A	SE	9129263
2	EXPRESS	12251t	97	20.0k	154.5m	12P	-	124T	A2S	FI	9131993
3	NORRLAND	5562t	90	14.5k	107.5m	0P	-	28T	A	AB	8818764
4 •	SC ABERDEEN	4234t	79	16.0k	109.0m	0P	-	29T	AS	BS	7800540
5	SC AHTELA	8610t	91	14.8k	139.5m	12P	-	92T	AS	MT	8911736
6	SC ASTREA	9528t	91	13.5k	129.1m	0p	-	58T	A	BS	8917895

SECTION 3 – FREIGHT ONLY FERRIES

| 7 | SEA-CARGO EXPRESS | 6693t | 12 | 16.0k | 117.4m | 0P | - | 35T | A | MT | 9358060 |
| 8 | TRANS CARRIER | 9953t | 94 | 14.5k | 145.2m | 0P | - | 94T | AS | BS | 9007879 |

BALTIC BRIGHT Built for *Ab Kungsvik* of Sweden and chartered to *Holmen Papper AB* of Sweden (shipping division trading as *Holmen Carrier*) to operate on their private paper carrying service between Hallstavik and Södertälje in Sweden and Chatham in the UK. Later operated on a number of short-term charters. In November 2009 chartered to *Sea-Cargo* to operate between Western Norway and Immingham.

EXPRESS Built as the UNITED EXPRESS by Fosen Mekaniske Verksteder A/S, Rissa, Norway for *United Shipping* (a subsidiary of *Birka Shipping*) of Finland and chartered to *Transfennica*. During 2000 used on their Kemi - Oulu - Antwerp - Felixstowe service. In 2001 the route was transferred to *Finnlines* and the vessel used sub-chartered to them (charter later transferred to *Finnlines*). In 2002 *United Shipping* was renamed *Birka Cargo* and she was renamed the BIRKA EXPRESS. In 2008 the charter was extended a further four years. In June 2013 renamed the EXPRESS. In November 2013 chartered to *Transfennica*. In April 2014 sold to *Sea-Cargo* but initially continued to operate for *Transfennica*. To be re-engined and modified to allow to side loading.

NORRLAND Built by J J Sietas KG, Hamburg, Germany for *Trailer Link* of Sweden. Chartered to *Sea-Cargo*.

SEA-CARGO EXPRESS One of two vessels ordered in 2005 from Bharati Ratnagiri Ltd, Mumbai, India for *Sea-Cargo*. The order for the second ship has been cancelled. Trailers are carried on the main deck only. Containers are carried on the weather deck and pallets on the lower decks. A crane is provided for the containers and a side door for pallets. She operates on the Aberdeen - Norway service.

SC ABERDEEN Con-ro vessel built by Fosen Mekaniske Verksteder, Rissa, Norway for *Nor-Cargo*. Launched as the ERIC JARL but renamed the ASTREA before entering service. In 1986 she sank and, after raising and refitting, she was, in 1992, renamed the TUNGENES. In 2001 she was renamed the SC ABERDEEN. In October 2012 laid up.

SC AHTELA Built as the AHTELA by Brodogradiliste "Sava", Macvanska Mitrovica, Yugoslavia, completed by Fosen Mekaniske Verksteder, Rissa, Norway for *Rederi AB Gustav Erikson* of Finland. Chartered to *Transfennica*. In 1995 chartered to *DFDS Tor Line*. In 1996 chartered to *Finncarriers Oy* of Finland and in 1997 renamed the FINNOAK. In 2007 sold to *Hollming Oy* of Finland and in 2008 the charter ended and she was renamed the AHTELA. Chartered to *Navirail* of Estonia to operate between Helsinki and Muuga (Estonia). Between February and May 2011 chartered to *Sea-Cargo* to operate between Esbjerg (Denmark) and Egersund (Norway). In October 2012 purchased by *Sea-Cargo* and renamed the SC AHTELA.

SC ASTREA Built as the ASTREA by Tangen Verft Kragerø A/S, Kragerø, Norway for *Finncarriers* of Finland. Operated between Finland and Spain - Portugal via Antwerp. In 2006 chartered to *Danish MoD*. In 2007 chartered to *Sea-Cargo*. In August 2011 purchased by *Sea-Cargo* and renamed the SC ASTREA. Currently chartered out.

TRANS CARRIER Built as the KORSNÄS LINK by Brodogradiliste Kraljevica, Kraljevica, Croatia for *SeaLink AB* of Sweden and due to be time-chartered to *Korsnäs AB*, a Swedish forest products company. However, due to the war in Croatia, delivery was seriously delayed and she was offered for sale. In 1994 sold to the *Swan Group* and renamed the SWAN HUNTER. She was placed on the charter market. In 1997 she was chartered to *Euroseabridge* and renamed the PARCHIM. In 1999 the charter ended and she resumed the name SWAN HUNTER. In 1999 she was sold to *SeaTrans* and renamed the TRANS CARRIER. She operated for *Sea-Cargo*. In 2005 chartered to *Finnlines* and used on the Finland to Spain/Portugal service. In 2006 returned to *Sea-Cargo*. In January and February 2009 lengthened by 18.9 metres in Poland.

SEATRUCK FERRIES

THE COMPANY *Seatruck Ferries Ltd* is a British private sector company. It is part of the *Clipper Group*.

MANAGEMENT Chairman Ole Frie, Managing Director Alistair Eagles.

ADDRESSES *Heysham (HQ)* North Quay, Heysham Port, Heysham, Morecambe, Lancs LA3 2UH, *Warrenpoint* Seatruck House, The Ferry Terminal, Warrenpoint, County Down BT34 3JR, *Liverpool:* Seatruck Ferry Terminal, Brocklebank Dock, Port of Liverpool, L20 1DB, *Dublin:* Seatruck Dublin, Alexandra Road, Dublin 1 Irish Republic.

Obbola (*Cees de Bijl*)

Clipper Pennant (*Gordon Hislip*)

Seatruck Progress (*Gordon Hislip*)

Hurst Point (*FotoFlite*)

TELEPHONE Administration +44 (0)1524 855377, Reservations *Heysham* +44 (0)1524 853512. *Warrenpoint* +44 (0)28 754400, *Liverpool* + (0)151 9333660, *Dublin* + (0) 353 18230492.

FAX Administration +44 (0)28 4175 4545, Reservations *Warrenpoint* +44 (0)28 4177 3737, *Heysham* +44 (0)1524 853549.

INTERNET Email aje@seatruckgroup.co.uk Websites www.seatruckferries.com *(English)*

ROUTES OPERATED Heysham - Warrenpoint (9 hrs; *CLIPPER PENNANT, SEATRUCK PANORAMA*; 2 per day), Heysham - Dublin (9 hrs; *SEATRUCK PACE*;1 per day), Liverpool - Dublin (9 hrs; *SEATRUCK POWER, SEATRUCK PROGRESS*; 1 or 2 per day).

1	CLIPPER PENNANT	14759t	09	22.0k	142.0m	12P	-	120T	A	CY	9372688
2	CLIPPER RANGER	7606t	98	17.0k	122.3m	12P	-	84T	A	IM	9119402
3	SEATRUCK PACE	14759t	09	22.0k	142.0m	12P	-	120T	A	CY	9350678
4	SEATRUCK PANORAMA	14759t	09	22.0k	142.0m	12P	-	120T	A	CY	9372676
5	SEATRUCK POWER	19722t	11	21.0k	142.0m	12P	-	151T	A	IM	9506215
6	SEATRUCK PROGRESS	19722t	11	21.0k	142.0m	12P	-	151T	A	IM	9506203

CLIPPER PENNANT Built by Astilleros Sevilla SA, Seville, Spain for *Seatruck Ferries*. In January 2013 chartered to *Stena RoRo*.

CLIPPER RANGER Built as the LEMBITU by Astilleros de Huelva SA, Huelva, Spain for the *Estonian Shipping Company*. On completion chartered to *P&O European Ferries (Irish Sea)* and placed on their Liverpool - Dublin route. In Autumn 1998 she was chartered to *Dart Line* and placed on the Dartford - Vlissingen route. In 1999 she was renamed the DART 7. In Autumn 1999 the charter was ended and she was chartered to *Cetam* of France, resumed the name LEMBITU and was used on services between Marseilles and Tunis. In 2000 she was chartered to *P&O European Ferries (Irish Sea)* and renamed the CELTIC SUN; she operated between Liverpool and Dublin. In 2001 the charter ended; she then reverted to the name LEMBITU and was chartered to *NorseMerchant Ferries* and placed on the Heysham - Dublin service. In late 2001 the charter ended and she returned to *ESCO* service in the Baltic. In 2003 chartered to *Scandlines AG* and placed on their Rostock - Helsinki - Muuga service. This service finished in December 2004 and she was chartered to *Channel Freight Ferries* in January 2005. In March 2005 chartered to *NorseMerchant Ferries* again and operated between Heysham and Belfast. Later purchased by *Elmira Shipping* of Greece and renamed the RR CHALLENGE. In June 2005 chartered to *Seatruck Ferries*. In October 2007 sold to *Attica Group* of Greece and renamed the CHALLENGE. She continued to be chartered to *Seatruck Ferries*. In January 2008 she was transferred to the Liverpool - Dublin route and in April sold to *Seatruck Ferries*. In July renamed the CLIPPER RANGER. In June 2009 replaced the SHIELD (now the HILDASAY) until the new CLIPPER PENNANT took over in October. In May 2010 inaugurated a new Heysham - Larne service. In October 2013 chartered to *Caledonian MacBrayne* to replace the MUIRNEAG. The charter may end in August 2014 when the LOCH SEAFORTH enters service.

SEATRUCK PACE Built as the CLIPPER PACE by Astilleros Sevilla SA, Seville, Spain for *Seatruck Ferries*. In March 2012 renamed the SEATRUCK PACE. In January 2013 chartered to *Blue Water Shipping* of Denmark to carry wind turbine parts between Mostyn (Wales) and Esbjerg. Now operates Heysham - Dublin.

SEATRUCK PANORAMA Built by Astilleros de Huelva SA, Huelva Spain for *Seatruck Ferries*. Launched as the CLIPPER PENNANT and renamed the CLIPPER PANORAMA before delivery. In December 2011 renamed the SEATRUCK PANORAMA.

SEATRUCK POWER, SEATRUCK PROGRESS Built by Flensburger Schiffbau-Gesellschaft, Flensburg, Germany for *Seatruck Ferries*.

Seatruck Ferries also own the ARROW currently on charter to *Isle of Man Steam Packet Company*, HELLIAR and HILDASAY, currently on charter to *NorthLink Ferries*, the STENA PERFORMER and STENA PRECISION, currently on charter to *Stena Line* and the CLIPPER POINT, currently on charter to *DFDS Seaways*.

SECTION 3 – FREIGHT ONLY FERRIES

FLOTA SUARDIAZ

THE COMPANY *Flota Suardiaz SL* is owned by *Grupo Suardiaz*, a Spanish private sector logistics company which operates divisions in ports, bunkering, warehousing, haulage, freight forwarding and shipping.

MANAGEMENT **Presidente** Juan Riva **Director General** Jesús Nieto.

ADDRESSES **Spain** Calle Ayala, 6 28001 Madrid, Spain, **UK** Suardiaz Shipping Ltd, Suardiaz House, 193 Shirley Road, Southampton, Hampshire, SO15 3FG.

TELEPHONE **Spain** +34 914 31 66 40, **UK** +44 (0) 2380 211 981.

FAX **Spain** + 34 914 36 46 74, **UK** +44 (0) 2380 335309.

INTERNET **Email** infoweb@suardiaz.com, **Website** www.suardiaz.com *(English, Spanish)*.

ROUTES OPERATED **Channel Line** (3 times per week) Sheerness – Calais, Grimsby – Calais **Cantabrian Line** (weekly) Teesport – Zeebrugge - Southampton – Le Havre – Santander **Northern Sea Line** (twice weekly) Cuxhaven – Immingham **Línea del Atlántico / Barcelona - Inglaterra** (weekly) Vlissingen – Zeebrugge – Southampton – Vigo – Setubal - Las Palmas – Tenerife – Casablanca – Barcelona – Sete – Barcelona – Casablanca – Setubal – Sheerness – Newcastle **Biscay Line** (3 per week) St Nazaire – Vigo **Canaries Line** (weekly) Barcelona – Tarragona – Las Palmas - Tenerife **Italy Line** (3 per week) Barcelona – Livorno.

Services listed carry unaccompanied ro-ro cargo together with large volumes of trade cars for vehicle manufacturers and distributors. The Cantabrian and Channel Line services are operated by SCSC (Suardiaz CAT Shipping Co) a joint venture with European Car distributor CAT. The Biscay Line is operated under contract to GEFCO. Vessels are regularly transferred between routes and are often chartered out for short periods to other operators and vehicle manufacturers. In view of this the following is a list of all vessels in the *Flota Suardiaz* fleet at the present time including those that do not currently serve the UK.

1	BOUZAS	15224t	02	18.5k	149.4m	12P	1265C	105T	A	ES	9249996
2	GALICIA	16361t	03	15.0k	149.4m	12P	1390C	490T	A	ES	9268409
3	GRAN CANARIA CAR	9600t	01	18.0k	132.5m	0P	1150C	42T	AS	ES	9218014
4	IVAN	8191t	96	14.6k	102.5m	0P	853C	73T	A	PT	9112040
5	L'AUDACE	15222t	99	18.5k	149.4m	12P	1233C	105T	A	ES	9187318
6	LA SURPRISE	15222t	00	18.5k	149.4m	12P	1233C	105T	A	ES	9198719
7	SUAR VIGO	16361t	03	18.5k	149.4m	12P	1356C	110T	A	ES	9250000
8	TENERIFE CAR	13122t	02	20.0k	149.4m	12P	1354C	54T	AS	ES	9249984

GRAN CANARIA CAR Built as HARALD FLICK by Hijos de J. Barreras SA, Vigo, Portugal for *Naviera del Odiel*, one of the shareholders in Barreras and placed on 10 year charter to *Flota Suardiaz* of Spain for use on services in the Mediterranean and to the Canaries, U.K. and Benelux. Renamed GRAN CANARIA CAR before entering service. In 2008 ownership passed to *Navicar SA* a subsidiary of *Flota Suardiaz*. In addition to operating for *Flota Suardiaz* has been chartered to UECC on a number of occasions.

BOUZAS, GALICIA, L'AUDACE, LA SURPRISE, SUAR VIGO Built by Hijos de J. Barreras SA, Vigo, Portugal for *Flota Suardiaz* of Spain for use on services in the Mediterranean and to the Canaries, U.K. and Benelux. In addition to operating for *Flota Suardiaz* a number of vessels have spent periods on charter to UECC. In February 2014 L'AUDACE was chartered to *P&O Ferries* to operate between Hull and Zeebrugge.

IVAN Built by Astilleros De Murueta, Vizcaya, Spain for *Adamastor - Sociedade de Navegação, Lda* a subsidiary of *Flota Suardiaz* for use on short sea services. In recent years she has been used on services between Sheerness, Grimsby and Calais.

TENERIFE CAR Built by Hijos de J. Barreras SA, Vigo, Portugal for *Navicar SA* a subsidiary of *Flota Suardiaz* for use on services in the Mediterranean and to the Canaries, U.K. and Benelux.

TRANSFENNICA

THE COMPANY *Transfennica Ltd* is a Finnish private sector company wholly owned by *Spliethoff Bevrachtingskantoor* of The Netherlands.

MANAGEMENT **Managing Director** Dirk P. Witteveen, **Sales Director (UK)** Andrew Clarke.

ADDRESSES *Finland* Eteläranta 12, 00130 Helsinki, Finland, **UK** Finland House, 47 Berth, Tilbury Port, Tilbury, Essex RM18 7EH.

TELEPHONE **Administration & Reservations** *Finland* + 358 (0)9 13262, **UK** + 44 (0)1375 363 900.

FAX **Administration & Reservations** *Finland* + 358 (0)9 652377, **UK** + 44 (0)1375 840 888.

INTERNET **Email** *Finland* info@transfennica.fi *UK* info.uk@transfennica.com *(English)*

Website www.transfennica.com *(English)*

ROUTES OPERATED Tilbury (twice weekly) to various destinations in Finland and Russia. Also Zeebrugge - Bilbao - Portsmouth - Zeebrugge (weekly) Please see the website. All *Transfennica* ships are listed below as ships are sometimes moved between routes.

1	CAROLINE RUSS	10488t	99	21.0k	153.5m	12P	-	134T	A2	AG	9197533
2	CARRIER	12251t	98	20.0k	154.5m	12P	-	124T	A2	FI	9132002
3	FRIEDRICH RUSS	10471t	99	20.0k	153.5m	12P	-	120T	A2	AG	9186429
4	GENCA	28301t	07	22.0k	205.0m	12P	-	200T	A2	NL	9307372
5	KRAFTCA	28301t	06	22.0k	205.0m	12P	-	200T	A2	NL	9307360
6	PAULINE RUSS	10488t	99	22.0k	153.5m	12P	-	120T	A2	AG	9198989
7	PLYCA	28301t	09	22.0k	205.0m	12P	-	200T	A2	NL	9345398
8	PULPCA	28301t	08	22.0k	205.0m	12P	-	200T	A2	NL	9345386
9	SEAGARD	10488t	99	21.0k	153.5m	12P	-	134T	A2	FI	9198977
10	STENA FORECASTER	24688t	03	22.0k	195.3m	12P	-	210T	A2	SE	9214666
11	STENA FORERUNNER	24688t	02	22.0k	195.3m	12P	-	210T	A2	SE	9214666
12	STENA FORETELLER	24688t	02	22.0k	195.3m	12P	-	210T	A2	SE	9214666
13	TIMCA	28301t	06	22.0k	205.0m	12P	-	200T	A2	NL	9307358
14	TRICA	28301t	07	22.0k	205.0m	12P	-	200T	A2	NL	9307384

CAROLINE RUSS Built by J J Sietas KG, Hamburg, Germany for *Ernst Russ* of Germany and chartered to *Transfennica*. Between January and September 2013 chartered to *Finnlines*. In January 2014 chartered to *Transfennica*.

CARRIER Built as the UNITED CARRIER by Fosen Mekaniske Verksteder A/S, Rissa, Norway for *United Shipping* (a subsidiary of *Birka Shipping*) of Finland and chartered to *Transfennica*. During 2000 she was used on their Kemi - Oulu - Antwerp - Felixstowe service. In 2001 the route was transferred to *Finnlines* and the vessel used sub-chartered to them (charter later transferred to *Finnlines*). In 2002 *United Shipping* was renamed *Birka Cargo* and the ship was renamed the BIRKA CARRIER. In 2006 the service ceased. In 2008 the charter was extended a further four years. In January 2013 chartered to *Transfennica*. In June 2013 she was renamed the CARRIER.

FRIEDRICH RUSS, PAULINE RUSS, Built by J J Sietas KG, Hamburg, Germany for *Ernst Russ* of Germany and chartered to *Transfennica*.

GENCA, KRAFTCA, PLYCA, PULPCA, TIMCA, TRICA Built by New Szczecin Shipyard (SSN), Szczecin, Poland for *Spliethoff Bevrachtingskantoor*, owners of *Transfennica*.

SEAGARD Built by J J Sietas KG, Hamburg, Germany for *Bror Husell Chartering* of Finland (later acquired by *Bore Shipowning* of Finland) and chartered to *Transfennica*.

STENA FORECASTER, STENA FORERUNNER Built by Dalian Shipyard Co Ltd, Dalian, China for *Stena RoRo* and chartered to *Transfennica*.

Pauline Russ *(J.J.Jager)*

Galicia *(FotoFlite)*

STENA FORETELLER Built as the STENA FORETELLER by Dalian Shipyard Co Ltd, Dalian, China for *Stena RoRo*. Initially chartered to *Cetam* of France to operate between Marseilles and Tunis and renamed the CETAM MASSILIA. In November 2003 the charter ended and she resumed her original name. A number of short-term commercial and military charters followed until June 2006 when she was chartered to *StoraEnso* paper group to operate between Gothenburg and Finnish ports. In September 2009 she was chartered to *Rederi AB Transatlantic* who took over responsibility to operate all *StoraEnso's* Baltic services. In February 2012 she was chartered to *Transfennica*.

UECC

THE COMPANY *United European Car Carriers AS* is a Norwegian private sector company jointly owned in equal shares by *Nippon Yusen Kabushiki Kaisha (NYK)* of Japan and *Wallenius Lines* of Sweden. UECC consists of companies in Norway, Germany, Spain, France, Portugal and the UK. The fleet technical and ship management department is based in Grimsby (UK).

MANAGEMENT **Chief Executive Officer** Glenn Edvardsen **Senior Commercial Manager UK** Peter Pegg.

ADDRESSES **Norway** Karenlyst Allè 57, 0277 Oslo, **UK** 17 St. Helen's Place, London EC3A 6DG.

TELEPHONE **Norway** +47 21 00 98 00, **UK** +44 (0)207 628 2855.

FAX **Norway** +47 21 00 98 01, **UK** +44 (0)207 628 2858.

INTERNET **Email** companymail@uecc.com, **Website** www.uecc.com *(English)*.

ROUTES OPERATED **Bristol Service** Portbury - Pasajes (*AUTOSUN*; every 4 days) **North Sea Line** Sheerness – Emden, Southampton – Cuxhaven, Zeebrugge – Malmo (*AUTOPRESTIGE; AUTOPRIDE*; weekly or twice weekly, **Biscay Services** Pasajes – Zeebrugge – Southampton – Santander - Pasajes (*AUTOSTAR*; weekly) Pasajes – Rotterdam – Zeebrugge – Santander – Pasajes (*AUTOSKY*; weekly) Santander – Zeebrugge – Southampton – Le Havre – Santander (*AUTOPREMIER*; weekly) **Atlantic Service** Vigo – Le Havre – Zeebrugge – Sheerness – Vigo (*VIKING CHANCE*; weekly) **Norway Service** Bremerhaven – Oslo/Drammen (*AUTORACER*; twice weekly) Bremerhaven – Drammen – Cuxhaven – Southampton – Zeebrugge – Bremerhaven (*AUTOPROGRESS*; weekly) **Baltic Long Loop Service** Southampton – Zebrugge – Gydnia – Hanko – Kotka – St Petersburg – Cuxhaven – Southampton (*ARABIAN BREEZE, ASIAN BREEZE*; weekly) **Baltic Short Loop Service** Bremerhaven – Wallhamn – Kotka – St Petersburg – Ust Luga – Bremerhaven (*AUTO BAY, AUTO BANK*; every 5 days) Bremerhaven –Hanko – St Petersburg – Bremerhaven (*AUTO BALTIC*; weekly) **North / South Service** Bremerhaven - Zeebrugge - Portbury - Vigo - Malaga - Tarragona - Livorno - Piraeus - Derince - Yenikoy - Borusan - Vigo - Bremerhaven (*OPAL LEADER, CORAL LEADER, EMERALD LEADER, MORNING MENAD, VIKING DRIVE*; weekly) **West-Med Service** Vigo - Djen Djen (*SPICA LEADER*; 3 per month) Fos – Mostaganem (*AUTORUNNER*; every 4 days) Gioia Tauro – Misurata – Djen Djen – Gioia Tauro (*BALTIC BREEZE; AEGEAN BREEZE*; weekly)

Services listed carry unaccompanied ro-ro cargo together with large volumes of trade cars and may call at additional ports for an inducement and regular additional ports include Cork, Dublin, Immingham, Sheerness, Portbury, Tilbury, and Newcastle. A number of short-sea contract sailings for vehicle manufacturers and distributors are also operated and these serve many additional ports in Northern Europe. Vessels are regularly transferred between routes and contracts and in view of this the following is a list of all owned and long term chartered vessels in the *UECC* fleet at the current time including those that do not presently serve the UK. Additionally the fleet is regularly supplemented by short term chartered vessels from *Flota Suardiaz* and *Fret Cetam* (the *Louis Dreyfus Armateurs* and *Höegh Auto-liners* Airbus joint venture) and with deep sea ocean-going ro-ro vessels from parent companies *NYK Line* and *Wallenius Lines* and Eukor. Chartered vessels at the time of preparation and considered out of the scope of this book were the CORAL LEADER, EMERALD LEADER, MORNING MENAD, OPAL LEADER, SPICA LEADER, VIKING DRIVE .

1	AEGEAN BREEZE	27876t	83	18.0k	164.0m	0P	3242C	260T	QRS	SG	8202367
2	ARABIAN BREEZE	27876t	83	18.0k	164.0m	0P	3242C	260T	QRS	SG	8202355
3	ASIAN BREEZE	27876t	83	18.0k	164.0m	0P	3242C	260T	QRS	SG	8202381
4	AUTO BALTIC	18979t	96	20.0k	138.5m	12P	1452C	105T	A2	FI	9121998

5	AUTO BANK	19107t	96	20.0k	138.8m	12P	1610C	105T	A2	FI	9160774
6	AUTO BAY	19094t	96	20.0k	138.8m	12P	1610C	105T	A2	FI	9122007
7	AUTOPREMIER	11591t	97	20.0k	128.8m	0P	1220C	-	AS	MD	9131943
8	AUTOPRESTIGE	11596t	99	20.0k	128.8m	0P	1220C	-	AS	MD	9190157
9	AUTOPRIDE	11591t	97	20.0k	128.8m	0P	1220C	-	AS	MD	9131955
10	AUTOPROGRESS	11591t	98	20.0k	128.8m	0P	1220C	-	AS	MD	9131967
11	AUTORACER	9693t	94	20.0k	119.9m	0P	1060C	-	AS	MD	9079200
12	AUTORUNNER	9693t	94	20.0k	119.9m	0P	1060C	-	AS	MD	9079212
13	AUTOSKY	21010t	00	20.9k	140.0m	0P	2080C	-	AS	MD	9206774
14	AUTOSTAR	21010t	00	20.9k	140.0m	0P	2080C	-	AS	MD	9206786
15	AUTOSUN	21094t	00	20.9k	140.0m	0P	1220C	-	AS	MD	9227053
16	BALTIC BREEZE	29979t	83	17.5k	164.0m	0P	3242C	260T	QRS	SG	8312590

AEGEAN BREEZE, ARABIAN BREEZE, ASIAN BREEZE Built by Kurushima Dockyard, Onishi, Japan for *Fuji Shipping* of Tokyo. Sold in 1988 to *Amon Shipping*. In 1990 sold to *Wallenius Lines*, Singapore and later chartered to UECC. Of deep-sea ocean-going ro-ro design with quarter ramps, they are normally used on the Baltic Long Loop and Mediterranean services.

AUTO BALTIC Built as the TRANSGARD by Umoe Sterkoder, Kristiansund, Norway for *Bror Husell Chartering* of Finland for long-term charter to *Transfennica* and used between Rauma and Antwerp and Hamina and Lübeck. Later chartered to *Finncarriers*. In 2005 she underwent conversion in Poland to add a garage on top of the original weather deck and was placed on long-term charter to UECC with options to purchase. Generally used on the Baltic or Iberian services. In 2007 renamed AUTO BALTIC.

AUTO BANK Built as the SERENADEN by Umoe Sterkoder AS, Kristiansund, Norway for *Rederi AB Engship* of Finland and chartered to *Transfennica*. In 2006 *Rederi AB Engship* was taken over by *Rettig Group Bore*. In 2007 converted at COSCO Shipyard, Nantong, China to add a garage on top of the weather deck, renamed AUTO BANK and placed on long-term charter to UECC. Generally used on the Baltic or Iberian services.

AUTO BAY Built as the HERALDEN by Umoe Sterkoder AS, Kristiansund, Norway for *Rederi AB Engship* of Finland and chartered to *Transfennica*. In 2006 *Rederi AB Engship* was taken over by *Rettig Group Bore*. In 2007 converted at COSCO Shipyard, Nantong, China to add a garage on top of the weather deck, renamed AUTO BAY and placed on long-term charter to UECC. Generally used on the Baltic or Iberian services.

AUTOPREMIER, AUTOPRESTIGE, AUTOPROGRESS, AUTOPRIDE Built by Frisian Shipyard Welgelegen, Harlingen, the Netherlands for UECC. Designated P-class, they are an enlarged version of the R-class and built to a 'Grimsby-Max' specification with greater capacity for ro-ro cargo. Normally used on scheduled sailings between Iberia, Belgium, Ireland and UK.

AUTORUNNER, AUTORACER. Built by Brattvaag Skipsverft, Brattvaag, Norway for UECC. Designated as R-class, they are normally used on scheduled sailings between Iberia, Belgium, Ireland and UK.

AUTOSKY, AUTOSTAR, AUTOSUN Built by Tsuneishi Zosen, Tadotsu, Japan for UECC. Designated S-class, they are a further enlargement of the P-class and R-class designs and are normally used on the longer routes to Iberia and in the Baltic.

BALTIC BREEZE Built by Kurushima Dockyard, Onishi, Japan for *Fuji Shipping Co* of Tokyo. Sold in 1988 to *Amon Shipping*. Sold to *Wallenius Lines*, Singapore in 1990. Chartered to *Eukor* then to UECC. Of deep-sea ocean-going ro-ro design with a quarter ramp, she is normally used on the Mediterranean services.

Under Construction

17	NEWBUILDING 1	-	16	-	181.0m	0P	3800C	-	QRS	-	-
18	NEWBUILDING 2	-	16	-	181.0m	0P	3800C	-	QRS	-	-

NEWBUILDING 1, NEWBUILDING 2 On order from Kawasaki Heavy Industries (KHI) of Japan. The vessels will be constructed at the NACKS shipyard in Nantong, China which is a joint venture between KHI and China Ocean Shipping (Group) Company. They will be dual fuel vessels - normal fuel oil and LNG.

SECTION 4 - GB & IRELAND - CHAIN, CABLE ETC FERRIES

CUMBRIA COUNTY COUNCIL

Address Environment Directorate, County Offices, Kendal, Cumbria LA9 4RQ **Tel** + 44 (0)1539 713040, **Fax** + 44 (0)1539 713035.

Internet Email tony.beaty@cumbria.gov.uk *(English)*

Website www.cumbria.gov.uk/roads-transport/highways-pavements/windermereferry.asp *(English)*

Route Bowness-on-Windermere - Far Sawrey.

1	MALLARD	-	90	-	25.9m	140P	18C	-	BA

MALLARD Chain ferry built by F L Steelcraft, Borth, Dyfed for *Cumbria County Council.*

DARTMOUTH - KINGSWEAR FLOATING BRIDGE CO LTD

Address Dart Marina, Sandquay Road, Dartmouth, Devon TQ6 9PH. **Tel** + 44 (0)1803 839622.

Internet Website www.dartmouthhigherferry.com *(English)*

Route Dartmouth - Kingswear (Devon) across River Dart (higher route) (forms part of A379).

1	HIGHER FERRY	540t	09	-	52.7m	240P	32C	-	BA

HIGHER FERRY Built by Ravestein BV, Deest, The Netherlands under contract to Pendennis Shipyard, Falmouth, who fitted the vessel out between January and June 2009.

ISLE OF WIGHT COUNCIL (COWES FLOATING BRIDGE)

Address Ferry Office, Medina Road, Cowes, Isle of Wight PO31 7BX. **Tel** + 44 (0)1983 293041.

Route West Cowes - East Cowes.

1	NO 5	-	76	-	33.5m	-	15C	-	BA

NO 5 Chain ferry built by Fairey Marine, East Cowes, UK for *Isle of Wight County Council*, now *Isle of Wight Council.*

KING HARRY FERRY AND CORNWALL FERRIES

Address 2 Ferry Cottages, Feock, Truro, Cornwall TR3 6QJ. **Tel** + 44 (0)1872 862312, **Fax** + 44 (0)1872 863355.

Internet Email info@falriver.co.uk **Website** www.falriver.co.uk *(English)*

Route Philliegh - Feock (Cornwall) (across River Fal)

1	KING HARRY FERRY	500t	06	-	55.2m	150P	34C	-	BA	UK	9364370

KING HARRY FERRY Chain ferry built by Pendennis Shipyard, Falmouth (hull constructed at Ravestein Shipyard, Deest, The Netherlands) to replace the previous ferry.

REEDHAM FERRY

Address Reedham Ferry, Ferry Inn, Reedham, Norwich NR13 3HA. **Tel** + 44 (0)1493 700999.

Internet Email info@reedhamferry.co.uk **Website** www.reedhamferry.co.uk *(English)*

Route Acle - Reedham - Norton (across River Yare, Norfolk).

| 1 | REEDHAM FERRY | - | 84 | - | 11.3m | 20P | 3C | - | BA | | |

REEDHAM FERRY Chain ferry built by Newsons, Oulton Broad, Lowestoft, UK for *Reedham Ferry*. Maximum vehicle weight: 12 tons.

SANDBANKS FERRY

Address *Company* Bournemouth-Swanage Motor Road and Ferry Company, Shell Bay, Studland, Swanage, Dorset BH19 3BA. **Tel** +44 (0)1929 450203, **Fax** +44 (0)1929 450498), **Ferry** Floating Bridge, Ferry Way, Sandbanks, Poole, Dorset BH13 7QN. **Tel** +44 (0)1929 450203.

Internet Email email@sandbanksferry.co.uk **Website** www.sandbanksferry.co.uk *(English)*

Route Sandbanks - Shell Bay (Dorset).

| 1 | BRAMBLE BUSH BAY | 625t | 93 | - | 74.4m | 400P | 48C | - | BA | UK | 9072070 |

BRAMBLE BUSH BAY Chain ferry, built by Richard Dunston (Hessle) Ltd, Hessle, UK for the *Bournemouth-Swanage Motor Road and Ferry Company*.

SOUTH HAMS DISTRICT COUNCIL

Address Lower Ferry Office, The Square, Kingswear, Dartmouth, Devon TQ6 0AA. **Tel** +44 (0)1803 861234.

Internet Website www.southhams.gov.uk/DartmouthLowerFerry *(English)*

Route Dartmouth - Kingswear (Devon) across River Dart (lower route).

| 1 | THE TOM AVIS | - | 94 | - | 33.5m | 50P | 8C | - | BA | | |
| 2 | THE TOM CASEY | - | 89 | - | 33.5m | 50P | 8C | - | BA | | |

THE TOM AVIS Float (propelled by tugs) built by Alan Toms, Fowey, UK for *South Hams District Council*.

THE TOM CASEY Float (propelled by tugs) built by Cozens, Portland, UK for *South Hams District Council*.

TORPOINT FERRY

Address 2 Ferry Street, Torpoint, Cornwall PL11 2AX. **Tel** +44 (0)1752 812233, **Fax** +44 (0)1752 816873.

Internet Website www.tamarcrossings.org.uk *(English)*

Route Devonport (Plymouth) - Torpoint (Cornwall) across the Tamar. The three ferries operate in parallel, each on her own 'track'. Pre-booking is not possible and the above numbers cannot be used for that purpose.

1	LYNHER II	748t	06	-	73.0m	350P	73C	-	BA	UK	9310941
2	PLYM II	748t	04	-	73.0m	350P	73C	-	BA	UK	9310927
3	TAMAR II	748t	05	-	73.0m	350P	73C	-	BA	UK	9310939

LYNHER II, PLYM II, TAMAR II Chain ferries built by Ferguson Shipbuilders Ltd, Port Glasgow, UK to replace 1960s-built ships. Unlike previous ferries, they are registered as 'Passenger/Ro-Ro Cargo' ships and thus have gross tonnage, nation of registry and, being over 100t, an IMO number.

WATERFORD CASTLE HOTEL

Address The Island, Waterford, Irish Republic. **Tel** +353 (0)51 878203.

Internet Email info@waterfordcastle.com **Website** www.waterfordcastle.com *(English (mainly about hotel; little about ferry))*

Route Grantstown - Little Island (in River Suir, County Waterford).

| 1 | LORELEY | 110t | 59 | - | 32.0m | 57P | 12C | - | BA | | |

LORELEY Chain ferry built as the LORELEY V by Ruthof, Mainz, Germany to operate between St Goarshausen and St Goar on the River Rhine. In 2004 replaced by a new vessel (the LORELEY VI) and became a reserve vessel In 2007, sold to the *Waterford Castle Hotel* and renamed the LORELEY and, in 2008 replaced the previous ferry. She is self propelled and guided by cable.

SECTION 5 - GB & IRELAND - MAJOR PASSENGER-ONLY FERRIES

There are a surprisingly large number of passenger-only ferries operating in the British Isles, mainly operated by launches and small motor boats. There are, however, a few 'major' operators who operate only passenger vessels (of rather larger dimensions) and have not therefore been mentioned previously.

Aran Island Ferries CEOL NA FARRAIGE (234t, 2001, 37.4m, 294 passengers, IMO 9246750), DRAÍOCHT NA FARRAIGE (318t, 1999, 35.4m, 294 passengers, IMO 9200897), GLÓR NA FARRAIGE (170t, 1985, 33.5m, 244 passenger, IMO 8522391) (ex ARAN FLYER 2007), BANRÍON NA FARRAIGE (117t, 27.4m, 1984, 188 passengers, IMO 8407709) (ex ARAN EXPRESS 2007), SEA SPRINTER (16t, 11.6m, 35 passengers). **Routes operated** Rossaveal (Co Galway) – Inishmor, Rossaveal - Inis Meáin, Rossaveal - Inisheer. **Tel** +353 (0)91 568903 (572050 after 19.00), **Fax** +353 (0)91 568538, **Email** info@aranislandferries.com **Website** www.aranislandferries.com *(English)*

Clydelink ISLAND PRINCESS (1996, 13.7m, 96 passengers), CAILIN OIR (1999, 15.2m, 72 passengers), **Route operated** Gourock - Kilcreggan (operated on behalf of *Strathclyde Partnership for Transport*) ISLAND TRADER (12 passengers), **Route operated** Renfrew - Yoker (operated on behalf of *Strathclyde Partnership for Transport*) **(Tel** 0871 705 0888, **Website** www.clydelink.co.uk *(English)* Note: The CAILIN OIR is spending summer 2014 on charter to *O'Brien Line*. She may return in the autumn.

Clyde Cruises (Clyde Marine Services Ltd) CHIEFTAIN (ex SEABUS, 2014) (54t, 2007, 19.5m, 100 passengers)CLYDE CLIPPER (125t, 2009, 27m, 250 passengers), CRUISER (ex POOLE SCENE, 2001, HYTHE HOTSPUR, 1995, SOUTHSEA QUEEN, 1978) (119t, 1974, 24.4m, 245 passengers), FENCER (18t, 1976, 11.0m, 33 passengers), ROVER (48t, 1964, 19.8m, 120 passengers), , THE SECOND SNARK (45t, 1938, 22.9m, 120 passengers). **Routes operated** Glasgow – Braehead, Aberdeen Harbour Tours, Dunstaffnage Marina (Oban) cruises, private charters around the Clyde area. **Tel** +44 (0)1475 721281, **Email** julie@clydecruises.com & enquiries@clyde-marine.co.uk **Website** www.clydecruises.com www.clyde-marine.co.uk *(English)*.

Dartmouth Steam Railway & Riverboat Company DARTMOUTH PRINCESS (22t, 1990, 18.3m, 156 passengers), KINGSWEAR PRINCESS (27t, 1978, 19.1m, 150 passengers) **Route operated** Dartmouth - Kingswear. CARLINA (5t, 8.5m, 12 passengers), CHAMPION (4t, 1952, 9.7m, 12 passengers), WARRIOR (3.5t, 1947, 9.7m, 12 passengers). **Route operated** Dartmouth - Dittisham. **Note:** Pleasure craft owned by this operator are also used for the ferry service on some occasions. **Tel** +44 (0)1803 834488, **Fax** +44 (0)1803 835248, **Email** bookings@dsrrb.co.uk **Website** www.dartmouthrailriver.co.uk *(English)*

Doolin2Aran Ferries DOOLIN DISCOVERY (2009, 15.2m, 72 passengers), JACK B (2005, 15.2m, 67 passengers), HAPPY HOOKER (77t, 1989, 19.8m, 96 passengers), MACDARA (2010, 8.5m, 12 passengers), ROSE OF ARAN (113t, 1976, 20.1m, 96 passengers. IMO 7527916). **Routes operated** Doolin - Inisheer, Doolin - Inishmore, Doolin - Inishmaan. **Tel** +353 (0)65 707 5949, **Email** info@doolin2aranferries.ie **Website** www.doolin2aranferries.com *(English)*

Exmouth to Sea Cruises MY QUEEN (1929, 37t, 18m, 127 passengers), ORCOMBE (1954, 14.3m, 100 passengers), PRINCESS MARINA (1936, 15.8m, 60 passengers). **Route operated** Exmouth - Starcross. **Tel** +44 (0)1626 774770, **Email** info@exe2sea.co.uk **Website** www.exe2sea.co.uk *(English)*

Fleetwood - Knott End Ferry (operated by *Wyre Marine Services Ltd*) WYRE ROSE (2005, 32 passengers). **Route operated** Fleetwood - Knott End. **Route operated** Fleetwood - Knott End. **Tel** +44 (0) 7793 270934, **Fax** +44 (0)1253 87 79 74 **Email** info@wyremarine.co.uk **Website** www.wyremarine.co.uk *(English)*

Gosport Ferry GOSPORT QUEEN (159t, 1966, 30.5m, 250 passengers, IMO 8633700), PORTSMOUTH QUEEN (159t, 1966, 30.5m, 250 passengers, IMO 8633695), SPIRIT OF GOSPORT (300t, 2001, 32.6m, 300 passengers, IMO 8972089), SPIRIT OF PORTSMOUTH (377t, 2005, 32.6m, 300 passengers, IMO 9319894). Under Construction HARBOUR SPIRIT (2015, 32.9m, 300 passengers. **Route operated** Gosport - Portsmouth. **Tel** +44 (0)23 9252 4551, **Fax:** +44(0)23 9252 4802, **Email** admin@gosportferry.co.uk **Website** www.gosportferry.co.uk *(English)*

Gravesend - Tilbury Ferry (operated by the *Lower Thames & Medway Passenger Boat Co Ltd*) DUCHESS M (ex VESTA 1979) (71t, 1956, 23.8m, 124 passengers), PRINCESS POCAHONTAS (ex FREYA II 1989, LABOE I 1985, LABOE 1984) (180t, 1962, 29.9m, 207 passengers, IMO 5201271). The PRINCESS POCAHONTAS is an excursion vessel operating regularly to Greenwich, Westminster, Chelsea and Southend, also occasionally to Rochester and Whitstable but sometimes covers the ferry roster. **Route operated** Gravesend (Kent) - Tilbury (Essex), **Tel** +44 (0)1732 353448, **Direct Line to Ferry** +44 (0)7973 390124, **Email** enquiry@princess-pocahontas.com **Websites** www.princess-pocahontas.com *(English)* www.gravesham.gov.uk/__data/assets/pdf_file/0004/74965/FerryTimetableSEPT2012.pdf *(English)*

Hamble - Warsash Ferry CLAIRE (2.1t, 1985, 7,3m, 12 passengers), EMILY (3.7t, 1990, 8.5m, 12 passengers), **Route operated** Hamble - Warsash (across Hamble River) . **Tel** +44 (0)23 8045 4512, **Mobile** +44 (0) 7720 438402 **Email** info@hamble-warsashferry.co.uk, **Website** www.hamble-warsashferry.co.uk *(English)*

Hayling Ferry PRIDE OF HAYLING (1989, 11.9m, 63 passengers). **Route operated** Eastney – Hayling Island. **Tel** +44 (0)7702 928154 , **Email:** haylingferry@yahoo.co.uk **Website** www.haylingferry.co.uk *(English)*

Hovertravel FREEDOM 90 (1990, 25.4m, 95 passengers, BHC AP1-88/100S hovercraft, converted from AP1-88/100 in 1999), ISLAND EXPRESS (ex FREJA VIKING, 2002) (1985, 25.4m, 95 passengers, BHC AP1-88/100S hovercraft, converted from BHC AP1-88/100 in 2001). **Route operated** Southsea - Ryde. **Tel** +44 (0)8434 878887, **Fax** +44 (0)1983 562216, **Email** info@hovertravel.com **Website** www.hovertravel.com *(English)*

Hythe Ferry (White Horse Ferries) GREAT EXPECTATIONS (66t, 1992, 21.3m, 162 passengers - catamaran), HOTSPUR IV (50t, 1946, 19.5m, 125 passengers). **Route operated** Southampton - Hythe (Hants). *Head Office* **Tel.** +44 (0)1793 618566, **Fax** +44 (0)1793 488428, *Local Office* **Tel** +44 (0)23 8084 0722, **Fax** +44 (0)23 8084 6611, **Email** post@hytheferry.co.uk **Website** www.hytheferry.co.uk *(English)*

Isle of Sark Shipping Company BON MARIN DE SERK (118t, 1983, 20.7m, 131 passengers, IMO 8303056), SARK BELLE (ex BOURNEMOUTH BELLE 2011) (50t, 1979, 26.2m, 180 passengers), SARK VENTURE (133t, 1986, 21.3m, 122 passengers, IMO 8891986), SARK VIKING (Cargo Vessel) (104t, 2007, 21.2m, 12 passengers, IMO 8648858). **Route operated** St Peter Port (Guernsey) - Sark. **Tel** +44 (0) 1481 724059, **Fax** +44 (0) 1481 713999, **Email** info@sarkshippingcompany.com **Website** www.sarkshippingcompany.com *(English)*

John O'Groats Ferries PENTLAND VENTURE (186t, 1987, 29.6m, 250 passengers, IMO 8834122). **Route operated** John O'Groats – Burwick (Orkney). **Tel** +44 (0)1955 611353, **Email** Office@jogferry.co.uk **Website** www.jogferry.co.uk *(English)*

Kintyre Express KINTYRE EXPRESS II (5.75t, 2011, 11.0m, 12 passengers), KINTYRE EXPRESS III (5.75t, 2012, 11.0m, 12 passengers), KINTYRE EXPRESS IV (5.75t, 2012, 11.0m, 12 passengers). **Routes operated** Campbeltown - Ballycastle, Campbeltown - Troon. **Tel** +44 (0) 1586 555895, **Fax** +44(0)1586 552344, **Email** info@kintyreexpress.com **Website** www.kintyreexpress.com *(English)*

KPMG Thames Clippers (trading name of Collins River Enterprises Ltd) AURORA CLIPPER (181t, 2007, 37.8m, 27.5k, 220 passengers, IMO 9451824), CYCLONE CLIPPER (181t, 2007, 37.8m, 27.5k, 220 passengers, IMO 9451880), HURRICANE CLIPPER (181t, 2002, 37.8m, 27.5k, 220 passengers, IMO 9249702), METEOR CLIPPER (181t, 2007, 37.8m, 27.5k, 220 passengers, IMO 9451812), MONSOON CLIPPER (181t, 2007, 37.8m, 27.5k, 220 passengers, IMO 9451795), MOON CLIPPER (ex DOWN RUNNER 2005) (98t, 2001, 32.0m, 25.0k, 138 passengers, IMO 9245586), SKY CLIPPER (ex VERITATUM 1995, SD10 2000) (60t, 1992, 25.0m, 62 passengers), STAR CLIPPER (ex CONRAD CHELSEA HARBOUR SD9 2000) (60t, 1992, 25.0m, 62 passengers), STORM CLIPPER (ex DHL WORLDWIDE EXPRESS 1995, SD11 2000) (60t, 1992, 25.0m, 62 passengers), SUN CLIPPER (ex ANTRIM RUNNER 2005) (98t, 2001, 32.0m, 25.0k, 138 passengers, IMO 9232292), TORNADO CLIPPER (181t, 2007, 37.8m, 27.5k, 220 passengers, IMO 9451783), TWIN STAR (45t, 1974, 19.2m, 120 passengers), TYPHOON CLIPPER (181t, 2007, 37.8m, 27.5k, 220 passengers, IMO 9451771. The 'Typhoon', 'Tornado', 'Cyclone' and 'Monsoon', 'Aurora' and 'Meteor' Clippers were designed by AIMTEK and built by Brisbane Ship Constructions in Australia in 2007. **Routes operated** Embankment - Waterloo - Blackfriars – Bankside - London Bridge - Tower - Canary Wharf – Greenland - Masthouse Terrace - Greenwich - North Greenwich – Woolwich, Bankside – Millbank - St George (Tate to Tate Service), Putney - Wandsworth - Chelsea Harbour - Cardogan - Embankment - Blackfriars, Canary Wharf - Rotherhithe Hilton Docklands Hotel (TWIN STAR). **Tel** +44

Hotspur IV *(Andrew Cooke)*

Freedom 90 *(Andrew Cooke)*

SECTION 5 – MAJOR PASSENGER ONLY FERRIES

Storm Clipper (*Andrew Cooke*)

Dartmouth Princess (*Nick Widdows*)

Spirit of the Tyne (*Miles Cowsill*)

Sark Belle (*Andrew Cooke*)

SECTION 5 – MAJOR PASSENGER ONLY FERRIES

(0)870 781 5049, **Fax** +44 (0)20 7001 2222, **Email** sean.collins@thamesclippers.com **Website** www.thamesclippers.com *(English)*.

Lundy Company OLDENBURG (294t, 1958, 43.6m, 267 passengers, IMO 5262146). **Routes operated** Bideford - Lundy Island, Ilfracombe - Lundy Island. Also North Devon coastal cruises and River Torridge cruises. **Tel** +44 (0)1237 470074, **Fax** +44 (0)1237 477779, **Email** info@lundyisland.co.uk **Website** www.lundyisland.co.uk *(English)*

Manche Iles Express (trading name of Société Morbihannaise de Navigation) GRANVILLE (ex BORNHOLM EXPRESS 2014) (325t, 2006, 41.0m, 245 passengers, IMO 9356476 - catamaran), VICTOR HUGO (ex SALTEN 2003) (387t, 1997, 35.0m, 195 passengers, IMO 9157806 - catamaran), MARIN MARIE (ex AREMETI 3 2003) (608t, 1994, 40.0m, 243 passengers, IMO 9112478) (laid up for sale), TOCQUEVILLE (269t, 2007, 37m, 260 passengers, IMO 9442823). **Route operated** Granville – Jersey - Sark - Guernsey, Portbail or Carteret – Jersey, Guernsey and Sark, Diélette - Alderney - Guernsey. **Tel** +33 0825 131 050, **Fax** +33 02 33 90 03 49, **Email** mancheilesexpress@cwgsy.net **Website** www.manche-iles-express.com *(French, English)*

Mersey Ferries ROYAL DAFFODIL (ex OVERCHURCH 1999) (751t, 1962, 46.6m, 860 passengers, IMO 4900868) (laid up), ROYAL IRIS OF THE MERSEY (ex MOUNTWOOD 2002) (464t, 1960, 46.3m, 750 passengers, IMO 8633712), SNOWDROP (ex WOODCHURCH 2004) (670t, 1960, 46.6m, 750 passengers, IMO 8633724). **Routes operated** Liverpool (Pier Head) - Birkenhead (Woodside), Liverpool - Wallasey (Seacombe) with regular cruises from Liverpool and Seacombe to Salford along the Manchester Ship Canal. **Tel Admin** +44 (0)151 639 0609, **Reservations** +44 (0)151 330 1444, **Fax** +44 (0)151 639 0578, **Email** customerservice@merseyferries.co.uk **Website** www.merseyferries.co.uk *(English)*

Mudeford Ferry (Derham Marine) FERRY DAME (4t, 1989, 9.1m, 48 passengers), JOSEPHINE (10.5t, 1997, 10.7m, 70 passengers - catamaran), JOSEPHINE II (10.5t, 2013, 11.0m, 86 passengers - catamaran). **Route operated** Mudeford Quay - Mudeford Sandbank. **Tel** +44 (0)7968 334441 **Email** information@mudefordferry.co.uk **Website** www.mudefordferry.co.uk *(English)*

Nexus (trading name of Tyne & Wear Integrated Transport Authority) PRIDE OF THE TYNE (222t, 1993, 24.0m, 240 passengers, IMO 9062166), SPIRIT OF THE TYNE (174t, 2006, 25.0m, 200 passengers). **Route operated** North Shields - South Shields. Also cruises South Shields - Newcastle. **Tel** +44 (0)191 2020747, **Fax** +44 (0)191 427 9510, **Website** www.nexus.org.uk *(English)*

Doolin Ferry (O'Brien Line) QUEEN OF ARAN (113t, 1976, 20.1m, 96 passengers, IMO 7527928), TRANQUILITY (62t, 1988, 15.8m, 100 passengers). **Routes operated** Doolin - Inisheer, Doolin - Inishmaan, Doolin - Inishmore. Also cruises to Cliffs of Mohr. **Tel** +353 (0)65 707 5555, **Fax** 00 353 (0)65 707 11 82, **Email** info@doolinferry.com **Website** www.doolinferry.com *(English)*

Travel Trident HERM TRIDENT V (79t, 1989, 25.9m, 250 passengers), TRIDENT VI (79t, 1992, 22.3m, 250 passengers). **Route operated** St Peter Port (Guernsey) - Herm. **Tel** +44 (0)1481 721379, **Fax** +44 (0)1481 700226, **Email** peterwilcox@cwgsy.net **Website** www.traveltrident.com *(English)*

Waverley Excursions BALMORAL (735t, 1949, 62.2m, 683 passengers, IMO 5034927) (laid up during 2013 and 2014), WAVERLEY (693t, 1947, 73.2m, 925 passengers, IMO 5386954). **Routes operated** Excursions all round British Isles. However, regular cruises in the Clyde, Bristol Channel, South Coast and Thames provide a service which can be used for transport purposes and therefore both vessels are, in a sense, ferries. The WAVERLEY is the only seagoing paddle steamer in the world. The BALMORAL will not operate during 2014, but may return in 2015. **Tel** +44 (0)845 130 4647, **Fax** +44 (0)141 248 2150, **Email** info@waverleyexcursions.co.uk **Website** www.waverleyexcursions.co.uk *(English)*

Western Isles Cruises Ltd WESTERN ISLES (46t, 1969, 19.5m, 81 passengers). **Route Operated** Mallaig - Inverie (Knoydart) - Tarbet. **Tel** +44 (0)1687 462233 or +44 (0)7939 386330, **Email** info@westernislescruises.co.uk, **Website** www.westernislescruises.co.uk *(English)*

Western Lady Ferry Service WESTERN LADY VI (50t, 1981, 19.2m, 173 passengers), WESTERN LADY VII (46t, 1984, 19.8m, 177 passengers). **Route Operated** Torquay - Brixham. **Tel** +44 (0)1803 293797, **Email** enquiries@dsrrb.co.uk, **Website** www.westernladyferry.com *(English)* Note: The service is now part of *Dartmouth Steam Railway & Riverboat Company* but is marketed separately.

SECTION 5 – MAJOR PASSENGER ONLY FERRIES

SCANDINAVIAN AND NORTHERN EUROPE REVIEW - 2013/14

The following geographical review again takes the form of a voyage along the coast of The Netherlands and Germany, round the southern tip of Norway, down the Kattegat, through the Great Belt and into the Baltic then up to the Gulf of Finland and Gulf of Bothnia.

FRISIAN ISLANDS

EVT, a private sector rival to Rederij Doeksen, who introduced the 55 car *Spathoek* onto the Harlingen - Terschelling route in 2012, ceased operations in April 2014 following the intervention of the Dutch Government. Doeksen took over EVT and its vessel and EVT received €9 million in compensation. Dutch Company TESO and German company Rederi Norden Frisia both ordered new tonnage.

SKAGERRAK & KATTEGAT

Fjord Lines' first newbuilding, the *Stavangerfjord* finally entered service in July 2013. The introduction of this LNG powered vessel was not without problems. As well as teething difficulties, the main cause of delay was the rule imposed by the Norwegian authorities that the ferry could not be refuelled with passengers on board. A revised timetable was devised to allow for refuelling in Denmark until the Norwegians relaxed their rules.

Sister vessel, the *Bergensfjord*, was delivered in February 2014 and entered service in March. Having learned lessons from the first ship, her introduction proved much smoother. The previous *Bergensfjord* was withdrawn at Christmas 2013 and sent to the STX Finland shipyard at Rauma for conversion to a day ferry suitable for the short Sandefjord - Strömstad crossing. Renamed *Oslsofjord*, she entered service in June 2014.

Despite reports that Color Line were about to order a new LNG ferry to replace the *Bohus* of 1971, no order was placed.

Stena Line operated the HSS 900 *Stena Carisma* between Gothenburg and Frederikshavn during summer 2013 but the vessel was laid up during summer 2014 so the future of the 17 year old vessel now looks uncertain.

DANISH DOMESTIC

In March 2013 Mols-Linien acquired a second Incat 112m vessel. Unlike the *KatExpress 1*, this vessel was almost new and had not served with a previous operator. She entered service in May as the *KatExpress 2*. Her entry into service led to the withdrawal of the company's original Danish built fast Ferries, the *Mai Mols* and *Mie Mols*. After being laid up for several months, with no buyers, they were both recycled locally.

Having tried unsuccessfully to launch a rival fast ferry service in 2012, German owned company Kattegat-Ruten continued with the ex-Mols-Linien ro-pax *Kattegat* on the Aarhus - Kalundborg route until November 2013, when the service ceased. The vessel joined her sister on the company's Straits of Gibraltar service.

The Samsø Municipality decided to take control of the Færgen operated Hou - Sælvig route and ordered a new ferry from Remontowa Shipbuilding in Gdansk, Poland. She will replace the *Kanhave* during autumn 2014. It was originally intended that the first of two new vessels ordered by Færgen from Sietas Werft, Hamburg for delivery in 2011 would operate on this route but the Municipality refused to pay for the necessary modifications to the facilities on the island, so she was instead placed on the Spodsbjerg - Tårs route. Færgeselskabet Læsø's vessel, the *Ane Læsø* will act as reserve vessel and Færgen's *Kanhave* will be deployed elsewhere, probably to the Kalundborg - Koby Kås (Samsø) route.

SOUTH BALTIC

Stena Line continued their programme of integrating the former Scandlines operation and vessels into its fleet although no names were changed apart from the *Watling Street* which, in April 2013, was

Prinsesse Benedikte *(Henk van der Lugt)*

Color Viking *(Matthew Punter)*

renamed the *Stena Flavia*. All vessels received Stena funnels, although the *Stena Flavia's* was not repainted until May 2014. Most received full Stena branding, apart from the chartered *Scottish Viking* which retained her Maersk light blue hull. In May 2014 services to Ventspils in Latvia were modified with the *Stena Flavia* operating a round weekly round trip to Nynäshamn in Sweden at the expense of one to Travemünde in Germany. This left the Nynäshamn route with six sailings per week and the Travemünde route just two.

In November Brittany Ferries' *Cotentin* was chartered to Stena RoRo and sub-chartered to Stena Line. Renamed the *Stena Baltica*, she replaced the *Stena Alegra* on the Karlskrona - Gdynia route. The *Stena Alegra* was then, in November, chartered to KiwiRail Interislander of New Zealand to operate on the Cook Strait.

DFDS Seaways made a number of changes on their South Baltic routes. Most significant was the replacement of the *Liverpool Seaways* on the Klaipėda - Kiel service with the former *Coraggio* of Grimaldi Lines, which was renamed the *Athena Seaways*. A sister vessel of the *Victoria Seaways*, in June 2014 she was moved to the Klaipėda - Karlshamn route. The Klaipėda - Sassnitz route closed at the end of September 2013 and the vessel used, the *Kaunas Seaways*, was transferred to the Paldiski - Kapellskär service.

TT-Line started a new service from Trelleborg to Świnoujście in Poland in January 2014. Operated by the ro-pax *Nils Dacke*, the once daily service represents further competition for Polferries rather aged fleet and one wonders how much longer they can continue.

Scandlines came under total control of the UK based private equity company 3i Group in November 2013 when they purchased the share of the company held by Allianz Capital Partners Gmbh of Germany. In March 2014 Scandlines purchased, at a knock down price, the *Copenhagen* and *Berlin*, the two ships built for them by Volkswerft Stralsund, Stralsund, Germany and rejected as being too heavy for the Gedser - Rostock route (earlier plans to have two LNG vessels built by STX Europe in Finland were dropped). The two vessels, one of which had undertaken sea trials, were towed to Blohm + Voss Shipyards, Hamburg and then to Fayard Shipyard, Odense, Denmark to be lightened by removing some of the upper superstructure and, in the case of the *Copenhagen*, completion of mechanical and electrical work. They are expected now to enter service in 2015.

During 2013 announcements were made that a new operator, Gotlandsbäten, would start an unsubsidised summer-only service from Västervik on the Swedish mainline to the Visby on the Swedish holiday island of Gotland. Initially the new service was linked to Caledonian MacBrayne's *Isle of Mull*, but in the event the chosen vessel was the 1986 built Greek ferry *Princess T* (originally the *Queen Diamond* in Japan), to be renamed the *Västervik*. Services have as of August 2014 yet to start. Meanwhile the franchise to operate all-year services to the island from 1st February 2017 until 1 February 2027, with the possibility of extension, was awarded to the incumbent operator, Destination Gotland.

In February 2013, Polferries reduced the Gdansk - Nynäshamn service to a single ship operation. One of the ships used, the *Baltivia* was transferred to the Świnoujście – Ystad route.

CROSS BALTIC

Finnlines withdrew the *Transrussia* from their Lübeck - St Petersburg service in early 2014. She reverted to her original name of *Finnhansa* and was placed on the Kotka - Rostock - Lübeck service. The service continued on a once weekly basis using one of the Travemünde - Malmö vessels - the *Finnclipper*, *Finnpartner* and *Finntrader* on a three week cycle - ie two weeks on the Malmö service and then a round trip to St Petersburg.

In May 2013, DFDS enhanced their service from Kiel to Russia by adding the chartered *Clipper Point* to the service operated by the *Botnia Seaways*. A call at Klaipėda in Lithuania was added. In October the *Clipper Point* was replaced by the ex Finnlines *Finlandia Seaways* as the *Clipper Point's* ice classification was insufficient to deal with the harsh winter conditions in the Gulf of Finland. In April 2014 the *Finlandia Seaways* was replaced by the *Anglia Seaways* and in May the service was once again reduced to a single crossing per week, operated by the *Anglia Seaways*, with the *Botnia Seaways* deployed on a Kiel - Klaipėda roster, supplementing the service provided by the passenger ferries.

Oslofjord *(Fjordline)*

Victoria Seaways *(Matthew Punter)*

Lofoten (*Henk van der Lugt*)

NORTH BALTIC

Viking Line took delivery of their newbuild, the *Viking Grace*, for the Turku - Stockholm route during December 2012, although she did not enter service until January. Powered by LNG, she replaced the *Isabella* which was laid up. It was planned that the *Isabella* would operate between Helsinki and Tallinn during summer 2013. However, in April 2013 she was sold to Tallink Grupp to operate on the Stockholm - Riga service, replacing the *Silja Festival*. In accordance with Tallink's naming and livery policy (ie not to have one) she was simply renamed the *Isabelle* and, apart from replacing the Viking Line logo on the funnel and changing the lettering on the side, she continued to sail in full Viking Line livery. The *Silja Festival* became an accommodation ship in Canada, being renamed the *Delta Spirit Lodge*.

Also at the start of 2014, Tallink/Silja Line replaced the *Silja Europa* on the Turku - Stockholm route with the smaller but 15 years newer *Baltic Princess*. The *Silja Europa* took over the Helsinki - Tallinn cruise roster.

Early in 2014 Viking Line announced that the overnight ship from Stockholm, alternately the *Mariella* or *Gabriella*, would undertake a round trip to from Helsinki to Tallinn during the day to provide extra capacity on the route during the busy summer period. This arrangement was to run from mid June until the end of August.

Eckerö Line introduced the *Finlandia* in January 2014. Formerly the *Moby Freedom*, she replaced both the *Nordlandia* and freight ferry *Translandia*.

In October 2013 Finnlines introduced calls at Långnäs on Åland on some of their sailings between Kapellskär and Naantali in order that duty free sales could be made on the vessels.

Navirail, who operate between Paldiski in Estonia and Hanko in Finland, upgraded their service in January 2014 by chartering the 320 passenger *Liverpool Seaways* from DFDS Seaways. The company now seeks to attract passengers, undercutting Silja Line and Viking Line for cars, but charges more for the night sailings.

NLC Ferry Oy Ab, the municipally owned company which took over the service between Vaasa and Umeå previous operated by RG-Line launched their new vessel, the *Wasa Express* (the one time *Sally Star*) at the beginning of 2013. They also branded themselves as Vasabåtarna (Vaasanlaivat in Finnish), the name of the traditional operator of this service before it was taken over by Silja Line in 1993. However, after a few months they changed the company banding to the English language Wasa Line.

St Peter Line's Stockholm and Helsinki to St Petersburg service was suspended during February 2014 when the ferries, the *Princess Maria* and *SPL Princess Anastasia*, went to the Black Sea to act as hotel vessels for the Winter Olympics at Sochi in Russia.

Isabelle (*Nick Widdows*)

Romantika (*Matthew Punter*)

6 - NORTHERN EUROPE

ÆRØ FÆRGERNE

THE COMPANY *Ærø Færgerne* is a Danish company, owned by the municipality of Ærø.

MANAGEMENT Managing Director & Marketing Manager Keld Moller.

ADDRESS Vestergade 1, 5970 Ærøskøbing, Denmark.

TELEPHONE Administration & Reservations +45 62 52 40 00.

FAX Administration & Reservations +45 62 52 20 88.

INTERNET Email info@aeroe-ferry.dk Website www.aeroe-ferry.dk *(Danish, English, German)*

ROUTE OPERATED Ærøskøbing (Ærø) - Svendborg (Fyn) (1hr 15mins; *ÆRØSKØBING, MARSTAL*; every 1/2 hours), Søby (Ærø) - Faaborg (Fyn) (1hr; *SKJOLDNÆS*; 3 per day), Søby (Ærø) - Fynshav (Als) (1hr 10mins; *SKJOLDNÆS*; 3 per day).

1	ÆRØSKØBING	1617t	99	12.0k	49.0m	395P	42C	L	BA	DK	9199086
2	MARSTAL	1617t	99	12.0k	49.0m	395P	42C	L	BA	DK	9199074
3	SKJOLDNÆS	986t	79	11.0k	47.1m	290P	36C	L	BA	DK	7925649

ÆRØSKØBING, MARSTAL Built by EOS, Esbjerg, Denmark for *Ærø Færgerne*.

SKJOLDNÆS Built as the SAM-SINE by Søren Larsen & Sønner Skibsværft A/S, Nykøbing Mors, Denmark for *Hou-Sælvig Ruten Aps* of Denmark. Operated between Hou (Jutland) and Sælvig (Samsø). In 1995 she was taken over by *Samsø Linien*. In 2001 she was lengthened by Ørskov Christensen's Staalskibsværft, Frederikshavn, Denmark. In 2009 sold to *Ærø Færgerne* and renamed the SKJOLDNÆS.

BASTØ FOSEN

THE COMPANY *Bastø Fosen* is a Norwegian private sector company, a subsidiary of *Torghatten ASA - Brønnøysund*.

MANAGEMENT Managing Director May Kristin Salberg.

ADDRESS PO Box 94, 3191 Horten, Norway.

TELEPHONE Administration +47 33 03 17 40, Reservations +47 33 03 17 40 (buses only).

FAX Administration +47 33 03 17 49, Reservations +47 33 03 17 49 (buses only).

INTERNET Email bastohorten@fosen.no Website www.basto-fosen.no *(Norwegian)*

ROUTE OPERATED Moss - Horten (across Oslofjord, Norway) (30 mins; *BASTØ I, BASTØ II, BASTØ III, BASTØ IV, BASTØ V* up to every 15 mins).

1	BASTØ I	5505t	97	14.0k	109.0m	550P	200C	18L	BA	NO	9144081
2	BASTØ II	5505t	97	14.0k	109.0m	550P	200C	18L	BA	NO	9144093
3	BASTØ III	7310t	05	18.0k	116.2m	540P	212C	18L	BA	NO	9299408
4	BASTØ IV	2835t	86	13.5k	80.1m	456P	140C	12L	BA	NO	8512114
5	BASTØ V	3397t	90	16.0k	92.0m	650P	155C	-	BA	NO	8917340

BASTØ I, BASTØ II Built by Fosen Mekaniske Verksteder, Frengen, Norway for *Bastø Fosen*.

BASTØ III Built by Stocznia Remontowa, Gdansk, Poland for *Bastø Fosen*.

BASTØ IV Built as the AUSTRHEIM by Trønderverftet A/S, Hommelvik, Norway for *A/S Bergen-Nordhordland Rutelag (BNR)*, operating between Steinestø and Knarvik. In 1993 chartered to *Rogaland Trafikkselskap A/S* and operated between Stavanger and Tau. In 1995 sold to *Hardanger Sunnhordlandske Dampskibsselskap (HSD)* of Norway and renamed the BJØRNEFJORD. Operated between Valevåg and Skjersholmane. In 2001 sold to *Boknafjorden Ferjeselskap A/S* and renamed the BOKNAFJORD. Later transferred to *Båtbygg A/S* and operated between Mortaviken and Arsvågen. In 2002 transferred to

Rogaland Trafikkselskap Ferjer A/S and in 2003 transferred to Stavangerska Ferjer A/S. In 2008 and 2009 she was briefly chartered to a number of operators and in 2008 sold to Tide Sjø AS. In December 2010 she was sold to Bastø Fosen and renamed the BASTØ IV.

BASTØ V Built as the NORDKAPPHORN by Trønderverftet A/S, Hommelvik, Norway for Finnmark Fylkesrederi og Ruteselskap AS of Norway. In 1992 chartered to Rogaland Trafikkselskap A/S and renamed the RENNESØY. In January 2012 sold to Torghatten Nord A/S and renamed the TRANØY. In September 2012 sold to Bastø Fosen and renamed the BASTØ V.

COLOR LINE

THE COMPANY Color Line ASA is a Norwegian private sector stock-listed limited company. The company merged with Larvik Scandi Line of Norway (which owned Larvik Line and Scandi Line) in 1996. In 1997 the operations of Larvik Line were incorporated into Color Line; Scandi Line continued as a separate subsidiary until 1999, when it was also incorporated into Color Line. The marketing name Color Scandi Line was dropped at the end of 2000.

MANAGEMENT Managing Director Trond Kleivdal.

ADDRESS Commercial Postboks 1422 Vika, 0115 Oslo, Norway, Technical Management Color Line Marine AS, PO Box 2090, 3210 Sandefjord, Norway.

TELEPHONE Administration & Reservations +47 22 94 42 00.

INTERNET Website www.colorline.com (English, Danish, German, Norwegian, Swedish,)

ROUTES OPERATED Conventional Ferries Oslo (Norway) - Kiel (Germany) (19 hrs 30 mins; COLOR FANTASY, COLOR MAGIC; 1 per day), Kristiansand (Norway) - Hirtshals (3 hrs 15 mins; SUPERSPEED 1; 4 per day), Larvik (Norway) - Hirtshals (Denmark) (3 hrs 45 mins; SUPERSPEED 2; up to 2 per day), Sandefjord (Norway) - Strömstad (Sweden) (2 hrs 30 mins; BOHUS, COLOR VIKING; up to 4 per day).

1	BOHUS	9149t	71	20.5k	123.4m	1165P	240C	34T	BA	NO	7037806
2	COLOR FANTASY	75027t	04	22.3k	224.0m	2750P	750C	90T	BA	NO	9278234
3	COLOR MAGIC	75100t	07	22.3k	223.7m	2750P	550C	90T	BA	NO	9349863
4	COLOR VIKING	19763t	85	16.4k	134.0m	2000P	320C	40T	BA2	NO	8317942
5	SUPERSPEED 1	36822t	08	27.0k	211.3m	2250P	525C	121T	BA2	NO	9374519
6	SUPERSPEED 2	34231t	08	27.0k	211.3m	1800P	525C	121T	BA2	NO	9378682

BOHUS Built as the PRINSESSAN DESIREE by Aalborg Værft A/S, Aalborg, Denmark for Rederi AB Göteborg-Frederikshavn Linjen of Sweden (trading as Sessan Linjen) for their service between Gothenburg and Frederikshavn. In 1981 the company was taken over by Stena Line and she became surplus to requirements. During 1981 she had a number of charters including B&I Line of Ireland and Sealink UK. In 1982 she was chartered to Sally Line to operate as second vessel on the Ramsgate - Dunkerque service between June and September. She bore the name 'VIKING 2' in large letters on her hull although she was never officially renamed. In September 1982 she returned to Stena Line and in 1983 she was transferred to subsidiary company Varberg-Grenaa Line for their service between Varberg (Sweden) and Grenaa (Denmark), renamed the EUROPAFÄRJAN. In 1985 she was renamed the EUROPAFÄRJAN II. In 1986, following a reorganisation within Stena Line, ownership was transferred to subsidiary company Lion Ferry AB and she was named the LION PRINCESS. In 1993 she was sold to Scandi Line and renamed the BOHUS. In 1999 Scandi Line operations were integrated into Color Line.

COLOR FANTASY Built by Kværner Masa-Yards, Turku, Finland for Color Line to replace the PRINSESSE RAGNHILD on the Oslo – Kiel service.

COLOR MAGIC Built by Aker Yards, Turku, Finland (hull construction) and Rauma, Finland (fitting out), for the Oslo - Kiel route.

COLOR VIKING Built as the PEDER PAARS by Nakskov Skibsværft A/S, Nakskov, Denmark for DSB (Danish State Railways) for their service between Kalundborg (Sealand) and Århus (Jutland). In 1990 purchased by Stena Line of Sweden for delivery in 1991. In that year renamed the STENA INVICTA and entered service on the Sealink Stena Line Dover - Calais service. She was withdrawn from the route in

February 1998, before the formation of P&O Stena Line, but ownership was transferred to that company. In Summer 1998, she was chartered to Silja Line to operate between Vaasa and Umeå under the marketing name 'WASA JUBILEE'. In Autumn 1998 she was laid up at Zeebrugge. She remained there until Autumn 1999 when she was chartered to Stena Line to operate between Holyhead and Dublin. In 2000 she was chartered to Color Line, renamed the COLOR VIKING and in April entered service on the Sandefjord - Strömstad service. In 2002 purchased by Color Line.

SUPERSPEED 1, SUPERSPEED 2 Built by Aker Yards, Rauma, Finland for the Kristiansand - Hirtshals and Larvik - Hirtshals routes. In January 2011, the SUPERSPEED 1 was modified to provide additional facilities and increase passenger capacity.

DESTINATION GOTLAND

THE COMPANY Destination Gotland AB is a Swedish private sector company owned by Rederi AB Gotland.

MANAGEMENT Managing Director Christer Bruzelius, Marketing Manager Per-Erling Evensen.

ADDRESS PO Box 1234, 621 23 Visby, Gotland, Sweden.

TELEPHONE Administration + 46 (0)498-20 18 00, Reservations + 46 (0)771-22 33 00.

FAX Administration & Reservations + 46 (0)498-20 18 90.

INTERNET Email info@destinationgotland.se Website www.destinationgotland.se (Swedish, English, Finnish, German)

ROUTES OPERATED Fast Conventional Ferries Visby (Gotland) - Nynäshamn (Swedish mainland) (3 hrs 15 mins; GOTLAND, VISBY; 1/2 per day), Visby - Oskarshamn (Swedish mainland) (2 hrs 55 mins; GOTLAND, VISBY; 1/4 per day). Fast Ferries (Summer only) Visby - Nynäshamn (3 hrs 15 mins; GOTLANDIA II; up to 3 per day), Visby - Oskarshamn (Swedish mainland) (2 hrs 55 mins; GOTLANDIA; 1 per day (selected)).

1	GOTLAND	29746t	03	28.5k	195.8m	1500P	500C	118T	BAS2 SE	9223796
2»	GOTLANDIA	5632t	99	35.0k	112.5m	700P	140C	-	A SE	9171163
3»	GOTLANDIA II	6554t	06	36.0k	122.0m	780P	160C	-	A SE	9328015
4	VISBY	29746t	03	28.5k	195.8m	1500P	500C	118T	BAS2 SE	9223784

GOTLAND, VISBY Built by Guangzhou Shipyard International, Guangzhou, China for Rederi AB Gotland for use on Destination Gotland services.

GOTLANDIA Alstom Leroux Corsair 11500 monohull vessel built as the GOTLAND at Lorient, France for Rederi AB Gotland and chartered to Destination Gotland. In 2003 renamed the GOTLANDIA. In 2006 laid up. In 2007 inaugurated a new route between Visby and Grankullavik (Öland). In 2014 will operate between Visby and Oskarshamn.

GOTLANDIA II Fincantieri SF700 monohull fast ferry built at Riva Trigoso, Italy for Rederi AB Gotland for use by Destination Gotland.

DFDS SEAWAYS

THE COMPANY DFDS Seaways is a division of DFDS A/S, a Danish private sector company.

MANAGEMENT CEO DFDS A/S Niels Smedegaard, Head of Shipping Division Peder Gellert Pedersen, Head of Baltic Sea Business Area Anders Refsgaard, Head of Passenger Business Area Kim Heiberg.

ADDRESS Copenhagen Sundkrogsgade 11, 2100 Copenhagen Ø, Denmark.

TELEPHONE Administration + 45 33 42 33 42, Reservations Denmark + 45 33 42 30 10, Germany + 49 (0)431 20976 420, Lithuania + 370 46 393616, Sweden + 46 454 33680

FAX Administration + 45 33 42 33 41.

Superspeed 2 (*Miles Cowsill*)

Visby (*Miles Cowsill*)

Pearl Seaways *(Henk van der Lugt)*

INTERNET   Administration   incoming@dfdsseaways.dk,   Reservations   *Denmark* incoming@dfdsseaways.dk *Germany* passage.kiel@dfds.com, *Lithuania* booking.lt@dfds.com, *Sweden* pax@dfds.com

Website www.dfdsseaways.com (*English, Danish, Dutch, German, Italian, Japanese, Norwegian, Polish, Swedish*)

ROUTES OPERATED *Passengers services* Copenhagen - Oslo (Norway) (16 hrs 30 mins; *CROWN SEAWAYS, PEARL SEAWAYS*; 1 per day), Klaipėda (Lithuania) - Kiel (Germany) (21 hrs; *OPTIMA SEAWAYS, REGINA SEAWAYS,* 6 per week), Klaipėda - Karlshamn (Sweden) (14 hrs; *ATHENA SEAWAYS, VICTORIA SEAWAYS,*; 7 per week), Paldiski (Estonia) - Kapellskär (Sweden) (10 hrs; *KAUNAS SEAWAYS, PATRIA SEAWAYS* ; 1 or 2 per day) (joint with *Baltic Scandinavia Line*), *Freight only services* Fredericia - Copenhagen - Klaipėda (call at Aarhus once per week) (*CORONA SEAWAYS*; 2 per week), Kiel - Klaipėda - Ust Luga - St Petersburg, (*BOTNIA SEAWAYS*; 1 per week), Travemünde - Klaipėda (*BOTNIA SEAWAYS; 2 per week*).

See Section 1 for services operating to Britain.

1F	ANGLIA SEAWAYS	13073t	00	18.5k	142.5m	12P	-	114T	A	DK	9186649
2	ATHENA SEAWAYS	24950t	07	23.0k	199.1m	500P	-	190T	A	LT	9350680
3F	BOTNIA SEAWAYS	11530t	00	20.0k	162.2m	12P	-	140T	A	LT	9192129
4F	CORONA SEAWAYS	25609t	08	20.0k	184.8m	12P	-	250T	AS	UK	9357597
5	CROWN SEAWAYS	35498t	94	22.0k	169.4m	1940P	450C	50T	BA	DK	8917613
6	KAUNAS SEAWAYS	25606t	89	16.3k	190.9m	262P	460C	93Tr	A2	LT	8311924
7	OPTIMA SEAWAYS	25206t	99	21.5k	186.3m	327P	164C	150T	A	LT	9188427
8	PATRIA SEAWAYS	18332t	92	17.0k	154.0m	242P	-	114T	BA2	LT	8917390
9	PEARL SEAWAYS	40039t	89	21.0k	178.4m	2090P	350C	70T	BA	DK	8701674
10	REGINA SEAWAYS	25518t	10	24.0k	199.1m	600P	-	190T	A	IT	9458535
11	VICTORIA SEAWAYS	24950t	09	23.0k	199.1m	600P	-	190T	A	LT	9350721
12	VILNIUS SEAWAYS	22341t	87	16.3k	190.9m	132P	460C	112Tr	A2	LT	8311900

ANGLIA SEAWAYS Built as the MAERSK ANGLIA by Guangzhou Shipyard International, Guangzhou, China for *Norfolkline*. Entered service as the GUANGZHOU 7130011 (unofficially the 'China II') but renamed shortly afterwards. Operated on the Scheveningen (from 2007 Vlaardingen) - Felixstowe service. In June 2009 moved to the Heysham - Dublin route. In August 2010 renamed the ANGLIA SEAWAYS. In January 2011 service withdrawn. In February 2011 chartered to *Seatruck Ferries* to inaugurate their new Heysham - Dublin service. In January 2012 returned to *DFDS Seaways* and placed on the Vlaardingen - Immingham route as an extra vessel. In April 2012 moved to the Zeebrugge - Rosyth service but proved too slow. In May chartered to *Seatruck Ferries* to operate between Heysham and Belfast. In August, this service ceased and she was switched to the Heysham - Dublin route and in September to the Heysham - Warrenpoint route. In April 2014 returned to *DFDS Seaways* and transferred to the Kiel - St Petersburg service.

ATHENA SEAWAYS Built as the CORAGGIO by Nuovi Cantieri Apuani, Marina di Carrara, Italy. First of an order of eight vessels for *Grimaldi Holdings* of Italy. Used on *Grimaldi Lines* Mediterranean services. In September 2010, bare-boat chartered to *Stena Line* to operate between Hook of Holland and Killingholme. In November 2011 replaced by the new STENA TRANSIT and returned to Mediterranean service. In December 2013 renamed the ATHENA SEAWAYS, chartered to *DFDS Seaways* and replaced the LIVERPOOL SEAWAYS on the Klaipėda - Kiel service. In June 2014 moved to the Klaipėda - Karlshamn route.

BOTNIA SEAWAYS Built as the FINNMASTER by Jinling Shipyard, Nanjing, China for the *Macoma Shipping Group* and chartered to *Finncarriers*. In 2008 sold to *DFDS Lisco* and in January 2009 delivered, chartered to *DFDS Tor Line* and renamed the TOR BOTNIA. Operated on the Immingham - Rotterdam route until December 2010. In January 2011 moved to the Kiel - St Petersburg route. In January 2013 renamed the BOTNIA SEAWAYS.

Corona Seaways (*Peter Therkildsen*)

Optima Seaways (*Gena Anfimov*)

CORONA SEAWAYS Built as the TOR CORONA by Jinling Shipyard, Nanjing, China for *Macoma Shipping Ltd* of the UK and time-chartered to *DFDS Tor Line* for ten years. Used on the Fredericia – Copenhagen – Klaipėda service. In April 2012 renamed the CORONA SEAWAYS.

CROWN SEAWAYS Launched as the THOMAS MANN by Brodogradevna Industrija, Split, Croatia for *Euroway AB* for their Lübeck – Travemünde – Malmö service. However, political problems led to serious delays and, before delivery, the service had ceased. She was purchased by *DFDS*, renamed the CROWN OF SCANDINAVIA and introduced onto the Copenhagen - Oslo service. In January 2013 renamed the CROWN SEAWAYS.

KAUNAS SEAWAYS Train ferry built as the KAUNAS by VEB Mathias-Thesen-Werft, Wismar, Germany (DDR) for *Lisco* of the former Soviet Union and operated between Klaipėda and Mukran in Germany (DDR). She was part of a series of vessels built to link the USSR and Germany (DDR), avoiding Poland. In 1994/95 she was modified to offer passenger facilities and placed on the Klaipėda – Kiel service. In 2003 transferred to the Klaipėda – Karlshamn route. Early in 2004 chartered to *DFDS Tor Line* to operate between Lübeck and Riga. In 2005 returned to the Klaipėda – Karlshamn route. In May 2009 replaced by the LISCO OPTIMA and laid up. In October 2009 placed on the Travemünde - Riga route; this route ceased in January 2010 and she was laid up again. In May 2010 chartered to *Scandlines* and placed on a new Travemünde - Liepaja (Latvia) service. In December 2010 returned to *DFDS Seaways*. In March 2011 chartered to *Baltic Scandinavian Line* to operate between Paldiski (Estonia) and Kapellskär. In May returned to *DFDS Seaways* and inaugurated a new service between Kiel and Ust Luga (Russia). In May 2012 she was renamed the KAUNAS SEAWAYS and in June transferred to the Klaipėda – Sassnitz route. At the end of September 2013 this route closed and in October she was transferred to the Paldiski – Kapellskär service.

OPTIMA SEAWAYS Ro-pax vessel built as the ALYSSA by C N Visentini di Visentini Francesco & C Donada, Italy for *Levantina Trasporti* of Italy for charter. Initially chartered to *CoTuNav* of Tunisia for service between Marseilles, Genoa and Tunis and in 2000 to *Trasmediterranea* of Spain for service between Barcelona and Palma de Mallorca. In 2001 chartered to *Stena Line Scandinavia AB*, renamed the SVEALAND and placed as second vessel on the *Scandlines AB* freight-only Trelleborg - Travemünde service. In 2003 sub-chartered to *Scandlines AG* and placed on the Kiel - Klaipėda route, replacing the ASK and PETERSBURG. In 2004 sold to *Rederia AB Hornet*, a *Stena* company. In late 2005 the *Scandlines* Kiel - Klaipėda service ended. In early 2006 she was chartered to *TT-Line* to cover for the rebuilding of the engines of their four newest vessels. Later sold to *DFDS*, renamed the LISCO OPTIMA and returned to the Kiel - Klaipėda route in Spring 2006. In May 2009 moved to the Klaipėda – Karlshamn route and in February 2011 moved to the Klaipėda - Kiel route but in September moved back. In April 2012 renamed the OPTIMA SEAWAYS. In June 2014 moved to the Klaipėda - Kiel route.

PATRIA SEAWAYS Ro-pax vessel built as the STENA TRAVELLER by Fosen Mekaniske Verksteder, Trondheim, Norway for *Stena RoRo*. After a short period with *Stena Line* on the Hook of Holland - Harwich service, she was chartered to *Sealink Stena Line* for their Southampton - Cherbourg route, initially for 28 weeks. At the end of the 1992 summer season she was chartered to *TT-Line* to operate between Travemünde and Trelleborg and was renamed the TT-TRAVELLER. In late 1995, she returned to *Stena Line*, resumed the name STENA TRAVELLER and inaugurated a new service between Holyhead and Dublin. In Autumn 1996 she was replaced by the STENA CHALLENGER (18523t, 1991). In early 1997 she was again chartered to *TT-Line* and renamed the TT-TRAVELLER. She operated on the Rostock - Trelleborg route. During Winter 1999/2000 her passenger capacity was increased to 250 and passenger facilities renovated. In early 2002 the charter ended and she was renamed the STENA TRAVELLER, chartered to *Stena Line* and placed on their Karlskrona - Gdynia service. This charter ended in May 2003 and she was sold to *Lisco Baltic Service* and renamed the LISCO PATRIA. Placed on the Klaipėda - Karlshamn service. In January 2006 transferred to the Klaipėda - Kiel service to replace the *Scandlines* vessel SVEALAND following that company's withdrawal from the joint route. In Spring 2006 returned to the Klaipėda – Karlshamn route. In May 2011 chartered to *Baltic Scandinavia Lines* and placed on their Paldiski - Kapellskär service. In September 2011 a controlling interest in this service was acquired by *DFDS Seaways*. In January 2012 renamed the PATRIA SEAWAYS.

PEARL SEAWAYS Built as the ATHENA by Wärtsilä Marine, Turku, Finland for *Rederi AB Slite* of Sweden (part of *Viking Line*) and used on 24-hour cruises from Stockholm to Mariehamn (Åland). In 1993 the company went into liquidation and she was sold to *Star Cruises* of Malaysia for cruises in the Far East.

ROPE 163

name

She was renamed the STAR AQUARIUS. Later that year she was renamed the LANGKAPURI STAR AQUARIUS. In February 2001 sold to *DFDS* and renamed the AQUARIUS. After rebuilding, she was renamed the PEARL OF SCANDINAVIA and introduced onto the Copenhagen - Oslo service. In January 2011 renamed the PEARL SEAWAYS.

REGINA SEAWAYS Built as the ENERGIA by Nuovi Cantieri Apuani, Marina di Carrara, Italy for *Grimaldi Holdings* of Italy. In August 2011 chartered to DFDS Seaways and moved to Klaipėda for modifications. In September 2011 renamed the REGINA SEAWAYS and placed on the Klaipėda - Kiel service.

VICTORIA SEAWAYS Built by Nuovi Cantieri Apuani, Marina di Carrara, Italy. Launched as the FORZA. Fifth of an order of eight vessels for *Grimaldi Holdings* of Italy. Whilst under construction, sold to *DFDS Tor Line*. On delivery renamed the LISCO MAXIMA. In March/April 2012 renamed the VICTORIA SEAWAYS. Originally operated between Kiel and Klaipėda. In January 2014 transferred to the Karlshamn - Klaipėda service.

VILNIUS SEAWAYS Train ferry as KAUNAS SEAWAYS. Built as the VILNIUS. In 1993 rebuilt in Liverpool to convert from a 12 passenger freight vessel to a 120 passenger ro-pax vessel. Operated on the Klaipėda – Kiel service until June 2003. Later chartered to *DFDS Tor Line* to operate between Lübeck and Riga. In Summer 2006 transferred to the *DFDS Lisco* Klaipėda - Sassnitz route. In January 2011 renamed the VILNIUS SEAWAYS. In June 2012 she was transferred to the Kiel - Ust Luga service. In June 2013 she was chartered to *Ukrferry* of the Ukraine for service in the Black Sea.

DFDS Seaways also owns the LIVERPOOL SEAWAYS, currently on charter to *NaviRail*.

REDERIJ DOEKSEN

THE COMPANY *Koninklijke Doeksen BV* is a Dutch private sector company. Ferries are operated by subsidiary *Terschellinger Stoomboot Maatschappij*, trading as *Rederij Doeksen*.

MANAGEMENT Managing Director P J M Melles, Marketing Manager Irene Smit.

ADDRESS Waddenpromenade 5, 8861 NT Harlingen, The Netherlands.

TELEPHONE *In The Netherlands* 0900-DOEKSEN (3635736), *From abroad* +31 562 442 002.

FAX +31 (0)517 413303.

INTERNET Email info@rederij-doeksen.nl Website www.rederij-doeksen.nl *(Dutch, English, German))* Facebook www.facebook.com/rederijdoeksen Twitter www.twitter.com/rederijdoeksen

ROUTES OPERATED Conventional Ferries Harlingen (The Netherlands) - Terschelling (Frisian Islands) (2 hrs; *FRIESLAND, MIDSLAND, SPATHOEK)* (up to 6 per day), Harlingen - Vlieland (Frisian Islands) (1 hr 45 mins; *VLIELAND*; 3 per day). Fast Passenger Ferries Harlingen - Terschelling (45 mins; *KOEGELWIECK, TIGER*; 3 to 6 per day), Harlingen - Vlieland (45 mins; *KOEGELWIECK, TIGER*; 2 per day), Vlieland - Terschelling (30 mins; *KOEGELWIECK, TIGER*; 2 per day). Freight Ferry Harlingen - Terschelling (2 hrs; *NOORD-NEDERLAND*), Harlingen - Vlieland (1hr 45 mins; *NOORD-NEDERLAND*).

1	FRIESLAND	3583t	89	14.0k	69.0m	1350P	122C	12L	BA	NL	8801058
2»p	KOEGELWIECK	439t	92	33.0k	35.5m	315P	0C	0L	-	NL	9035527
3	MIDSLAND	1812t	74	15.5k	77.9m	1200P	55C	6L	BA	NL	7393066
4F	NOORD-NEDERLAND	361t	02	14.0k	48.0m	12P	-	9L	BA	NL	9269611
5	SPATHOEK	1743t	88	12.0k	67.4m	975P	55C	-	BA	NL	8800975
6»p	TIGER	660t	02	37.0k	52.0m	414P	0C	0L	BA	NL	9179191
7	VLIELAND	2726t	05	15.0k	64.1m	1300P	58C	4L	BA	NL	9303716

FRIESLAND Built by Van der Giessen-de Noord, Krimpen aan den IJssel, Rotterdam, The Netherlands for *Rederij Doeksen*. Used on the Harlingen - Terschelling route.

KOEGELWIECK Harding 35m catamaran built at Rosendal, Norway for *Rederij Doeksen* to operate between Harlingen and Terschelling, Harlingen and Vlieland and Terschelling and Vlieland.

Eckerö *(William Barham)*

Finlandia *(William Barham)*

MIDSLAND Built as the RHEINLAND by Werftunion GmbH & Co, Cassens-Werft, Emden, Germany for *AG Ems* of Germany. In 1993 purchased by *Rederij Doeksen* and renamed the MIDSLAND. Used mainly on the Harlingen - Terschelling route but also used on the Harlingen - Vlieland service. She is now a reserve vessel.

NOORD-NEDERLAND Catamaran built by ASB, Harwood, New South Wales, Australia for *Rederij Doeksen*. Used on freight services from Harlingen to Terschelling and Vlieland.

SPATHOEK Built by Husumer Schiffswerft, Husum, Germany as the SCHLESWIG-HOLSTEIN for *Wyker Dampfschiffs-Reederei Föhr-Amrum GmbH* of Germany. She operated between Föhr and Amrum. In March 2011 sold to *EVT* and renamed the SPATHOEK. In March 2012 began operating between Harlingen and Terschelling. In April 2014 acquired by *Rederij Doeksen* following that company's acquisition of EVT.

TIGER Catamaran built as the SUPERCAT 2002 by FBMA Babcock Marine, Cebu, Philippines for *SuperCat* of the Philippines. In 2007 purchased by *Rederij Doeksen* and renamed the TIGER. Operates from Harlingen to Terschelling and Vlieland.

VLIELAND Catamaran built by FBMA Babcock Marine, Cebu, Philippines for *Rederij Doeksen* to operate between Harlingen and Vlieland.

REDERI AB ECKERÖ

THE COMPANY *Rederi AB Eckerö* is an Åland Islands company. It operates two ferry companies, a cruise operation from Stockholm (*Birka Cruises*), a ro-ro time chartering company (*Eckerö Shipping*) and a bus company on Åland (*Williams*).

ADDRESS PB 158, AX-22101 Mariehamn, Åland, Finland.

TELEPHONE Administration +358 (0)18 28 030.

FAX Administration +358 (0)18 12 011.

INTERNET Email info@rederiabeckero.ax Website www.rederiabeckero.ax *(Swedish)*

ECKERÖ LINE

THE COMPANY *Eckerö Line Ab Oy* is a Finnish company, 100% owned by *Rederi Ab Eckerö* of Åland, Finland. Until January 1998, the company was called *Eestin-Linjat*.

MANAGEMENT Managing Director Irja Hanelius, Marketing Director Ida Toikka-Everi.

ADDRESS PO Box 307, 00181 Helsinki, Finland.

TELEPHONE Administration & Reservations +358 6000 4300.

FAX Administration & Reservations +358 (0)9 22885541.

INTERNET Email info@eckeroline.fi Website www.eckeroline.fi *(Swedish, Finnish, English)*

ROUTE OPERATED Passenger Service Helsinki (Länsisatama) - Tallinn (Estonia) (2 hrs 30 mins; *FINLANDIA*; up to 2 per day).

1	FINLANDIA	36093t	01	27.0k	175.0m	1880P	665C	116T	BA	FI	9214379

FINLANDIA Built as the MOBY FREEDOM by Daewoo Shipbuilding & Heavy Machinery Ltd., Okpo, South Korea for *Moby SpA (Moby Line)* of Italy. Operated on their Genoa/Civitavecchia/Livorno - Olbia routes. In March 2012 sold to *Eckerö Line*, and renamed the FREEDOM. Refitted at Landskrona and, in June, renamed the FINLANDIA. She entered service on 31st December 2012.

ECKERÖ LINJEN

THE COMPANY Eckerö Linjen is an Åland Islands company 100% owned by Rederi AB Eckerö.

MANAGEMENT Managing Director Tomas Karlsson, Marketing Manager Maria Hellman.

ADDRESS Torggatan 2, Box 158, AX-22100 Mariehamn, Åland.

TELEPHONE Administration +358 (0)18 28 000, Reservations +358 (0)18 28 300.

FAX Administration & Reservations +358 (0)18 28 380.

INTERNET Email info@eckerolinjen.ax Website www.eckerolinjen.se (Swedish, Finnish, English)

ROUTE OPERATED Eckerö (Åland) - Grisslehamn (Sweden) (2 hrs; ECKERÖ; 3 per day).

1	ECKERÖ	12358t	79	19.5k	121.1m	1500P	265C	34T	BA	SE	7633155

ECKERÖ Built as the JENS KOFOED by Aalborg Værft A/S, Aalborg, Denmark for Bornholmstrafikken. Used on the Rønne - Copenhagen, Rønne - Ystad and (until December 2002) Rønne - Sassnitz services. Rønne - Copenhagen service became Rønne – Køge in September 2004. In October 2004 sold to Eckerö Linjen for delivery in May 2005. Renamed the ECKERÖ and substantially rebuilt before entering service in early 2006. In January 2009 transferred from the Finnish to the Swedish flag.

AG EMS

THE COMPANY AG Ems is a German public sector company.

MANAGEMENT Managing Director & Chief Executive B W Brons, Marine Superintendent Knut Gerdes, Operations Manager Hans-Jörd Oltmanns.

ADDRESS Am Aussenhafen, Postfach 1154, 26691 Emden, Germany.

TELEPHONE Administration & Reservations +49 (0)1805-180182.

INTERNET Email info@ag-ems.de Website www.ag-ems.de (German) www.borkumlijn.nl (Dutch) www.helgolandlinie.de (German)

ROUTES OPERATED Conventional Ferries Emden (Germany) - Borkum (German Frisian Islands) (2 hrs; MÜNSTERLAND, OSTFRIESLAND; up to 4 per day), Eemshaven (The Netherlands) - Borkum (55 mins; GRONINGERLAND; up to 4 per day), Wilhelmshaven - Heligoland (3 hrs; HELGOLAND; 1 per day) (Operated by subsidiary Helgoland Linie - tourist cars not conveyed). Fast Ferries Emden - Borkum (1 hr; NORDLICHT up to 4 per day), Eemshaven - Borkum (30 mins; NORDLICHT; 1 per week in summer).

1	GRONINGERLAND	1070t	91	12.0k	44.4m	621P	30C	-	BA	DE	9002465
2	HELGOLAND	1812t	72	15.5k	77.9m	1200P	65C	10L	BA	DE	7217004
3	MÜNSTERLAND	1859t	86	15.5k	78.7m	1200P	70C	10L	BA	DE	8601989
4p»	NORDLICHT	435t	89	33.0k	38.8m	272P	0C	0L	-	DE	8816015
5	OSTFRIESLAND	1859t	85	15.5k	78.7m	1200P	70C	10L	BA	DE	8324622
6p	WAPPEN VON BORKUM	287t	76	11.5k	42.8m	358P	0C	0L	-	DE	7525918

GRONINGERLAND Built by Husumer Schiffswerft, Husum, Germany as the HILLIGENLEI for Wyker Dampfschiffs-Reederei Föhr-Amrum GmbH of Germany. Operated Schlüttsiel - Halligen – Wittdün (North Frisian Islands). In 2004 laid up. In late 2005 sold to AG Ems. In 2006 renamed the GRONINGERLAND and placed on the Eemshaven – Borkum route.

HELGOLAND Built by as the WESTFALEN C Cassens Schiffswerft, Emden, Germany for AG Ems. Rebuilt in 1994. In 2006 renamed the HELGOLAND and inaugurated a new Wilhelmshaven - Heligoland service for subsidiary Helgoland Linie.

MÜNSTERLAND, OSTFRIESLAND Built by Martin Jansen GmbH & Co KG Schiffswerft, Leer, Germany for AG Ems.

NORDLICHT Fjellstrand 38m passenger-only catamaran built at Mandal, Norway for AG Ems.

WAPPEN VON BORKUM Built as the HANNOVER by Schiffswerft Schlömer GmbH & Co KG, Oldersum, Germany for *Friesland Fahrlinie* of Germany. In 1979 sold to *AG Ems* and renamed the STADT BORKUM. In 1988 sold to *ST-Line* of Finland, operating day trips from Rauma and renamed the PRINCESS ISABELLA. In 1994 returned to *AG Ems* and renamed the WAPPEN VON BORKUM.

FÆRGEN

THE COMPANIES *Danske Færger A/S* trading as *Færgen (previously Nordic Ferry Services A/S)* is a Danish mixed public and private sector company.

MANAGEMENT CEO John Steen-Mikkelsen.

ADDRESSES Dampskibskajen 3, 3700 Rønne, Denmark.

TELEPHONE Administration +45 70 23 15 15. Reservations *(BornholmerFaergen* only) +45 70 10 18 66.

INTERNET Website www.faergen.com *(Danish, German, English)*

ROUTES OPERATED

AlsFærgen Fynshav (Als) - Bøjden (Fyn) (50 mins; *FRIGG SYDFYEN, ODIN SYDFYEN;* hourly (summer) two-hourly (winter)), *BornholmerFærgen* Conventional Ferries Rønne (Bornholm, Denmark) - Køge (6 hrs 30 mins; *HAMMERODDE;* 1 per day, *April-October only:* Rønne – Sassnitz (Germany) (3 hrs 30 mins; *POVL ANKER;* 1 per day). Fast Ferry Rønne - Ystad (Sweden) (1 hr 20 mins; *LEONORA CHRISTINA, VILLUM CLAUSEN;* Peak season: departure every 2 hours. Low season: 3 trips a day), *FanøFærgen* Esbjerg (Jutland) - Nordby (Fanø) (12 mins; *FENJA, MENJA, SØNDERHO;* every 20-40 mins), *LangelandsFærgen* Spodsbjerg (Langeland) - Tårs (Lolland) (40 mins; *LANGELAND, LOLLAND;* hourly), *SamsøFærgen* Hou – Sælvig (Samsø) (50 min; *KANHAVE;* up to 8 per day), Kalundborg - Koby Kås (Samsø) (1 hr 50 min; *KYHOLM;* up to 4 per day).

1	FENJA	751t	98	11.5k	49.9m	396P	34C	4L	BA	DK	9189378
2	FRIGG SYDFYEN	1676t	84	13.5k	70.1m	338P	50C	8L	BA	DK	8222824
3	HAMMERODDE	13906t	05	18.5k	124.9m	400P	342C	106T	A	DK	9323699
4	KANHAVE	4250t	08	16.0k	91.4m	600P	122C	30L	BA	DK	9548562
5	KYHOLM	3380t	98	14.5k	69.2m	450P	96C	8L	BA	DK	9183025
6	LANGELAND	4500t	12	16.0k	99.9m	600P	122C	36L	BA	DK	9596428
7»	LEONORA CHRISTINA	8235t	11	40.0k	112.6m	1400P	359C	-	BA	DK	9557848
8	LOLLAND	4500t	12	16.0k	99.9m	600P	122C	36L	BA	DK	9594690
9	MENJA	751t	98	11.5k	49.9m	396P	34C	4L	BA	DK	9189380
10	ODIN SYDFYEN	1698t	82	12.5k	70.4m	338P	50C	8L	BA	DK	8027896
11	POVL ANKER	12131t	78	19.5k	121.0m	1500P	262C	26T	BA	DK	7633143
12p	SØNDERHO	93t	62	10.0k	26.3m	163P	0C	0L	-	DK	
13»	VILLUM CLAUSEN	6402t	00	40.0k	86.6m	1055P	200C	-	BA	DK	9216250

FENJA Built by Morsø Værft A/S, Nykøbing Mors, Denmark for *Scandlines Sydfyenske A/S* for the Esbjerg - Nordby service.

FRIGG SYDFYEN Built by Svendborg Skibsværft A/S, Svendborg, Denmark for *Sydfyenske Dampskibsselskab (SFDS)* of Denmark for the service between Spodsbjerg and Tårs. In June 2012 moved to the Fynshav - Bøjden route.

HAMMERODDE Built by Merwede Shipyard, Hardinxveld-Giessendam, The Netherlands for *Bornholmstrafikken.* In Winter 2010 an additional vehicle deck was added for freight and some additional cabins.

KANHAVE Built by Frantzis Shipyard, Perama, Greece. Used on the Hou - Sælvig route.

KYHOLM Built by Ørskov Staalskibsværft, Frederikshavn, Denmark for *Samsø Linien* of Denmark. In October 2008 chartered to *Samsøtrafikken* (now *SamsøFærgen*).

LANGELAND Built by Sietas Werft, Hamburg, Germany for the Spodsbjerg - Tårs route.

LEONORA CHRISTINA Austal Auto-Express 113 catamaran built at Fremantle, Australia for *Færgen*. Used on the Rønne - Ystad route.

LOLLAND Built by Sietas Werft, Hamburg, Germany. She was launched as the SAMSØ and it was intended that she would be operated on the Hou - Sælvig service, being owned by *Samsø Linien* and operated by *Færgen*. However, these plans were dropped and in February 2012 she was renamed the LOLLAND. After delivery in March 2012 she was, in April, placed on the Spodsbjerg - Tårs route.

MENJA Built by Morsø Værft A/S, Nykøbing Mors, Denmark for *Scandlines Sydfyenske A/S* for the Esbjerg - Nordby service.

ODIN SYDFYEN Built by Svendborg Skibsværft A/S, Svendborg, Denmark for *Sydfyenske Dampskibsselskab (SFDS)* of Denmark for the service between Spodsbjerg and Tårs. In June 2012 moved to the Fynshav - Bøjden route.

POVL ANKER Built by Aalborg Værft A/S, Denmark for *Bornholmstrafikken*. Used on the Rønne - Copenhagen (until September 2004), Rønne - Køge (October 2004-date), Rønne - Ystad and Rønne - Sassnitz services. In recent years she has operated between Rønne and Sassnitz and Rønne and Ystad in the peak summer period.

SØNDERHO Passenger-only ferry built by Esbjerg Jernstøberi & Maskinfabrik A/S, Esbjerg, Denmark for *Post & Telegrafvæsenet* (Danish Post Office). In 1977 taken over by *DSB*. Used on extra peak sailings and late night and early morning sailings between Esbjerg and Nordby.

VILLUM CLAUSEN Austal Auto-Express 86 catamaran built at Fremantle, Australia for *Bornholmstrafikken*. Used on the Rønne - Ystad service. Car capacity increased in 2005.

FINNLINES

THE COMPANY *Finnlines plc* is a Finnish private sector company. The Italian company *Grimaldi Compagnia de Navigazione SpA* has a controlling interest. It operates four passenger brands: *Finnlines HansaLink, Finnlines NordöLink* and *FinnLink* and *TransRussiaExpress*.

MANAGEMENT President and CEO Uwe Bakosch, Vice-President Mrs Seija Turunen.

ADDRESS PO Box 197, 00180 Helsinki, Finland.

TELEPHONE Administration + 358 (0)10 343 50, Reservations + 358 (0)10 343 4500.

FAX Administration + 358 (0)10 343 5200.

INTERNET *Finnlines* Email info.fi@finnlines.com Website *Finnlines* www.finnlines.com *(English, Finnish, German, Polish, Swedish)*

ROUTES OPERATED *Finnlines Hansalink branded routes* Helsinki - Travemünde (27 hrs; FINNLADY, FINNMAID, FINNSTAR; 7 per week), Helsinki - Rostock (32 hrs; FINNHANSA; 1 per week).

Finnlines NordöLink branded route Malmö - Travemünde (9 hrs; FINNCLIPPER, FINNPARTNER, FINNTRADER, NORDLINK; up to 4 per day).

FinnLink branded route Naantali (Finland) - Långnäs - Kapellskär (Sweden) (6 hrs; FINNEAGLE FINNFELLOW, FINNSAILOR; up to 2 per day).

TranRussia Express branded route Lübeck - Travemünde - Sassnitz - Ventspils - St Petersburg (60 hours; FINNCLIPPER or FINNPARTNER or FINNTRADER,; 1 per week),

1	EUROFERRY BRINDISI	25996t	96	21.0k	168.0m	200P	-	154T	BA2	SE	9010814
2	FINNCLIPPER	29841t	99	22.0k	188.3m	440P	-	210T	BA2	SE	9137997
3	FINNEAGLE	29841t	99	22.0k	188.3m	440P	-	185T	BA2	SE	9138006
4	FINNFELLOW	33769t	00	22.0k	188.3m	452P	-	220T	BA	SE	9145164
5	FINNHANSA	32531t	94	21.3k	183.0m	90P	-	236T	A2	FI	9010151
6	FINNLADY	45923t	07	25.0k	216.0m	500P	-	300T	BA2	FI	9336268
7	FINNMAID	45923t	06	25.0k	216.0m	500P	-	300T	BA2	FI	9319466
8	FINNPARTNER	32534t	94	21.3k	183.0m	90P	-	236T	A2	SE	9010163

Hammerodde *(John Bryant)*

Villum Clausen *(John Bryant)*

9	FINNSAILOR	20783t	87	20.3k	157.6m	119P	-	146T	A	SE	8401444
10	FINNSTAR	45923t	06	25.0k	216.0m	500P	-	300T	BA2	FI	9319442
11	FINNTRADER	32534t	95	21.3k	183.0m	114P	-	220T	BA2	SE	9017769
12	NORDLINK	45923t	07	25.0k	216.0m	500P	-	300T	BA2	SE	9336256

EUROFERRY BRINDISI Built as the GOTLAND by Pt Dok Kodja Bahri, Kodja, Indonesia for *Rederi AB Gotland* for charter. In 1997 briefly chartered to *Tor Line* and then to *Nordic Trucker Line*, to operate between Oxelösund and St Petersburg (a ro-ro service). In June 1997 she was chartered to *SeaWind Line*, enabling a twice-daily passenger service to be operated. In late 1997 she was sold to *Finnlines* and renamed the FINNARROW. She started operating twice weekly between Helsinki and Travemünde. During Summer 1998 she was transferred to *FinnLink*; a bow door was fitted and she was modified to allow for two-level loading. In 2003 transferred to *Nordö Link*. In 2005 returned to *FinnLink*. In 2006 transferred to *Finnlines Nordö Link* again. In 2007 chartered to *Stena Line* to operate between Karlskrona and Gdynia. In December 2011 transferred to the Hook of Holland - Killingholme route. In March 2011 replaced by the STENA TRANSPORTER and returned to *Finnlines*. Placed on the Travemünde - Malmö service. In October 2011 transferred to *FinnLink*. Between January and March 2013 chartered to *Stena Line* to cover Irish Sea routes during the refit period but withdrawn from service prematurely following an accident. In April 2013 chartered to *Grimaldi Line* of Italy for five years and renamed the EUROFERRY BRINDISI.

FINNCLIPPER 'Ro-pax' ferry built by Astilleros Españoles, Cadiz, Spain. Ordered by *Stena RoRo* of Sweden and launched as the STENA SEAPACER 1. In 1998 sold, before delivery, to *Finnlines* and renamed the FINNCLIPPER. Entered service on the Helsinki - Travemünde route in 1999. During Winter 1999/2000 she was converted to double-deck loading. In 2003 transferred to *FinnLink*. In 2007 an additional freight deck was added. Currently operating on the Travemünde - Malmö and Lübeck - St Petersburg services.

FINNEAGLE 'Ro-pax' vessel built by Astilleros Españoles, Cadiz, Spain. Ordered by *Stena RoRo* of Sweden and launched as the STENA SEAPACER 2. In 1998 sold, before delivery, to *Finnlines* and renamed the FINNEAGLE. Although expected to join her sister the FINNCLIPPER on the Helsinki - Travemünde route, on delivery in November 1999 she entered service with *FinnLink*. During Winter 1999/2000 she was modified for two-deck loading. She has operated on both the *FinnLink* and *Finnlines NordöLink* services.

FINNFELLOW 'Ro-pax' ferry built as the STENA BRITANNICA by Astilleros Españoles, Cadiz, Spain for *Stena RoRo* and chartered to *Stena Line BV* to operate between Hook of Holland and Harwich. In 2003 replaced by a new STENA BRITANNICA, sold to *Finnlines*, renamed the FINNFELLOW and placed on the Helsinki – Travemünde route. In 2004 transferred to *FinnLink*.

FINNHANSA 'Ro-pax' vessel built as the FINNHANSA by Stocznia Gdanska SA, Gdansk, Poland for *Finnlines Oy* of Finland to operate between Helsinki - Travemünde. In April 2009 sold to Finnlines' parent company, *Grimaldi PLC* of Italy and renamed the EUROFERRY SICILIA. Operated between Genoa and Catania. In May 2010 sold back to *Finnlines* and in July 2010 renamed the TRANSRUSSIA and placed on the *TransRussia Express* service. In February 2014 renamed the FINNHANSA. Currently operating on the Kotka - Rostock - Lübeck service.

FINNLADY, FINNMAID Built by Fincantieri-Cantieri Navali Italiani SpA, Ancona, Italy to operate between Helsinki and Travemünde.

FINNPARTNER 'Ro-pax' vessel built by Stocznia Gdanska SA, Gdansk, Poland for *Finnlines Oy* of Finland to provide a daily service conveying both freight and a limited number of cars and passengers on the previously freight-only route between Helsinki and Travemünde. In February 2007 replaced by the FINNLADY and placed on the Turku - Travemünde freight service; in May sent to the Remontowa Shipyard in Gdansk for rebuilding to increase passenger capacity and allow for two-deck through loading. Currently operating on the Travemünde - Malmö and Lübeck - St Petersburg services.

FINNSAILOR Built by Gdansk Shipyard, Gdansk, Poland for *Finnlines* of Finland for freight service between Finland and Germany. In 1996 converted to ro-pax format to inaugurate a new passenger/freight service between Helsinki and Norrköping (Sweden) for subsidiary *FinnLink*. In 1997 this service was transferred to the Kapellskär - Naantali route and passengers (other than lorry drivers) ceased to be conveyed. In 2000 she was chartered to *Nordö-Link* to operate between Travemünde and Malmö. In 2002 she returned to *FinnLink*. In 2004 transferred to *Nordö-Link*. In 2007 returned to *FinnLink* as fourth ship. In early 2009 transferred to *Finnlines'* freight service operating between Helsinki, Turku and Travemünde but in April transferred back. In March 2011 moved back to *Finnlines NordöLink*. In November 2013 chartered to *Navirail* of Estonia to operate between Paldiski and Hanko. In January 2014 returned to *Finnlines* and placed on the Naantali - Kapellskär route.

FINNSTAR Built by Fincantieri-Cantieri Navali Italiani SpA, Castellamare, Italy to operate between Helsinki and Travemünde.

FINNTRADER 'Ro-pax' vessel built by Stocznia Gdanska SA, Gdansk, Poland for *Finnlines Oy* of Finland to provide a daily service conveying both freight and a limited number of cars and passengers on the previously freight-only route between Helsinki and Travemünde. In 2006/07 rebuilt to increase passenger capacity and allow for two-deck through loading. In 2007 transferred to the Malmö - Travemünde route. Currently operating on the Travemünde - Malmö and Lübeck - St Petersburg services.

NORDLINK Built by Fincantieri-Cantieri Navali Italiani SpA, Castellamare, Italy for *Finnlines* to operate for *Finnlines NordöLink* between Travemünde and Malmö. Currently operating on the Travemünde - Malmö service.

FJORD LINE

THE COMPANY *Fjord Line* is a Norwegian company. During 2007 most of the shares of the company were purchased by *Frode and Ole Teigen*. The company bought and merged with *Master Ferries* during December 2007 and all operations are branded as *Fjord Line*.

MANAGEMENT **Managing Director** Ingvald Fardal, **Sales and Marketing Director** Eva Sørås Mellgren, **CFO** Svein Ege, **Director Fjord Line Denmark** Gert Balling, **Technical & Nautical Director** Morten Larsen.

ADDRESS PO Box 513, 4379 Egersund, Norway.

TELEPHONE **Administration** + 47 55 54 87 00, **Reservations** + 47 51 46 40 99.

FAX **Administration & Reservations** + 47 51 49 24 30.

INTERNET **Email** info@fjordline.com **Website** www.fjordline.com *(English, Danish, German, Dutch, Polish, Norwegian,)*

ROUTE OPERATED **Conventional Ferry** Bergen (Norway) – Stavanger - Hirtshals (Denmark) (17 hrs; *BERGENSFJORD, STAVANGERFJORD*; daily), Langesund (Norway) - Hirtshals (4 hrs 30 mins; *BERGENSFJORD, STAVANGERFJORD*, daily), Sandefjord (Norway) - Strömstad (Sweden) (2 hrs 30 mins; *OSLOFJORD*; 2 per day), **Fast Ferry May-August** Kristiansand (Norway) - Hirtshals (Denmark) (2 hrs 15 min; *FJORD CAT*; up to 3 per day).

1	BERGENSFJORD	31678t	13	21.5k	170.0m	1500P	600C	90T	BA	NO	9586617
2»	FJORD CAT	5619t	98	43.0k	91.3m	663P	220C	-	A	DK	9176060
3	OSLOFJORD	16794t	93	19.0k	134.4m	882P	350C	44T	BA	DK	9058995
4	STAVANGERFJORD	31678t	13	21.5k	170.0m	1500P	600C	90T	BA	NO	9586605

BERGENSFJORD, STAVANGERFJORD Built by Bergen Group Fosen AS, Rissa, Norway for *Fjord Line*. They operate on LNG.

FJORD CAT Incat 91-metre catamaran, built speculatively at Hobart, Tasmania, Australia. In Spring 1998, following *Incat's* acquisition of a 50% share in *Scandlines Cat-Link A/S*, she was chartered by *Nordic Catamaran Ferries K/S* to that company, operating between Århus and Kalundborg and named the CAT-LINK V. She is the current holder of the Hales Trophy for fastest crossing of the Atlantic during her delivery voyage between the USA and Falmouth, UK (although this claim is disputed because it was not a genuine commercial service). In 1999 the charter was transferred to *Mols-Linien*, she was renamed the MADS MOLS and operated between Århus and Odden. Charter ended in July 2005. Laid up and renamed the INCAT 049. In 2006 sold to *Gabriel Scott Rederi (Master Ferries)* and renamed the

MASTER CAT. In December 2008 purchased by *Fjord Line* and renamed the FJORD CAT. Did not operate in 2009 but service resumed in 2010.

OSLOFJORD Built by Fosen Mekaniske Verksteder, Rissa, Norway for *Rutelaget Askøy-Bergen* as the BERGEN and used on the *Fjord Line* Bergen - Egersund - Hanstholm service. In April 2003 chartered to *DFDS Seaways*, renamed the DUCHESS OF SCANDINAVIA and, after modifications, introduced onto the Harwich - Cuxhaven service. In 2004 sold to *Bergensfjord KS* of Norway and chartered to *DFDS Seaways*. In 2005 sub-chartered to *Fjord Line* for 5 months (with *DFDS* officers and deck-crew) and renamed the ATLANTIC TRAVELLER. In 2006 chartered directly to *Fjord Line*. In March 2008 purchased by *Fjord Line* and renamed the BERGENSFJORD. In January 2014 renamed the OSLOFJORD, rebuilt as a day ferry by STX Finland, Rauma, Finland and, in June 2014, inaugurated a new service between Sandefjord and Strömstad.

GOTLANDSBÅTEN

THE COMPANY *Gotlandsbåten* is a Swedish private sector company.

MANAGEMENT CEO Lars Meijer, **Marketing Manager** Julia Bendelin.

ADDRESS Färjevägen 10, 593 50 Västervik, Sweden.

TELEPHONE *International* + 46(0)8 519 77 640, *Sweden* 0900-75 55

INTERNET Email info@gotlandsbaten.se Website www.gotlandsbaten.se *(Swedish)*

ROUTE OPERATED Västervik (Sweden) - Visby (Gotland) (3hrs 20 mins; *VÄSTERVIK*, up to 2 per day). Service now due to start Summer 2015.

1	VÄSTERVIK	9022t	86	22.0k	150.9m	1200P	260C	60T	BA	PA	8604345

VÄSTERVIK Built as the QUEEN DIAMOND Kurushima Dockyard Co., Ltd. Onishi, Japan for *KK Diamond Ferry* of Japan. In January 2004 sold to *Sea World Express Ferry Co. Ltd.* of South Korea and renamed NEW SEA WORLD EXPRESS FERRY. In November sold to *Effect Shipholding Co* of the Marshall Island (a subsidiary of *Endeavor Shipping Co of Greece*). Renamed the PRINCESS T. In 2012, she was rebuilt at Yalova, Turkey. In November 2013 chartered to *Gotlandsbåten*. She was due to be renamed the VÄSTERVIK and enter service in June 2014 but this has been delayed by various problems.

HURTIGRUTEN

THE COMPANY *Hurtigruten ASA* is a Norwegian private sector company. The service was originally provided by a consortium of companies. By 2006, through mergers and withdrawal from the operation, there were just two companies - *Troms Fylkes D/S* and *Ofotens og Vesteraalens D/S* and in that year *Hurtigruten ASA* was formed.

MANAGEMENT **Chairman** Trygve Hegnar, **Managing Director** Daniel Skjeldam.

ADDRESS Hurtigruten ASA, Postboks 6144 Langnes, 9291 Tromsø, Norway.

TELEPHONE **Administration** + 47 97 05 70 30, **Reservations *Norway*** + 47 81 00 30 30, **UK** + 44 (0) 203 051 3869. *Central Europe* Tel. (040) 874 083 58, *France* Tel + 33 1 58 30 86 86, **US** 1-(866) 552-0371.

FAX **Administration & Reservations Nordic** + 47 97 05 70 31 **UK** + 44 (0)20 8846 2678.

DE Fax (040) 36 41 77.

INTERNET Email firmapost@hurtigruten.com uk.sales@hurtigruten.com

Websites www.hurtigruten.co.uk *(English)* www.hurtigruten.no *(Norwegian)* www.hurtigruten.de *(German)* www.hurtigruten.fr *(French)* www.hurtigruten.us *(US English)*

ROUTE OPERATED 'Hurtigruten' sail every day throughout the year from Bergen and calls at 34 ports up to Kirkenes and takes you along one of the world's most exciting coast lines, where you will find

Ane Laesø (*Peter Therkildsen*)

Fjord Cat (*Miles Cowsill*)

yourself close to nature, people and traditions. Daily departures throughout the year. The round trip takes just under 11 days.

1	FINNMARKEN	15539t	02	18.0k	138.5m	1000P	50C	0L	S	NO	9231951
2P	FRAM	11647t	07	18.0k	110.0m	500P	47C	0L	S	NO	9370018
3	KONG HARALD	11204t	93	18.0k	121.8m	691P	50C	0L	S	NO	9039119
4	LOFOTEN	2621t	64	16.0k	87.4m	410P	4C	0L	C	NO	5424562
5	MIDNATSOL	16151t	03	18.0k	135.7m	1000P	50C	0L	S	NO	9247728
6	NORDKAPP	11386t	96	18.0k	123.3m	691P	50C	0L	S	NO	9107772
7	NORDLYS	11204t	94	18.0k	121.8m	691P	50C	0L	S	NO	9048914
8	NORDNORGE	11384t	97	18.0k	123.3m	691P	50C	0L	S	NO	9107784
9	POLARLYS	11341t	96	18.0k	123.0m	737P	50C	0L	S	NO	9107796
10	RICHARD WITH	11205t	93	18.0k	121.8m	691P	50C	0L	S	NO	9040429
11	TROLLFJORD	16140t	02	18.0k	135.7m	822P	50C	0L	S	NO	9233258
12	VESTERÅLEN	6262t	83	18.0k	108.6m	560P	40C	0L	S	NO	8019368

FINNMARKEN Built by Kværner Kleven Skeppsvarv, Ulsteinvik, Norway for *Ofotens og Vesteraalens D/S*. In October 2009 chartered as a support vessel for the Gorgon Project (natural gas) in Western Australia. In November 2011 returned to *Hurtigruten* and, in February 2012, returned to service.

FRAM Built by Fincantieri-Cantieri Navali Italiani SpA at Trieste for *Hurtigruten Group ASA* (ordered by OVDS). Since 2007 she has operated cruises around Greenland and Svalbad during the summer period and in South America during the winter and this has been the pattern since. She is named after Fridtjof Nansen's expedition ship Fram and has ice class 1A/1B.

KONG HARALD Built by Volkswerft, Stralsund, Germany for *Troms Fylkes D/S*.

LOFOTEN Built by A/S Aker Mekaniske Verksted, Oslo, Norway for *Vesteraalens D/S*. In 1988 she was sold to *Finnmark Fylkesrederi og Ruteselskap*. In 1996 she was sold to *Ofotens og Vesteraalens D/S*. In 2002 she was replaced by the FINNMARKEN but she then operated summer cruises and in the winter months substituted for the NORDNORGE when that vessel was sailing in the Chilean Fjords and Antarctica. Since 2008 she has operated on the main Hurtigruten roster.

MIDNATSOL Built by Fosen Mekaniske Verksteder, Rissa, Norway for *Troms Fylkes D/S*.

NORDKAPP Built by Kværner Kleven Skeppsvarv, Ulsteinvik, Norway for *Ofotens og Vesteraalens D/S*. During the winters of 2005/06 and 2006/07 she operated cruises in South America but following the delivery of the FRAM she now remains on the Hurtigruten throughout the year.

NORDLYS Built by Volkswerft, Stralsund, Germany for *Troms Fylkes D/S*. In 2002 sold to *Kilberg Shipping KS* of Norway and leased back on 15 year bareboat charter with options to repurchase. She was laid up during winter 2008/09 until required to replace the damaged RICHARD WITH from the end of January. She now operates full-time on the Hurtigruten roster.

NORDNORGE Built by Kværner Kleven, Ulsteinvik, Norway for *Ofotens og Vesteraalens D/S*. During winters 2002/03 - 2007/08 she operated cruises in South America. During most of Winter 2008/09 she was used as an accommodation vessel for a liquefied natural gas field. Laid up at Bremerhaven during winter 2009/10.

POLARLYS Built by Ulstein Verft A/S, Ulsteinvik, Norway for *Troms Fylkes D/S*.

RICHARD WITH Built by Volkswerft, Stralsund, Norway for *Ofotens og Vesteraalens D/S*. In 2002 sold to *Kystruten KS*, of Norway and leased back on 15 year bareboat charter with options to re-purchase.

TROLLFJORD Built by Fosen Mekaniske Verksteder, Rissa, Norway for *Troms Fylkes D/S*.

VESTERÅLEN Built by Kaarbös Mekaniske Verksted A/S, Harstad, Norway for *Vesteraalens D/S*. From 1987 owned by *Ofotens og Vesteraalens D/S* and from 2006 by *Hurtigruten Group ASA*.

FÆRGESELSKABET LÆSØ

THE COMPANY *Færgeselskabet Læsø K/S* is a Danish public sector company, 50% owned by the county of North Jutland and 50% by the municipality of Læsø.

MANAGEMENT **Managing Director** Lars Ricks, **Marketing Manager** Bente Faurholt.

ADDRESS Havnepladsen 1, Vesterø Havn, 9940 Læsø, Denmark.

TELEPHONE **Administration & Reservations** +45 98 49 90 22

FAX **Administration** +45 98 49 95 22.

INTERNET **Email** info@laesoe-line.dk **Website** www.laesoe-line.dk *(Danish, English, German)*

ROUTE OPERATED Læsø - Frederikshavn (Jutland) (1 hr 30 mins; *ANE LÆSØ, MARGRETE LÆSØ*; up 7 per day).

| 1 | ANE LÆSØ | 2208t | 95 | 12.0k | 53.8m | 440P | 72C | - | BA | DK | 9107370 |
| 2 | MARGRETE LÆSØ | 3668t | 97 | 13.5k | 68.5m | 586P | 76C | 12L | BA | DK | 9139438t |

ANE LÆSØ Built as the VESBORG by Ørskov Stålskibsværft, Ørskov, Denmark for Samsø Linien. In March2012 sold to *Læsø Færgen*. Rebuilt by Soby Yard, Aerø, Denmark and renamed the ANE LÆSØ. She will also act as reserve vessel for the new Samsø ferry, owned by the municipality, which will be replace the KANHAVE of *Færgen* on the Hou - Sælvig (Samsø) service at the end of September 2014.

MARGRETE LÆSØ Built as the LÆSØ FÆRGEN by A/S Norsdsøværftet, Ringkøbing, Denmark for *Andelsfærgeselskabet Læsø* of Denmark. In June 1997 renamed the MARGRETE LÆSØ. In July 1999 transferred to *Færgeselskabet Læsø*.

LINDA LINE

Lindaliini AS (trading as *Linda Line*) is an Estonian Company owned by three Estonian investors - Enn Rohula (26.8%), Urmas Sardis & Janek Veeber (73.2%).

MANAGEMENT **CEO** Enn Rohula.

ADDRESS 4A Adala Tallinn 10614.

TELEPHONE **Administration** +372 6999 340 **Reservations** *Tallinn* +372 69990 333, *Helsinki* +358 (0)600 066 8970.

FAX **Administration** +372 6999341.

INTERNET **Email** info@lindaline.ee **Website** www.lindaline.ee *(Estonian, Finnish, English Russian)*

ROUTE OPERATED Tallinn (Estonia) – Helsinki (Finland) (1hr 40 mins, *KAROLIN, MERILIN*; up 6 to per day (April – December) depending on winter ice conditions).

| 1P | KAROLIN | 636t | 00 | 40.0k | 42.0m | 402P | 0C | 0L | EE | 9124433 |
| 2P | MERILIN | 963t | 99 | 37.0k | 52.0m | 450P | 0C | 0L | EE | 9194256 |

KAROLIN Construction began 1995 at Austal Ships Pty Ltd (Hendersons) initially as the OCEANFAST FERRIES NO 16 and later the CARAIBE-JET but not completed until 2000. In 2000 sold to *AG Ems of Germany* as the POLARSTERN for services between from Emden and Frisian Island of Borkum and Helgoland (summer only). In 2009 sold to *Lindaliini AS* and renamed the KAROLIN.

MERILIN Built 1999 by Austal Freemantle for AG Reederei Norden-Frisa, Germany, for services between Norddeich and Norderney (German Frisian Islands). Originally named the NO 1 (1999) but upon entering service immediately renamed CAT 1. In 2007 bought by *Lindaliini AS* and renamed the MERILIN.

MOLS-LINIEN

THE COMPANY *Mols-Linien A/S* is a Danish private sector company; previously a subsidiary of *J Lauritzen A/S*, it was sold in 1988 to DIFKO No LXII *(Dansk Investeringsfond)*. Since 1994 shares in the company have been traded on the Stock Exchange. In January 1999 a 40% share in the company was acquired by *Scandlines Danmark A/S*. Their *Scandlines Cat-Link* Århus - Kalundborg service became part of *Mols-Linien* in February 1999 and the service was switched from Kalundborg to Odden in April 1999. The *Scandlines* share in the company was acquired by the *Clipper Group* in 2007.

MANAGEMENT **Managing Director** Preben Wolff, **Marketing Manager** Mikkel Hybel.

ADDRESS Færgehavnen, 8400 Ebeltoft, Denmark.

TELEPHONE **Administration** + 45 89 52 52 00, **Reservations** + 45 70 10 14 18 (press 1).

FAX **Administration** + 45 89 52 53 93.

INTERNET **Email** mols-linien@mols-linien.dk **Website** www.mols-linien.dk *(Danish, English, German)*

ROUTES OPERATED Århus - Odden (Sealand) (1 hr 5 mins; *KATEXPRESS 1, KATEXPRESS 2, MAX MOLS*; up to 7 per day), Ebeltoft (Jutland) - Odden (45 mins; *KATEXPRESS 1, KATEXPRESS 2, MAX MOLS*; up to 4 per day).

1»	KATEXPRESS 1	10841	09	40.0k	112.6m	1200P	417C	34L	A	DK	9501590
2»	KATEXPRESS 2	10841	13	40.0k	112.6m	1000P	417C	34L	A	DK	9561356
3»	MAX MOLS	5617t	98	43.0k	91.3m	800P	220C	-	A	DK	9176058

KATEXPRESS 1 Incat 112m catamaran built by Incat Tasmania Pty Ltd for *MGC Chartering* of the Irish Republic. Launched as the INCAT 066. On completion, sold to for *MGC Chartering* of the Irish Republic and renamed the MGC 66. In April 2009 chartered to *LD Lines*, renamed the NORMAN ARROW and, in June, placed on the Dover - Boulogne route. In November 2009 withdrawn and laid up for the winter. In April 2010 began operating on the Portsmouth Le Havre - route. In March 2012 chartered to *Mols-Linien* and renamed the KATEXPRESS 1 (Note: in upper and lower case spelt 'KatExpress 1'). Entered service in May 2012.

KATEXPRESS 2 Incat 112m catamaran built by Incat Tasmania Pty Ltd. Launched as INCAT 067. In March 2013 chartered to *Mols-Linien* and renamed the KATEXPRESS 2 for ten years with a purchase option. (Note: in upper and lower case spelt 'KatExpress 2'). Entered service in May 2013.

MAX MOLS Incat 91-metre catamaran, built speculatively at Hobart, Tasmania, Australia. In Spring 1998, following *Incat's* acquisition of a 50% share in *Scandlines Cat-Link A/S*, she was sold to that company and named the CAT-LINK IV. In 1999 purchased by *Mols-Linien* and renamed the MAX MOLS. In 2000 chartered to *Marine Atlantic* of Canada to operate between Port aux Basques (Newfoundland) and North Sydney (Nova Scotia). Returned to *Mols-Linien* in Autumn 2000. In Summer 2002 chartered to *Riga Sea Lines* to operate between Riga and Nynäshamn. Returned to *Mols-Linien* in Autumn 2002. In 2004 chartered to *P&O Ferries* to operate between Portsmouth and Caen. Operated under the marketing name 'Caen Express'. In November 2004 returned to *Mols-Linien* and placed on the Århus – Odden route to enhance the service as second vessel.

NAVIRAIL

THE COMPANY *Navirail* is an Estonian company.

ADDRESS Liimi 1, 10621 Tallinn, Estonia.

TELEPHONE **Administration** + 372 666 16 81, **Reservations** + 372 66 616 83.

FAX **Administration & Reservations** + 372 66 616 59.

INTERNET **Email** navirail@navirail.com **Websites** www.navirail.com *(English, Estonian, Finnish, Polish, Russian)*

ROUTE OPERATED Paldiski (Estonia) - Hanko (Finland) (3 hrs; *LIVERPOOL SEAWAYS*; 1 per day).

Nordnorge (*Hurtigruten*)

Trollfjord (*Miles Cowsill*)

1   LIVERPOOL SEAWAYS 21856t   97   20.0k 186.0m   320P   100C   135T   A   LT   9136034

LIVERPOOL SEAWAYS Built as the LAGAN VIKING by CN Visentini, Donada, Italy for *Levantina Trasporti* of Italy and chartered to *Norse Irish Ferries*, operating between Liverpool and Belfast. In 1999 the charter was taken over by *Merchant Ferries*. Purchased by *NorseMerchant Ferries* in 2001. In 2002 the service transferred to Twelve Quays River Terminal, Birkenhead. In January 2005 renamed the LIVERPOOL VIKING and in December moved to the Birkenhead – Dublin route. In August 2010 renamed the LIVERPOOL SEAWAYS. In February 2011 moved to the Klaipėda - Karlshamn service. In January 2014 chartered to *NaviRail*.

REEDEREI NORDEN-FRISIA

THE COMPANY *Aktiengesellschaft Reederei Norden-Frisia* is a German public sector company.

MANAGEMENT President/CEO C U Stegmann, Managing Director/CFO Prok. Graw, Technical Manager Prok. H Stolle.

ADDRESS Postfach 1262, 26534 Norderney, Germany.

TELEPHONE *Administration* + 49 (0)4931 987 0.

FAX *Administration* + 49 (0)4931 987 1131.

INTERNET *Email* info@reederei-frisia.de *Website* www.reederei-frisia.de *(German)*

ROUTES OPERATED **Car Ferries & Passenger Ferries** Norddeich (Germany) - Norderney (German Frisian Islands) (1 hr; FRISIA I, FRISIA IV, FRISIA VI; up to 15 per day), Norddeich - Juist (German Frisian Islands) (1 hr 20 mins; FRISIA II, FRISIA V, FRISIA VII; up to 15 per day). **Excursion Vessels** *(FRISIA IX, FRISIA X, RÜM HART 2, WAPPEN VON NORDENEY; varies)*.

1	FRISIA I	1020t	70	12.3k	63.7m	1500P	53C	-	BA	DE	7018604
2	FRISIA II	1125t	78	12.0k	63.3m	1340P	53C	-	BA	DE	7723974
3	FRISIA IV	1574t	02	12.0k	71.7m	1342P	60C	-	BA	DE	9246839
4	FRISIA V	1007t	65	11.0k	63.8m	1442P	53C	-	BA	DE	8827181
5	FRISIA VI	768t	68	12.0k	54.9m	1096P	35C	-	BA	DE	8827179
6F	FRISIA VII	363t	84	12.0k	53.0m	12P	30C	-	BA	DE	8891807
7p	FRISIA IX	571t	80	11.0k	57.0m	785P	0C	-	-	DE	7924310
8p	FRISIA X	187t	72	12.0k	36.3m	290P	0C	-	-	DE	7222308
9p	RÜM HART 2	105t	69	12.0k	35.4m	940P	0C	-	DE		-
10p	WAPPEN VON NORDENEY	154t	67	14.0k	31.1m	200P	0C	-	DE		7935395

FRISIA I, FRISIA II, FRISIA V, FRISIA VI Built by Jos L Meyer Werft, Papenburg, Germany for *Reederei Norden-Frisia*. Passenger capacities relate to the summer season. Capacity is reduced during the winter.

FRISIA IV Built by Schiffswerft und Maschinenfabrik Cassens GmbH, Emden, Germany for *Reederei Norden-Frisia* to replace the FRISIA VIII.

FRISIA VII Built by Schlömer Werft, Oldersum, Germany for *Reederei Norden-Frisia*. Conveys ro-ro freight to Norderney and Juist.

FRISIA IX, FRISIA X Built by Schiffswerft Julius Diedrich GmbH & Co. KG, Oldersum, Germany for *Reederei Norden-Frisia*. The FRISIA IX was built to convey 9 cars at the bow end but is now used in passenger-only mode. These ships are generally used for excursions.

RÜM HART 2 Built by Julius Diedrich Schiffswerft, Odersum, Germany as the BALTRUM IV for *Baltrum-Linie* of Germany. In November 1982 sold to *Wyker Dampfschiffs-Reederei* and renamed the RÜM HART 2. In March 2014 sold to *Reederei Norden-Frisia*.

WAPPEN VON NORDENEY Built by Cassens-Werft, Emden, Germany for *Reederei Norden-Frisia*. Used for excursions.

Under Construction

| 11 | FRISIA III | | 1574t | 15 | 12.0k | 71.7m | 1342P | 60C | - | BA | DE |

FRISIA III Under construction by Cassen-Werft, Emden, Germany.

POLFERRIES

THE COMPANY Polferries is the trading name of Polska Zegluga Baltycka SA (Polish Baltic Shipping Company), a Polish state-owned company.

MANAGEMENT Financial Director and Board Member Piotr Redmerski.

ADDRESS ul Portowa 41, PL 78-100 Kolobrzeg, Poland.

TELEPHONE Administration + 48 94 35 52 103, + 48 94 35 52 102, Passenger Reservations Świnoujście + 48 91 32 26 140, Gdansk + 48 58 34 31 887, Ystad + 46 40 12 17 00, Nynäshamn + 46 8 520 686 60 Freight Reservations Świnoujście + 48 91 32 26 104, Gdansk + 48 58 34 30 212, Ystad + 46 411 55 88 50, Nynäshamn + 46 8 520 202 60.

FAX Administration + 48 94 35 52 208, Passenger Reservations Świnoujście + 48 91 32 26 168, Gdansk + 48 58 34 36 574, Ystad + 46 411 55 88 51, Nynäshamn + 46 8 520 172 54 Freight Reservations Świnoujście + 48 91 32 26 169, Gdansk + 48 58 34 30 975, Ystad + 46 411 55 88 51, Nynäshamn + 46 8 520 178 01.

INTERNET Email info@polferries.pl Passenger Reservations Świnoujście boas.pax@polferries.pl Gdansk pax.gdansk@polferries.pl, Ystad info@polferries.se Nynäshamn pax.nynashamn@polferries.se Freight Reservations Świnoujście boas.cargo@polferries.pl, Gdansk cargo.gdansk@polferries.pl Ystadspedition@polferries.se Nynäshamn frakt@polferries.se Website www.polferries.pl (Polish, Danish, English, German, Swedish)

ROUTES OPERATED Świnoujście - Ystad (7 hrs; BALTIVIA, WAWEL; 2 per day), Gdansk - Nynäshamn (Sweden) (18 hrs; SCANDINAVIA; 3 per week).

1	BALTIVIA	17790t	81	19.0k	146.9m	250P	30C	80L	BA	BS	7931997
2	SCANDINAVIA	23842t	80	20.0k	146.1m	1800P	510C	38L	BA2	BS	7826788
3	WAWEL	25318t	80	19.0k	163.9m	900P	550C	75L	A2	BS	7814462

BALTIVIA Built as the SAGA STAR by Fartygsentreprenader AB, Kalmar, Sweden for TT-Saga-Line and, from 1982, used on freight services between Travemünde and Trelleborg/Malmö. (Originally ordered by Rederi AB Svea as the SAGALAND). In 1989 sold to Cie Meridionale of France, renamed the GIROLATA and used on SNCM (later CMR) services in the Mediterranean. In 1993 she was chartered back to TT-Line, resumed her original name and was used on the Travemünde - Trelleborg service. Following delivery of the ROBIN HOOD and the NILS DACKE in 1995, she was transferred to the Rostock - Trelleborg route. In July 1997 she was purchased by TT-Line and in 1998 passenger facilities were completely renovated to full ro-pax format; following the delivery of the TOM SAWYER she was transferred back to the Travemünde - Trelleborg route, operating additional freight sailings. Briefly transferred back to Rostock - Trelleborg when the charter of the TT-TRAVELLER ended. Withdrawn in 2002, sold to Transmanche Ferries and renamed the DIEPPE. In 2006 replaced by the SEVEN SISTERS, sold to Polferries, renamed the BALTIVIA and, in 2007, placed on the Gdansk Nynäshamn route. In February 2013 transferred to the Świnoujście - Ystad service.

SCANDINAVIA Built as the VISBY by Öresundsvarvet AB, Landskrona, Sweden for Rederi AB Gotland of Sweden for their services between the island of Gotland and the Swedish mainland. In 1987 the franchise to operate these services was lost by the company and awarded to Nordström & Thulin of Sweden. A subsidiary called N&T Gotlandslinjen AB was formed to operate the service. The VISBY was chartered to this company and managed by Johnson Line, remaining owned by Rederi AB Gotland. In early 1990 she was chartered to Sealink and renamed the FELICITY. After modifications, she was, in March 1990, introduced onto the Fishguard - Rosslare route. Later in 1990 she was renamed the STENA FELICITY. In Summer 1997 she was returned to Rederi AB Gotland for rebuilding, prior to her entering service with Destination Gotland in January 1998. She was renamed the VISBY. In late 2002 she was renamed the VISBORG. In March 2003 replaced by the new VISBY and laid up for sale or charter. In July sold to Polferries, renamed the SCANDINAVIA and placed on the Gdansk - Nynäshamn route.

WAWEL Built as the SCANDINAVIA by Kockums Varvet AB, Malmö, Sweden for *Rederi AB Nordö* of Sweden. After service in the Mediterranean for *UMEF*, she was, in 1981, sold to *SOMAT* of Bulgaria, renamed the TZAREVETZ and used on *Medlink* services between Bulgaria and the Middle East, later on other routes. In 1986 she was chartered to *Callitzis* of Greece for a service between Italy and Greece. In 1988 she was sold to *Sealink*, re-registered in The Bahamas and renamed the FIESTA. She was then chartered to *OT Africa Line*. During Autumn 1989 she was rebuilt at Bremerhaven to convert her for passenger use and in March 1990 she was renamed the FANTASIA and placed on the Dover - Calais service. Later in 1990 she was renamed the STENA FANTASIA. In 1998 transferred to *P&O Stena Line*. In 1999 she was renamed the P&OSL CANTERBURY. In 2002 renamed the PO CANTERBURY. In Spring 2003 replaced by the PRIDE OF CANTERBURY and laid up at Dunkerque. Later in the year sold to *GA Ferries* and renamed the ALKMINI A. In 2004 moved to Greece and, after a partial rebuild (including the welding up of the bow door) placed on the Igoumenitsa – Brindisi route. Later in 2004 sold to *Polferries* and renamed the WAWEL; rebuilt to increase the number of cabins. In 2005 placed on the Świnoujście – Ystad service.

SASSNITZ - UST LUGA FERRY

THE COMPANY The *Sassnitz - Ust Luga Ferry* is operated by *Black Sea Ferry* in partnership with *Russian Railways* and *AnRuss Trans*. *Trans-Exim* act as agents.

ADDRESS Trans-Exim, 45 Suvorova street, Kaliningrad, Russia.

TELEPHONE Administration and Reservations + 7 4012 66 04 68.

FAX Administration and Reservations + 7 4012 66 04 69.

INTERNET Email ferrytransexim.ru Website www.transexim.ru/eng *(English, Russian)*

ROUTE OPERATED Ust Luga (Russia) - Baltiysk (Kaliningrad, Russia) - Sassnitz (Germany) *(PETERSBURG;* 1 per week).

1	PETERSBURG	25353t	86	16.0k	190.8m	144P	329C	110T	A2	RU	8311883

PETERSBURG Built Mathias Thesen Werft, Wismar, East Germany as the MUKRAN for *DSR* of Germany (DDR) to operate between Mukran (Sassnitz) and Klaipėda, a joint service with *Lisco* of Lithuania. In 1994 the service was taken over by *Euroseabridge*. In 1995 she was rebuilt to introduce road vehicle and additional passenger capacity and was renamed the PETERSBURG. In 2001 she was transferred to the Kiel - Klaipėda service, replacing the sister vessel GREIFSWALD whose charter was ended. In April 2003, the service became part of *Scandlines* and she was transferred to transferred to the Karlshamn - Liepaja (Latvia) route. In 2009, the charter ended and she returned to her owners. In October 2010 she was sold to *Baltic Fleet LLC* of Russia and the following month placed on a service between Baltiysk (Kaliningrad) and Ust Luga. In June 2012 she inaugurated a new service between Sassnitz and Ust Luga via Baltiysk.

SCANDLINES

THE COMPANY In 2007, the owners of *Scandlines AG*, the Danish Ministry of Transport and Energy and Deutsche Bahn AG, decided to sell their shares. The new owner was a consortium of the 3i Group (UK), Allianz Capital Partners GmbH (Germany) (40% of the shares each) and *Deutsche Seereederei GmbH* (Germany) (20% of the shares). The company was subsequently transformed into a private limited company and now trades under the name Scandlines GmbH, uniting the companies *Scandlines Deutschland GmbH* and *Scandlines Danmark A/S*. With *Deutsche Seereederei GmbH* selling its shares in *Scandlines GmbH* in 2010, 3i and Allianz Capital Partners held 50% of the shares each. During 2012 *Stena Line* took over the Travemünde - Ventspils, Travemünde - Liepaja and Nynäshamn - Ventspils routes, took full control of the joint routes - Rostock - Trelleborg and Sassnitz - Trelleborg services and took over the vessels used. The freight-only route between Rostock and Hanko passed to *SOL*. The Helsingborg - Helsingør service remains jointly operated and continues to be branded *Scandlines*. In November 2013 3i Group purchased Allianz Capital Partners' share and now control 100% of the company.

Wawel *(John Bryant)*

Baltivia *(John Bryant)*

MANAGEMENT CEO Søren Poulsgaard Jensen, CCO Morten Haure-Petersen, Business Development Volker Schiemann.

TELEPHONE Administration *Denmark* + 45 33 15 15 15, *Germany* + 49 (0)381 5435899,

Reservations *Denmark* + 45 33 15 15 15, *Germany* + 49 (0)1802 116699.

FAX Administration *Denmark*, + 45 72 68 64 80, *Germany* + 49 (0)381 5435 678.

INTERNET Email info@scandlines.com Website www.scandlines.com *(Danish, German, English),*

ROUTES OPERATED Helsingør (Sealand, Denmark) - Helsingborg (Sweden) (25 mins; *HAMLET, TYCHO BRAHE*; every 20 mins) (joint with *Scandlines* AB of Sweden), Rødby (Lolland, Denmark) - Puttgarden (Germany) (45 mins; *DEUTSCHLAND, HOLGER DANSKE, PRINS RICHARD, PRINSESSE BENEDIKTE, SCHLESWIG-HOLSTEIN (HOLGER DANSKE specially for dangerous goods)*; half-hourly train/vehicle ferry + additional road freight-only sailings), Gedser (Falster, Denmark) - Rostock (Germany) (2 hours; *KRONPRINS FREDERIK, PRINS JOACHIM*; every 2 hours.

1	DEUTSCHLAND	15187t	97	18.5k	142.0m	1200P	364C	30Lr	BA2	DE	9151541
2	HAMLET	10067t	97	13.5k	111.2m	1000P	244C	34L	BA	DK	9150030
3F	HOLGER DANSKE	2779t	76	14.9k	86.8m	12P	-	12L	BA	DK	7432202
4	KRONPRINS FREDERIK	16071t	81	20.5k	152.0m	1082P	210C	46T	BA	DK	7803205
5	PRINS JOACHIM	16071t	80	21.0k	152.0m	922P	210c	46Lr	BA	DK	7803190
6	PRINS RICHARD	14822t	97	18.5k	142.0m	1100P	364C	36Lr	BA2	DK	9144419
7	PRINSESSE BENEDIKTE	14822t	97	18.5k	142.0m	1100P	364C	36Lr	BA2	DK	9144421
8	SCHLESWIG-HOLSTEIN	15187t	97	18.5k	142.0m	1200P	364C	30Lr	BA2	DE	9151539
9	TYCHO BRAHE	11148t	91	14.5k	111.2m	1250P	240C	35Lr	BA	DK	9007116

DEUTSCHLAND Train/vehicle ferry built by Van der Giessen-de Noord, Krimpen aan den IJssel, Rotterdam, The Netherlands for *DFO* for the Puttgarden - Rødby service. During Winter 2003/04 a new hoistable deck was added for cars by Neptun Yard Rostock, (Germany).

HAMLET Road vehicle ferry built by Finnyards, Rauma, Finland for *Scandlines* (50% owned by *Scandlines* AG and 50% owned by *Scandlines* AB of Sweden) for the Helsingør - Helsingborg service. Sister vessel of the TYCHO BRAHE but without rail tracks.

HOLGER DANSKE Built by Aalborg Værft A/S, Aalborg, Denmark as a train/vehicle ferry for *DSB* for the Helsingør - Helsingborg service. In 1991 transferred to the Kalundborg - Samsø route (no rail facilities). In 1997 transferred to subsidiary *SFDS A/S*. Withdrawn at the end of November 1998 when the service passed to *Samsø Linien*. In 1999 began operating between Rødby and Puttgarden as a road-freight-only vessel, carrying, among others, loads which cannot be conveyed on passenger vessels.

KRONPRINS FREDERIK Train/vehicle ferry built by Nakskov Skibsværft A/S, Nakskov, Denmark for *DSB* for the Nyborg - Korsør service. Withdrawn in 1997. After conversion to a car/lorry ferry, she was transferred to the Gedser - Rostock route (no rail facilities).

PRINS JOACHIM Train/vehicle ferry, built by Nakskov Skibsværft A/S, Nakskov, Denmark for *DSB* for the Nyborg - Korsør service. Withdrawn in 1997 and laid up. During Winter 2000/2001 modified in the same way as KRONPRINS FREDERIK and transferred to the Gedser - Rostock route.

PRINS RICHARD, PRINSESSE BENEDIKTE Train/vehicle ferries, built by Ørskov Christensen Staalskibsværft A/S, Frederikshavn, Denmark for *Scandlines A/S* for the Rødby - Puttgarden service. During Winter 2003/04 a new hoistable deck was added for cars by Neptun Yard Rostock, (Germany).

SCHLESWIG-HOLSTEIN Train/vehicle ferry built by Van der Giessen-de Noord, Krimpen aan den IJssel, Rotterdam, The Netherlands for *DFO* for the Puttgarden - Rødby service. During Winter 2003/04 a new hoistable deck was added for cars by Neptun Yard Rostock, (Germany).

TYCHO BRAHE Train/vehicle ferry, built by Tangen Verft A/S, Tomrefjord, Norway for *DSB* for the Helsingør - Helsingborg service.

Under Construction

| 10 | BERLIN | 24000t | 14 | 20.5k | 169.0m | 1500P | 480C | 96L | BA2 | DK | 9587855 |
| 11 | COPENHAGEN | 24000t | 14 | 20.5k | 169.0m | 1500P | 480C | 96L | BA2 | DK | 9587867 |

BERLIN, COPENHAGEN Partly built by Volkswerft Stralsund, Stralsund, Germany for *Scandlines* to operate on the Gedser - Rostock route. The propulsion system allows for adaption to LNG. Originally due to enter service in Spring 2012, the construction of these vessels was seriously delayed. It was then found that the vessels did not meet the specification and the order was cancelled. The BERLIN was 90% finished and had undertaken sea trials; the COPENHAGEN had been launched and was 50% finished. In March 2014 *Scandlines* purchased the two vessels and they were towed to Blohm + Voss Shipyards, Hamburg and then to Fayard Shipyard, Odense, to be completed and modified to make them suitable for the Gedser - Rostock route. They are expected to enter service in 2015.

SMYRIL LINE

THE COMPANY *Smyril Line* is a Faroe Islands company.

MANAGEMENT **Admin. Director** Mr. Rúni Vang Poulsen, **Accounting and Department Manager**, Ms. Nina Djurhuus.

ADDRESS Yviri við Strond 1, PO Box 370, 110 Tórshavn, Faroe Islands.

TELEPHONE **Administration & Reservations** + 298-345900.

FAX + 298-345901.

INTERNET **Email** office@smyrilline.com **Website** www.smyrilline.com *(English, French, Dutch German)* www.smyrilline.fo *(Danish, Faroese, Icelandic)*

ROUTES OPERATED *Winter/Early Spring* Tórshavn (Faroes) - Hirtshals (Denmark) (36 hrs; *NORRÖNA*; 1 per week), *Spring/Early Summer/Autumn* Tórshavn - Hirtshals (36 hrs; *NORRÖNA*; 1 per week), Tórshavn - Seyðisfjördur (Iceland) (19 hrs; *NORRÖNA*; 1 per week), *Summer* Tórshavn - Hirtshals (Denmark) (30 hrs; *NORRÖNA*; 2 per week), Tórshavn - Seyðisfjördur (Iceland) (19 hrs; *NORRÖNA*; 2 per week).

| 1 | NORRÖNA | 35966t | 03 | 21.0k | 164.0m | 1482P | 800C | 134T | BA | FO | 9227390 |

NORRÖNA Built by Flender Werft, Lübeck, Germany for *Smyril Line*, to replace the existing NORRÖNA. Originally due to enter service in Summer 2002, start of building was delayed by financing difficulties. She was to have been built at Flensburger Schiffbau-Gesellschaft, Flensburg, Germany, but delays in arranging finance led to change of shipyard.

ST. PETER LINE

THE COMPANY *St. Peter Line* is a Russian owned, EU registered private sector company.

MANAGEMENT **CEO** Andrey Mushkarev.

ADDRESS Ostrovskogo sq. 7, St. Petersburg, 191025 Russia.

TELEPHONE *Russia* + 7 812 386-11 47, *Finland* + 358 (0)9 6187 2000.

INTERNET **Email** sales@stpeterline.com **Website** www.stpeterline.ru *(Russian, English, Estonian, Finnish, Swedish)*

ROUTES OPERATED Helsinki (Finland) - St Petersburg (Russia) (12 hours 30 mins; *PRINCESS MARIA*; 3/4 per week), St Petersburg - Helsinki - Stockholm - Tallinn - St Petersburg; *SPL PRINCESS ANASTASIA*; 1/2 per week).

| 1 | PRINCESS MARIA | 34093t | 81 | 20.0k | 168.1m | 1638P | 360C | 54T | A | MT | 7911533 |
| 2 | SPL PRINCESS ANASTASIA | 37583t | 86 | 22.0k | 177.0m | 2500P | 380C | 42L | BA | MT | 8414582 |

PRINCESS MARIA Built as the FINLANDIA by Oy Wärtsilä Ab, Turku, Finland for *EFFOA* of Finland for *Silja Line* services between Helsinki and Stockholm. In 1990 she was sold to *DFDS*, renamed the QUEEN

Skåne (*Frank Lose*)

Kronprins Frederik (*Frank Lose*)

OF SCANDINAVIA and introduced onto the Copenhagen - Helsingborg - Oslo service. In 2000 rebuilt at Gdynia. In 2001 transferred to the Newcastle - IJmuiden route. In May 2007 moved to the Newcastle - Norway route. This service ended at the end of August 2008 and she was laid up. In 2009 used for ten weeks as an accommodation vessel at Oskarshamn and in December in Copenhagen. In April 2010 time chartered to *Inflot Cruise and Ferry Ltd* of Russia for three years for use by *St. Peter Line* and in renamed the PRINCESS MARIA.

SPL PRINCESS ANASTASIA Built as the OLYMPIA by Oy Wärtsilä Ab, Turku, Finland for *Rederi AB Slite* of Sweden for *Viking Line* service between Stockholm and Helsinki. In 1993 she was chartered to *P&O European Ferries* to inaugurate a new service between Portsmouth and Bilbao. Renamed the PRIDE OF BILBAO. During the summer period she also operated, at weekends, a round trip between Portsmouth and Cherbourg. In 1994 she was purchased by the *Irish Continental Group* and re-registered in the Bahamas. In 2002 her charter was extended for a further five years and again for a further three years from October 2007. The Cherbourg service ended at the end of 2004. In September 2010 redelivered to *Irish Continental Group*. In October 2010 renamed the BILBAO. In November 2010 chartered to *St. Peter Line*, in February 2011 renamed the SPL PRINCESS ANASTASIA and in April 2011 inaugurated a new Stockholm - St Petersburg service. In February 2011 purchased by an associated company of *St. Peter Line*. During January and February 2014 she served as a floating hotel at the Winter Olympics in Sochi, Russia.

STENA LINE

THE COMPANY *Stena Line Scandinavia AB* is a Swedish private sector company. During 2012, the operations of subsidiary *Scandlines AB* of Sweden were absorbed and some of the Baltic operations and vessels of *Scandlines GmbH* of Germany were taken over.

MANAGEMENT CEO Carl-Johan Hagman, **Communication Director** Joakim Kenndal.

ADDRESS 405 19 Gothenburg, Sweden (*Visitors' address* Danmarksterminalen, Masthuggskajen, Gothenburg, Sweden).

TELEPHONE Administration + 46 (0)31-85 80 00, **Reservations** + 46 (0)31-704 00 00.

FAX Administration & Reservations + 46 (0)31-24 10 38.

INTERNET Email info@stenaline.com Website www.stenaline.com (*Czech, Danish, Dutch, English, French, German, Latvian, Lithuanian, Norwegian, Polish, Russian, Swedish*)

ROUTES OPERATED *Stena Line branded routes* **Conventional Ferries** Gothenburg (Sweden) - Frederikshavn (Denmark) (3 hrs 15 mins; *STENA DANICA, STENA JUTLANDICA*; up to 6 per day), Gothenburg - Kiel (Germany) (14 hrs; *STENA GERMANICA, STENA SCANDINAVICA*; 1 per day), Frederikshavn - Oslo (Norway) (8 hrs 45 mins; *STENA SAGA*; 1 per day), Varberg (Sweden) - Grenaa (Denmark) (4 hrs; *STENA NAUTICA*; 2 per day), Karlskrona (Sweden) - Gdynia (Poland) (10 hrs 30 mins; *STENA BALTICA, STENA SPIRIT, STENA VISION*; 2 per day), Rostock (Germany) - Trelleborg (Sweden) (5 hrs 45 mins (7 hrs night); *MECKLENBURG-VORPOMMERN, SKÅNE*; 3 per day)), Sassnitz (Germany) - Trelleborg (3 hrs 45 mins; *SASSNITZ, TRELLEBORG*; 4-5 per day), Travemünde (Germany) - Ventspils (Latvia) (25 hrs; *STENA FLAVIA*; 2 per week), Travemünde (Germany) - Liepaja (Latvia) (28 hrs 30 mins; *ASK, URD*; 4 per week), Nynäshamn (Sweden) – Ventspils (Latvia) (12 hrs; *SCOTTISH VIKING, STENA FLAVIA*; 3 per week). **Freight Ferry** Gothenburg - Frederikshavn (Train Ferry) (3 hrs 45 mins; *STENA SCANRAIL*; 2 per day).

Scandlines branded route (joint with Scandlines) Helsingør (Sealand, Denmark) - Helsingborg (Sweden) (25 mins; *AURORA AF HELSINGBORG, HAMLET, MERCANDIA IV*; up to every 15 mins).

1	ASK	13144t	82	18.0k	171.0m	186P	-	104T	AS	DK	7826867
2	AURORA AF HELSINGBORG	10918t	92	14.0k	111.2m	1250P	225C	25Lr	BA	SE	9007128
3	MECKLENBURG-VORPOMMERN	36185t	96	22.0k	199.9m	600P	445C	230Tr	A2	DE	9131797
4	MERCANDIA IV	4296t	89	13.0k	95.0m	420P	170C	18L	BA	DK	8611685
5	MERCANDIA VIII	4296t	87	13.0k	95.0m	420P	170C	18L	BA	DK	8611623

Smyril (*Peter Therkildsen*)

Spl Princess Anastasia (*Nick Widdows*)

6	SASSNITZ	21154t	89	18.5k	171.5m	875P	314C	50Tr	BA2	DE	8705383
7	SCOTTISH VIKING	26500t	09	24.0k	186.5m	800P	185C	120L	A	IT	9435454
8	SKÅNE	42705t	98	21.0k	200.2m	600P	520C	240Tr	AS2	SE	9133915
9	STENA BALTICA	22542t	07	23.0k	167.0m	160P	-	140L	BA2	UK	9364978
10»	STENA CARISMA	8631t	97	40.0k	88.0m	900P	210C	-	A	SE	9127760
11	STENA DANICA	28727t	83	19.5k	154.9m	2274P	555C	120T	BAS2	SE	7907245
12	STENA FLAVIA	26904t	08	24.0k	186.5m	852P	185C	120L	A	UK	9417919
13	STENA GERMANICA	44372t	01	22.0k	240.1m	900P	-	250L	BA	SE	9145176
14	STENA JUTLANDICA	29691t	96	21.5k	183.7m	1500P	550C	156T	BAS2	SE	9125944
15	STENA NAUTICA	19504t	86	19.4k	134.0m	700P	330C	70T	BA2	SE	8317954
16	STENA SAGA	33750t	81	22.0k	166.1m	2000P	510C	76T	BA	SE	7911545
17	STENA SCANDINAVICA	55050t	03	22.0k	240.1m	900P	-	260L	BA	SE	9235517
18	STENA SCANRAIL	7504t	73	16.5k	142.4m	65P	-	64Tr	A	SE	7305772
19	STENA SPIRIT	39169t	88	20.0k	175.4m	2400P	550C	120T	BAS2	BS	7907661
20	STENA VISION	39178t	87	20.0k	175.4m	2400P	550C	120T	BAS2	SE	7907659
21	TRELLEBORG	20028t	82	21.0k	170.2m	900P	200C	90Tr	A2	SE	7925297
22	URD	13144t	81	17.5k	171.0m	186P	-	104T	AS	DK	7826855

ASK Built as the LUCKY RIDER by Nuovi Cantieri Apuania S.P.A., Marina De Carrara, Italy, a ro-ro freight ferry, for *Delpa Maritime* of Greece. In 1985 she was acquired by *Stena Line* and renamed the STENA DRIVER. Later that year she was acquired by *Sealink British Ferries* and renamed the SEAFREIGHT FREEWAY to operate freight-only services between Dover and Dunkerque. In 1988 she was sold to *SOMAT* of Bulgaria for use on *Medlink* services in the Mediterranean and renamed the SERDICA. In 1990 she was sold and renamed the NORTHERN HUNTER. In 1991 she was sold to *Blæsbjerg* of Denmark, renamed the ARKA MARINE and chartered to *DSB*. She was then converted into a ro-pax vessel, renamed the ASK and introduced onto the Århus - Kalundborg service. Purchased by *Scandlines A/S* of Denmark in 1997. In 1999 she was, after some modification, transferred to *Scandlines Euroseabridge* and placed on the Travemünde - Klaipéda route. In 2000 she was transferred to the Rostock - Liepaja route. Lengthened by 20m in 2001 and, in late 2001, chartered to *Nordö Link* to operate between Travemünde and Malmö. In late 2002 replaced by the FINNARROW and returned to *Scandlines*. She was transferred to the Rostock - Trelleborg route whilst the MECKLENBURG-VORPOMMERN was being rebuilt. She was then transferred to the Kiel - Klaipéda route. In 2003 chartered to *Scandlines AB* to operate on the Trelleborg - Travemünde route. In April 2005 the charter ended and she returned to *Scandlines AG*. Initially she was due to replace the FELLOW on the Nynäshamn – Ventspils route during her annual refit. In Autumn 2005 moved to the Rostock - Ventspils route. In January 2009 moved to the Nynäshamn – Ventspils route. In January 2011 moved to the Travemünde - Liepaja route. In May 2011 laid up. In November introduced as second vessel. In September 2012 sold to *Stena Line*.

AURORA AF HELSINGBORG Train/vehicle ferry built by Langsten Verft A/S, Tomrefjord, Norway for *SweFerry* for *ScandLines* joint *DSB/SweFerry* service between Helsingør and Helsingborg. Now owned by *Scandlines AB* (subsidiary of *Stena Line*) (previously leased from finance company).

MECKLENBURG-VORPOMMERN Train/vehicle ferry built by Schichau Seebeckwerft, Bremerhaven, Germany for *DFO* for the Rostock - Trelleborg service. During Winter 2002/03 modified to increase freight capacity and reduce passenger capacity. In September 2012 sold to *Stena Line*.

MERCANDIA IV Built as the SUPERFLEX NOVEMBER by North East Shipbuilders Ltd, Sunderland, UK for *Vognmandsruten* of Denmark. In 1989 sold to *Mercandia* and renamed the MERCANDIA IV. In 1990 she began operating on their *Kattegatbroen* Juelsminde - Kalundborg service. In 1996 she was transferred to their *Sundbroen* Helsingør - Helsingborg service. In 1997 the service and vessel were leased to *HH-Ferries*. In 1999 she was purchased by *HH-Ferries*. She has been equipped to carry dangerous cargo.

MERCANDIA VIII Built as the SUPERFLEX BRAVO by North East Shipbuilders Ltd, Sunderland, UK for *Vognmandsruten* of Denmark and used on their services between Nyborg and Korsør and Copenhagen (Tuborg Havn) and Landskrona (Sweden). In 1991 she was chartered to *Scarlett Line* to operate on the

Copenhagen and Landskrona route. In 1993 she was renamed the SVEA SCARLETT but later in the year the service ceased and she was laid up. In 1996 she was purchased by *Mercandia*, renamed the MERCANDIA VIII and placed on their *Sundbroen* Helsingør - Helsingborg service. In 1997 the service and vessel were leased to *HH-Ferries*. In 1999 she was purchased by *HH-Ferries*. Now reserve vessel.

SASSNITZ Train/vehicle ferry built by Danyard A/S, Frederikshavn, Denmark for *Deutsche Reichsbahn*. In 1993 ownership transferred to *DFO*. Used on the Sassnitz - Trelleborg service. In September 2012 sold to *Stena Line*.

SCOTTISH VIKING Built by CN Visentini, Porto Viro, Italy for *Epic Shipping* of the UK and chartered to *Norfolkline*. Operated between Zeebrugge and Rosyth until December 2010. In January 2010 chartered to *Scandlines* and placed on the Nynäshamn - Ventspils service. In September 2012 charter transferred to *Stena Line*.

SKÅNE Train/vehicle ferry built by Astilleros Españoles, Cadiz, Spain for an American trust and chartered to *Scandlines*. She is used on the Trelleborg - Rostock service.

STENA BALTICA Built as the COTENTIN by STX Finland, Helsinki, Finland for *Brittany Ferries*. Used on freight service from Poole to Cherbourg and Santander. In March 2013 replaced by the BARFLEUR (operating to Cherbourg only). During summer 2013 operated twice weekly from Poole to Bilbao and Santander. In October 2013 sold to *Stena RoRo* and renamed the STENA BALTICA. In November 2013 chartered to *Stena Line* and replaced the STENA ALEGRA on the Karlskrona - Gdynia route.

STENA CARISMA Westamarin HSS 900 craft built at Kristiansand, Norway for *Stena Line* for the Gothenburg - Frederikshavn service. Work on a sister vessel, approximately 30% completed, was ceased. Not due to operate during 2014.

STENA DANICA Built by Chantiers du Nord et de la Méditerranée, Dunkerque, France for *Stena Line* for the Gothenburg - Frederikshavn service.

STENA FLAVIA Built by CN Visentini, Porto Viro, Italy for *Epic Shipping* of the UK. Launched as the WATLING STREET. On delivery, chartered to *ISCOMAR* of Spain and renamed the PILAR DEL MAR. In 2009 laid up until February 2010 when she was chartered to *Acciona Trasmediterranea* of Spain and operated between Barcelona and Tangiers. Later that month, chartered to *T-Link* and resumed the name WATLING STREET. In May 2011 chartered to *Scandlines* and placed on the Travemünde - Ventspils service. In April 2012, sold to *Stena RoRo*; she continued to be chartered to *Scandlines*. In September 2012 charter transferred to *Stena Line*. In April 2013 renamed the STENA FLAVIA. Now also operates once weekly Ventspils - Travemünde.

STENA GERMANICA Ro-pax ferry built as the STENA HOLLANDICA by Astilleros Españoles, Cadiz, Spain for *Stena RoRo* and chartered to *Stena Line BV* to operate between Hook of Holland and Harwich. In 2007 lengthened by 50m at Lloyd Werft, Bremerhaven and passenger capacity increased to 900. Between May and August 2010 refurbished at Gdansk and had an 100 additional cabins added. At the end of August entered service on the Gothenburg - Kiel route, renamed the STENA GERMANICA III. In September, after the previous STENA GERMANICA had been renamed the STENA VISION, she was renamed the STENA GERMANICA.

STENA JUTLANDICA Train/vehicle 'ro-pax' vessel built by Van der Giessen-de Noord, Krimpen aan den IJssel, Rotterdam, The Netherlands for *Stena Line* to operate between Gothenburg and Frederikshavn. She was launched as the STENA JUTLANDICA III and renamed on entry into service.

STENA NAUTICA Built as the NIELS KLIM by Nakskov Skibsværft A/S, Nakskov, Denmark for *DSB (Danish State Railways)* for their service between Århus (Jutland) and Kalundborg (Sealand). In 1990 she was purchased by *Stena Rederi* of Sweden and renamed the STENA NAUTICA. In 1992 she was chartered to *B&I Line*, renamed the ISLE OF INNISFREE and introduced onto the Rosslare - Pembroke Dock service, replacing the MUNSTER (8093t, 1970). In 1993 she was transferred to the Dublin - Holyhead service. In early 1995 she was chartered to *Lion Ferry*. She was renamed the LION KING. In 1996 she was replaced by a new LION KING and renamed the STENA NAUTICA. During Summer 1996 she was chartered to *Trasmediterranea* of Spain but returned to *Stena RoRo* in the autumn and remained laid up during 1997. In December 1997 she was chartered to *Stena Line* and placed on the Halmstad - Grenaa route. This route ended on 31st January 1999 and she was transferred to the Varberg - Grenaa route. During Winter 2001/02 she was rebuilt to heighten the upper vehicle deck and allow separate

Mecklenburg-Vorpommern *(Frank Lose)*

Stena Danica *(Miles Cowsill)*

Stena Jutlandicia (*Miles Cowsill*)

Stena Carisma (*Miles Cowsill*)

loading of vehicle decks; passenger capacity was reduced. On 16th February 2004 she was hit by the coaster JOANNA and holed. Returned to service at the end of May 2004 after repairs at Gothenburg and Gdansk.

STENA SAGA Built as the SILVIA REGINA by Oy Wärtsilä Ab, Turku, Finland for *Stockholms Rederi AB Svea* of Sweden. She was registered with subsidiary company *Svea Line* of Turku, Finland and was used on *Silja Line* services between Stockholm and Helsinki. In 1981 she was sold to *Johnson Line* and in 1984 sold to a Finnish Bank and chartered back. In 1990 she was purchased by *Stena RoRo* of Sweden for delivery in 1991. In 1991 she was renamed the STENA BRITANNICA and took up service on the Hook of Holland - Harwich service for Dutch subsidiary *Stena Line BV*, operating with a British crew. In 1994 she was transferred to the Oslo - Frederikshavn route and renamed the STENA SAGA. During Winter 2002/03 rebuilt to increase passenger capacity by 200.

STENA SCANDINAVICA Ro-pax vessel built by Hyundai Heavy Industries, Ulsan, South Korea, for *Stena RoRo*. Launched and delivered in January 2003 as the STENA BRITANNICA II. Chartered to *Stena Line* for use on the Hook of Holland - Harwich service, replacing the 2000-built STENA BRITANNICA, now the FINNFELLOW of *FinnLink*. In March 2003 renamed the STENA BRITANNICA. In 2007 lengthened at Lloyd Werft, Bremerhaven. In September 2010 renamed the BRITANNICA. Between October 2010 and April 2011 refurbished and had 100 additional cabins added at Gdansk. In April 2011 renamed the STENA SCANDINAVICA IV and entered service on the Gothenburg - Kiel route. In May, after the previous STENA SCANDINAVICA had been renamed the STENA SPIRIT, she was renamed the STENA SCANDINAVICA.

STENA SCANRAIL Built by Van der Giessen-de Noord, Krimpen aan den IJssel, Rotterdam, The Netherlands. Launched as the STENA SEATRADER for *Stena AB* and entered service as the SEATRADER. In 1976 she was lengthened and then demise-chartered to *Bahjah Navigation* of Cyprus and renamed the BAHJAN. In 1981 the charter ended and she was renamed the STENA SEARIDER. In 1983 chartered to *Snowdrop Shipping* of Cyprus and renamed the SEARIDER. The charter ended the following year and she resumed the name STENA SEARIDER. Later in 1984 she was renamed the TRUCKER and in 1985 again reverted to the name STENA SEARIDER. In 1987 she was converted to a train ferry to operate between Gothenburg and Frederikshavn, chartered to *Stena Line* and renamed the STENA SCANRAIL.

STENA SPIRIT Built as the STENA SCANDINAVICA by Stocznia i Komuni Paryski, Gdynia, Poland for *Stena Line* for the Gothenburg - Kiel service (launched as the STENA GERMANICA and names swapped with sister vessel before delivery). There were originally intended to be four vessels. Only two were delivered to *Stena Line*. The third (due to be called the STENA POLONICA) was sold by the builders as an unfinished hull to *Fred. Olsen Lines* of Norway and then resold to *ANEK* of Greece who had her completed at Perama and delivered as EL VENIZELOS for service between Greece and Italy. The fourth hull (due to be called the STENA BALTICA) was sold to *A Lelakis* of Greece and was to be rebuilt as a cruise ship to be called REGENT SKY; however, the project was never completed. The hull was broken up in 2004. During the summer period on some days, the vessel arriving in Gothenburg overnight from Kiel operates a round trip to Frederikshavn before departing for Kiel the following evening. During Winter 1998/99 she was modified to increase freight capacity and reduce the number of cabins. In April 2011 replaced by the former STENA BRITANNICA (renamed the STENA SCANDINAVICA IV) and entered CityVarvet in Gothenburg for refurbishment. In June 2011 she was renamed the STENA SPIRIT and, in July 2011, transferred to the Karlskrona - Gydnia route.

STENA VISION Built as the STENA GERMANICA by Stocznia im Lenina, Gdansk, Poland for *Stena Line* for the Gothenburg - Kiel service. During the summer period on some days, the vessel arriving in Gothenburg overnight from Kiel operates a round trip to Frederikshavn before departing for Kiel the following evening. During Winter 1998/99 modified to increase freight capacity and reduce the number of cabins. In August 2010 replaced by the former STENA HOLLANDICA (renamed the STENA GERMANICA III initially) and entered CityVarvet in Gothenburg for refurbishment. In September she was renamed the STENA VISION and, in November, transferred to the Karlskrona - Gydnia route.

TRELLEBORG Train/vehicle ferry built by Öresundsvarvet AB, Landskrona, Sweden for *Svelast* of Sweden (an *SJ* subsidiary). In 1990 ownership transferred to *SweFerry*. She is used on the Trelleborg - Sassnitz service.

URD Built as the EASY RIDER by Nouvi Cantieri Aquania SpA, Venice, Italy, a ro-ro freight ferry, for *Delpa Maritime* of Greece and used on Mediterranean services. In 1985 she was acquired by *Sealink British Ferries* and renamed the SEAFREIGHT HIGHWAY to operate a freight-only service between Dover and Dunkerque. In 1988 she was sold to *SOMAT* of Bulgaria for use on *Medlink* services in the Mediterranean and renamed the BOYANA. In 1990 she was sold to *Blæsbjerg* of Denmark, renamed the AKTIV MARINE and chartered to *DSB*. In 1991 she was converted into a ro-pax vessel, renamed the URD and introduced onto the Århus - Kalundborg service. Purchased by *Scandlines* in 1997. Withdrawn at the end of May 1999 and, after modification, transferred to the *Balticum Seaways* (later *Scandlines Balticum Seaways*) Århus - Aabenraa - Klaipėda route. In 2001 lengthened and moved to the Rostock - Liepaja route. In Autumn 2005 this route became Rostock - Ventspils. Withdrawn from Rostock - Ventspils in November 2009. Vessel inaugurated new service Travemünde - Ventspils in January 2010. Replaced by the WATLING STREET in May 2011 and moved to the Travemünde - Liepaja route. In October 2012 sold to *Sol Dru A/S* (a subsidiary of *Swedish Orient Line*) and chartered to *Stena Line*. In August 2013 sold to *Stena Line*.

SYLTFÄHRE

THE COMPANY *Syltfähre* (*Syltfærge* in Danish) is the trading name of *Römö-Sylt Linie GmbH & Co. KG*, a German private sector company, a subsidiary of *FRS* (*Förde Reederei Seetouristik*) of Flensburg.

MANAGEMENT **Managing Director** Birte Dettmers, **CEO** Christian Baumberger, Götz Becker, Jan Kruse.

ADDRESS *Germany* Hafenstraße, 25992 List, Germany, *Denmark* Kilebryggen, 6792 Rømø, Denmark.

TELEPHONE **Administration** + 49 (0)461 864 0, **Reservations** + 49 (0)461 864 601.

INTERNET **Email** info@rsl.de **Website** www.syltfaehre.de *(Danish, English, German)*

ROUTE OPERATED List auf Sylt (Sylt, Germany) - Havneby (Rømø, Denmark) (approx. 40 mins; SYLTEXPRESS; variable - approx two-hourly). **Note:** The island of Rømø is linked to the Danish mainland by a toll-free road causeway; the island of Sylt is linked to the German mainland by a rail-only causeway on which cars are conveyed on shuttle wagons.

1	SYLTEXPRESS	3650t	05	16.0k	88.2m	600P	80C	10L	BA	CY	9321823

SYLTEXPRESS Built by Fiskerstrand Verft A/S, Aalesund, Norway for *Römö-Sylt Linie*.

STRANDFARASKIP LANDSINS

THE COMPANY *Strandfaraskip Landsins* is owned by the Faroe Islands Government.

ADDRESS Sjógøta 5, Postboks 30, 810 Tvøroyri, Faroe Islands.

TELEPHONE **Administration** + 298 34 30 30, **Reservations** + 298 34 30 00.

FAX **Administration & Reservations** + 298 34 30 01.

INTERNET **Email** fyrisitingssl.fo **Website** www.ssl.fo *(Faroese)*

ROUTES OPERATED **Passenger and Car Ferries** Tórshavn (Streymoy) - Tvøroyri (Suduroy) (1 hr 50 mins; SMYRIL; up to 2 per day), Klaksvík - Syðradali (20 min; SAM; up to 6 per day), Skopun – Gamlarætt (30 mins; TEISTIN; up to 9 per day). **Passenger-only Ferries** Sørvágur - Mykines (1 hr 15 mins; SILJA STAR/FROYUR *(chartered ships)*; up to 3 per day), Hvannasund - Svínoy (40 mins) - Kirkja (20 mins) - Hatlarvik (10 mins) - Svínoy (30 mins; RITAN; up to 4 per day), Sandur - Skúvoy (35 mins; SILDBERIN; up to 5 per day), Tórshavn - Nólsoy (25 mins; TERNAN; up to 5 per day).

1p	RITAN	81t	71	10.5k	22.1m	125P	0C	0L	-	FO	
2	SAM	217t	75	9.7k	30.2m	115P	17C	-	A	FO	7602168
3p	SILDBERIN	34t	79	7.5k	11.2m	30P	0C	0L	-	FO	
4	SMYRIL	12670t	05	21.0k	135.0m	976P	200C	32L	A	FO	9275218
5p	SÚLAN	11t	87	-	12.0m	40P	0C	0L	-	FO	
6	TEISTIN	1260t	01	11.0k	45.0m	288P	33C	2L	BA	FO	9226102

| 7 | TERNAN | 927t | 80 | 12.0k | 39.7m | 319P | 0C | 0L | BA | FO | 7947154 |

RITAN Built by Monnickenda, Volendam, The Netherlands. Used on the Hvannasund – Svínoy-Kirkja-Hattarvik service.

SAM Built by Blaalid Slip & Mek Verksted, Raudeberg, Norway. Used on the Klaksvik - Syòradali route and the Leirvik - Syòradali route.

SILDBERIN Built at Tvøroyri, Faroe Islands. Used on the Sandur - Skúvoy route.

SMYRIL Built by IZAR, San Fernando, Spain for *Strandfaraskip Landsins*. Operates on the Tórshavn – Tvøroyri service.

SÚLAN Built by Faaborg Værft A/S, Faaborg, Denmark. Used on the Sørvágur - Mykines service.

TEISTIN Built by P/F Skipasmidjan a Skala, Skala, Faroe Islands for *Strandfaraskip Landsins*. Used on the Skopun – Gamlarætt service.

TERNAN Built by Tórshavnar Skipasmidja P/f, Tórshavn, Faroe Islands for *Strandfaraskip Landsins*. Used on the Tórshavn –Nólsoy service.

TALLINK/SILJA LINE

THE COMPANY AS *Tallink Grupp* is an Estonian private sector company. *Tallink Silja Oy* is a Finnish subsidiary, *Tallink Silja AB* is a Swedish subsidiary.

MANAGEMENT *AS Tallink Grupp:* Chairman of Management Board Enn Pant, *Tallink Silja Oy* Managing Director Margus Schults, *Tallink Silja AB* Managing Director Kadri Land.

ADDRESSES *AS Tallink Grupp* Sadama 5/7, Tallinn 10111, Estonia, *Tallink Silja Oy* P.O. Box 100, 00181 Helsinki, Finland, *Tallink Silja AB* Box 27295, 10253 Stockholm, Sweden.

TELEPHONE *AS Tallink Grupp* + 372 (0)640 9800, *Tallink Silja Oy* Administration + 358 (0)9 18041, Reservations + 358 (0)600 15700 and + 358 (0)600 15700, *Tallink Silja AB* Administration + 46 (0)8 6663300, Reservations + 46 (0)8 222140.

FAX *AS Tallink Grupp* Administration + 372 (0)640 9810, *Tallink Silja Oy* Administration + 358 (0)9 1804262, *Tallink Silja AB* Administration + 46 (0) 8 6638149.

INTERNET www.tallinksilja.com (*English, Danish, Estonian, Finnish, German, Latvia, Norwegian, Swedish, Russian),* www.tallink.com (corporate site)

ROUTES OPERATED Tallink branded services *Passenger Ferries* Helsinki - Tallinn: *Shuttle* (2 hrs; STAR, SUPERSTAR; 5 per day), *Cruise Ferry* (3 hrs 30 mins; *BALTIC QUEEN;* 1 per day), Stockholm - Mariehamn (Åland) - Tallin (14 hrs; *ROMANTIKA, VICTORIA I;* daily), Stockholm - Riga (Latvia) (16 hrs; *ISABELLE;* alternate days), *Freight-only Ferries* Kapellskär - Paldiski (9 hrs - 11 hrs; *REGAL STAR,* 1 per day), Stockholm (Sweden) - Turku (Finland) (10 hrs 45 mins; *SEA WIND;* 1 per day).

Silja Line branded services Helsinki (Finland) - Mariehamn (Åland) - Stockholm (Sweden) (16 hrs; *SILJA SERENADE, SILJA SYMPHONY;* 1 per day), Turku (Finland) - Mariehamn (Åland) (day)/Långnäs (Åland) (night) - Stockholm (11 hrs; *BALTIC PRINCESS, GALAXY;* 2 per day).

1	ATLANTIC VISION	30285t	02	27.9k	203.3m	728P	695C	110L	BA2	CY	9211509
2	BALTIC PRINCESS	48300t	08	24.5k	212.0m	2800P	300C	82T	BA	EE	9354284
3	BALTIC QUEEN	48300t	09	24.5k	212.0m	2800P	300C	82T	BA	EE	9443255
4	DELTA SPIRIT LODGE	34414t	85	22.0k	170.7m	2000P	400C	80T	BA	LV	8306498
5	GALAXY	48915t	06	22.0k	212.0m	2800P	300C	82T	BA	SE	9333694
6	ISABELLE	35154t	89	21.5k	170.9m	2420P	364C	30T	BA	LV	8700723
7F	REGAL STAR	15281t	00	17.5k	156.6m	100P	-	120T	A	EE	9087116
8	REGINA BALTICA	18345t	80	21.3k	145.2m	1450P	500C	68T	BA	LV	7827225
9	ROMANTIKA	40803t	02	22.0k	193.8m	2178P	300C	82T	BA	LV	9237589
10F	SEA WIND	15879t	72	17.5k	154.4m	260P	55C	88Tr	BAS	SE	7128332
11	SILJA EUROPA	59912t	93	21.5k	201.8m	3000P	400C	68T	BA	EE	8919805

12	SILJA SERENADE	58376t	90	21.0k	203.0m	2641P	450C	70T	BA	FI	8715259
13	SILJA SYMPHONY	58377t	91	21.0k	203.0m	2641P	450C	70T	BA	SE	8803769
14	STAR	36249t	07	27.5k	185.0m	1900P	450C	120L	BA	EE	9364722
15	SUPERSTAR	36000t	08	29.0k	175.0m	1800P	600C	140T	BA	EE	9365398
16	VICTORIA I	40975t	04	22.0k	193.8m	2500P	300C	823T	BA	EE	9281281

ATLANTIC VISION Built as the SUPERFAST IX by Howaldtswerke Deutsche Werft AG, Kiel, Germany for *Attica Enterprises* for use by *Superfast Ferries*. She operated between Rostock and Södertälje from January until April 2002. In May 2002 she began operating between Rosyth and Zeebrugge (with the SUPERFAST X). In 2004 fitted with additional cabins and conference/seating areas. In 2005 transferred to the Rostock – Hanko (later Helsinki) route. In 2006 sold to *Tallink*. In October 2008 chartered to *Marine Atlantic* of Canada to operate on the North Sydney-Port aux Basques service and renamed the ATLANTIC VISION.

BALTIC PRINCESS Built by Aker Yards, Helsinki. A large part of the hull was built at St Nazaire, France. In August 2008 replaced the GALAXY on the Tallinn - Helsinki route. In February 2013 transferred to the Stockholm - Turku service.

BALTIC QUEEN Built by STX Europe, Rauma, Finland. Operates between Helsink and Tallinn.

GALAXY Built by Aker Yards, Rauma, Finland to operate as a cruise ferry on the Tallinn - Helsinki route. In July 2008 transferred to the Stockholm - Turku route and rebranded as a *Silja Line* vessel.

ISABELLE Built as the ISABELLA by Brodogradevna Industrija, Split, Yugoslavia for *SF Line*. Used on the *Viking Line* Stockholm - Naantali service until 1992 when she was switched to operating 24-hour cruises from Helsinki and in 1995 she was transferred to the Stockholm - Helsinki route. During 1996 she additionally operated day cruises to Muuga in Estonia during the 'layover' period in Helsinki. In 1997 she was transferred to the Stockholm - Turku route. in January 2013 she was replaced by the VIKING GRACE. After covering for the AMORELLA during her refit period she was laid up. In April 2013 sold to *Hansa Link Limited*, a subsidiary of *AS Tallink Grupp* and renamed the ISABELLE. In May placed on the Stockholm - Riga service, replacing the SILJA FESTIVAL.

REGAL STAR Partly built by Sudostroitelnyy Zavod Severnaya Verf, St Petersburg. Work started in 1993 (as a deep-sea ro-ro) but was never completed. In 1999 the vessel was purchased, taken to Palumba SpA, Naples and completed as a short-sea ro-ro with accommodation for 80 drivers. In 2000 she was delivered to *MCL* of Italy and placed on a route between Savona and Catania. In September of that year she was chartered by *Grimaldi Ferries* and operated on a route Salerno – Palermo – Valencia. In late 2003 she was sold to *Hansatee Shipping* of Estonia and, in 2004, placed on the Kapellskär – Paldiski route, replacing the KAPELLA. From February 2006 she was transferred to the Helsinki – Tallinn service, replacing the KAPELLA due to the hard ice conditions. She continued in this service for the summer, but she returned to the Paldiski – Kapellskär service. In June 2010 moved to the *SeaWind Line* Stockholm – Turku service for the summer seasons and returned to the Kapellskär - Paldiski route in the autumn.

REGINA BALTICA Built as the VIKING SONG by Oy Wärtsilä Ab, Turku, Finland for *Rederi AB Sally* of Finland and used on the *Viking Line* service between Stockholm and Helsinki. In 1985 replaced by the MARIELLA of *SF Line* and sold to *Fred. Olsen Lines*. She was named BRAEMAR and used on services between Norway and Britain as well as between Norway and Denmark. Services to Britain ceased in June 1990 and she continued to operate between Norway and Denmark. She was withdrawn in 1991 and sold to *Rigorous Shipping* of Cyprus (a subsidiary of *Fred. Olsen Lines*). She was chartered to the *Baltic Shipping Company* of Russia, renamed the ANNA KARENINA and inaugurated a service between Kiel and St Petersburg. In 1992 a Nynäshamn call was introduced. In 1996 the service ceased and she was returned to her owners and renamed the ANNA K. Later in 1996 she was sold to *Empremare Shipping Co Ltd* of Cyprus (a company jointly owned by *Nordström & Thulin* and *Estonian Shipping Company*), chartered to *EstLine* and renamed the REGINA BALTICA. In 2000 the charter transferred to *Tallink*; she continued to operate between Stockholm and Tallinn. Purchased by *Tallink* in 2002. In May 2006 replaced by the ROMANTIKA and succeeded the FANTAASIA on the Stockholm - Riga service. In May 2009 replaced by the ROMANTIKA and laid up. In May 2010 chartered to *Acciona Trasmediterranea*, of Spain and operated between Almeria (Spain) and Nador (Morocco). In October 2011 returned to Tallinn

Star *(Miles Cowsill)*

Galaxy *(Miles Cowsill)*

and laid up. In February 2012 chartered to *Scira* of Norway to act as an accommodation vessel for the Sheringham Shoal Offshore Wind Farm off the North Norfolk coast.

ROMANTIKA Built by Aker Finnyards, Rauma, Finland for *Tallink Grupp* to operate for *Tallink* between Tallinn and Helsinki. In Spring 2006 moved to the Tallinn - Stockholm route. In May 2009 transferred to the Stockholm - Riga route. In August 2014 moved to Stockholm - Tallinn.

SEA WIND Train/vehicle ferry built as the SVEALAND by Helsingørs Skipsværft, Helsingør, Denmark for *Stockholms Rederi AB Svea* and used on the *Trave Line* Helsingborg (Sweden) - Copenhagen (Tuborg Havn) - Travemünde freight service. In 1981 she was sold to *TT-Saga Line* and operated between Travemünde and Malmö. In 1984 she was rebuilt to increase capacity and renamed the SAGA WIND. In 1989 she was acquired by *SeaWind Line*, renamed the SEA WIND and inaugurated a combined rail freight, trailer and passenger service between Stockholm and Turku. Now freight-only.

SILJA EUROPA Built by Jos L Meyer, Papenburg, Germany. Ordered by *Rederi AB Slite* of Sweden for *Viking Line* service between Stockholm and Helsinki and due to be called EUROPA. In 1993, shortly before delivery was due, *Rederi AB Slite* went into liquidation and the order was cancelled. A charter agreement with her builders was then signed by *Silja Line* and she was introduced onto the Stockholm - Helsinki route as SILJA EUROPA. In early 1995 she was transferred to the Stockholm - Turku service. In January 2013 she was transferred to the Helsinki - Tallinn route. In August 2014 chartered to Australian interests as an accommodation vessel.

DELTA SPIRIT LODGE Built as the WELLAMO by Oy Wärtsilä Ab, Helsinki, Finland for *EFFOA* for the *Silja Line* Stockholm - Mariehamn - Turku service. In 1990, following the sale of the FINLANDIA to *DFDS*, she was transferred to the Stockholm - Helsinki service until the SILJA SERENADE was delivered later in the year. In 1991 she was renamed the SILJA FESTIVAL. During Winter 1991/92 she was extensively rebuilt and ownership was transferred to *Silja Line*. In 1993 she was transferred to the Malmö - Travemünde service of *Euroway*, which was at this time managed by *Silja Line*. This service ceased in 1994 and she was transferred to the Vaasa - Sundsvall service. In 1994 and 1995 she operated on this route during the peak summer period and on the Helsinki - Tallinn route during the rest of the year. The Vaasa - Sundsvall service did not operate in Summer 1996 and she continued to operate between Helsinki and Tallinn. In 1997 she was transferred to the Stockholm - Turku route replacing the SILJA SCANDINAVIA (see the GABRIELLA, *Viking Line*). In Autumn 2008 transferred to the Stockholm - Riga route and operated under the *Tallink* brand. In May 2013 replaced by the ISABELLE and laid up. In February 2014 chartered to *Rio Tinto Alcan* and, after a refit in Vancouver for a CAD 4 million refit before being moved to Kitimat, British Columbia as an accommodation ship to serve the construction of a new aluminium smelter. Renamed the DELTA SPIRIT LODGE.

SILJA SERENADE, SILJA SYMPHONY Built by Masa-Yards Oy, Turku, Finland for *Silja Line* for the Stockholm - Helsinki service. In 1993, SILJA SERENADE was transferred to the Stockholm - Turku service but in early 1995 she was transferred back to the Helsinki route.

STAR Built by Aker Yards, Helsinki, Finland for *Tallink* to operate as a normal ferry on the Tallinn - Helsinki route, reducing the crossing time to 2 hours.

SUPERSTAR Built by Fincantieri-Cantieri Navali Italiani SpA, Riva Trigoso, Italy to operate on the Tallinn - Helsinki route from May 2008.

VICTORIA I Built by Aker Finnyards, Rauma, Finland for *Tallink*. Operates between Tallinn and Stockholm.

AS Tallink Grupp also own the STENA SUPERFAST VII and STENA SUPERFAST VIII, currently on charter to *Stena Line (UK)*.

TESO

THE COMPANY *TESO* is a Dutch private company, with most shares owned by inhabitants of Texel. Its full name is *Texels Eigen Stoomboot Onderneming*.

MANAGEMENT Managing Director C H S de Waal.

ADDRESS Pontweg 1, 1797 SN Den Hoorn, Texel, The Netherlands.

TELEPHONE Administration +31 (0)222 36 96 00, **Reservations** Not applicable.

FAX Administration +31 (0)222 36 96 59.

INTERNET Email info@teso.nl **Website** www.teso.nl *(Dutch, English, German)*

ROUTE OPERATED Den Helder (The Netherlands) - Texel (Dutch Frisian Islands) (20 minutes; *DOKTER WAGEMAKER, SCHULPENGAT*; hourly).

| 1 | DOKTER WAGEMAKER | 13256t | 05 | 15.6k | 130.0m | 1750P | 320C | 44L | BA2 | NL | 9294070 |
| 2 | SCHULPENGAT | 8311t | 90 | 13.6k | 110.4m | 1750P | 156C | 25L | BA2 | NL | 8802313 |

DOKTER WAGEMAKER Built at Galatz, Romania (hull and superstructure) and Royal Schelde, Vlissingen (fitting out) for *TESO*.

SCHULPENGAT Built by Verolme Scheepswerf Heusden BV, Heusden, The Netherlands for *TESO*.

Under Construction

| 3 | TEXELSTROOM | - | 16 | 15.0k | 135.4m | 1750P | 350C | 44L | BA2 | NL | - |

TEXELSTROOM Under construction by LaNaval Shipyard, Sestao, Spain to replace the SCHULPENGAT.

TT-LINE

THE COMPANY *TT-Line GmbH & Co KG* is a German private sector company.

MANAGEMENT **Managing Directors** Hanns Heinrich Conzen & Jens Aurel Scharner, **Sales Manager** Dirk Lifke.

ADDRESS Zum Hafenplatz 1, 23570, Travemünde, Germany.

TELEPHONE Administration *Travemünde* +49 (0)4502 801 452, *Rostock* +49 (0)381 6707911, **Reservations** *Travemünde* +49 (0)4502 801 81, *Rostock* +49 (0)381 670790.

FAX Administration & Reservations *Travemünde* +49 (0)4502 801 407, *Rostock* +49 (0)381 6707980.

INTERNET Email info@ttline.com **Website** www.ttline.com *(English, German, Swedish)*

ROUTES OPERATED *Passenger Ferries* Travemünde (Germany) - Trelleborg (Sweden) (8 hrs 30 mins/9 hrs 30 mins; *NILS HOLGERSSON, PETER PAN*; 2 per day). *Ro-pax Ferries* Travemünde (Germany) - Trelleborg (Sweden) (7 hrs 30 mins/8 hrs 15 mins; *ROBIN HOOD*; 1 per day), Rostock (Germany) - Trelleborg (Sweden) (5 hrs 30 mins/6 hrs 30 mins/7 hrs 30 mins; *HUCKLEBERRY FINN, TOM SAWYER*; 3 per day), Świnoujście (Poland) - Trelleborg (Sweden) (7 hrs; *NILS DACKE*; 1 per day).

1	HUCKLEBERRY FINN	26391t	88	18.0k	177.2m	400P	280C	121T	BAS2	SE	8618358
2	NILS DACKE	26790t	95	18.5k	179.7m	317P	-	157T	BA	PO	9087477
3	NILS HOLGERSSON	36468t	01	18.0k	190.8m	744P	-	171T	BAS2	DE	9217230
4	PETER PAN	36468t	01	18.0k	190.8m	744P	-	171T	BAS2	SE	9217242
5	ROBIN HOOD	26796t	95	18.5k	179.7m	300P	-	157T	BA	DE	9087465
6	TOM SAWYER	26478t	89	18.0k	177.2m	400P	280C	121T	BAS2	DE	8703232

HUCKLEBERRY FINN Built as the NILS DACKE by Schichau Seebeckwerft AG, Bremerhaven, Germany, as a ro-pax vessel. During Summer 1993 rebuilt to transform her into a passenger/car ferry and renamed the PETER PAN, replacing a similarly named vessel (31356t, 1986). On arrival of the new PETER PAN in Autumn 2001 she was renamed the PETER PAN IV. She was then converted back to ro-pax format, renamed the HUCKLEBERRY FINN and, in early 2002, transferred to the Rostock -Trelleborg route.

NILS DACKE, ROBIN HOOD Ro-pax vessels built by Finnyards, Rauma, Finland for *TT-Line*. Primarily freight vessels but accompanied cars - especially camper vans and cars towing caravans - are conveyed. They operated on the Travemünde - Trelleborg and Travemünde - Helsingborg routes. In January 2014, the NILS DACKE was transferred to a new Trelleborg - Świnoujście service and changed to Polish registry.

Tom Sawyer *(FotoFlite)*

Peter Pan *(FotoFlite)*

NILS HOLGERSSON, PETER PAN Built by SSW Fähr und Spezialschiffbau GmbH, Bremerhaven, Germany for *TT-Line* for the Travemünde - Trelleborg route.

TOM SAWYER Built as the ROBIN HOOD by Schichau Seebeckwerft AG, Bremerhaven, Germany, as a ro-pax vessel. During Winter 1992/93 rebuilt to transform her into a passenger/car ferry and renamed the NILS HOLGERSSON, replacing a similarly named vessel (31395t, 1987) which had been sold to *Brittany Ferries* and renamed the VAL DE LOIRE. In 2001 converted back to ro-pax format and renamed the TOM SAWYER. Transferred to the Rostock - Trelleborg route.

TUULE LAEVAD

THE COMPANY *Tuule Laevad* is the trading name of *Tulule Gruup* an Estonian company. Subsidiary companies are *AS Saaremaa Laevakompanii* and *OÜ Väinamere Liinid*.

MANAGEMENT General Director Tõnis Rihvk.

ADDRESS Kohtu 1, 93819 Kuressaare, Estonia.

TELEPHONE Administration +372 452 4350, Reservations +372 14204.

FAX Administration +372 452 4355.

INTERNET Email slk@laevakompanii.ee Website www.tuulelaevad.ee *(Estonian, English)*

ROUTES OPERATED Vehicle Ferries Kuivastu - Virtsu (30 mins, *MUHUMAA, SAAREMAA*, up to 27 per day), Heltermaa (Hiiumaa) – Rohuküla (1 hr 30 mins; *HIIUMA, REGULA*; up to 10 per day), Triigi - Sõru (1 hr 5 mins; *KÕRGELAID*; up to 8 per day).

1P•	AEGNA	101t	79	18.0k	25.9 m	93P	0C	0L	-	EE	8874366
2	HARILAID	1028t	85	9.9k	49.9m	120P	35C	0L	BA	EE	8727367
3	HIIUMAA	5900t	11	15.0k	97.9m	600P	150C	12L	BA	EE	9481805
4	KÕRGELAID	1028t	87	9.9k	49.9m	200P	35C	0L	BA	EE	8725577
5	MUHUMAA	5900t	10	15.0k	97.9m	600P	150C	12L	BA	EE	9474060
6	REGULA	3774t	71	14.5k	71.2m	580P	105C	12L	BA	EE	7051058
7	SAAREMAA	5900t	10	15.0k	97.9m	600P	150C	12L	BA	EE	9474072
8•	ST OLA	4833t	71	16.0k	85.9m	500P	140C	12L	BA	EE	7109609

AEGNA Built as the RÅSA by Fjellstrand, Omastrand, Norway for *Helgeland Trafikkselskap* of Norway. In 2003 sold to *Jan og Torleif Charter DA*. In 2005 sold to *Saaremaa Laevakompanii* and renamed the AEGNA. Inaugurated a passenger-only service between Saaremaa and Ruhnu and Pärnu. This no longer operates and she is now laid up.

HARILAID, KÕRGELAID Built by Riga Shiprepair Yard, Riga, Latvia (USSR) for *ESCO* of Estonia. In 1994 transferred to *Saaremaa Laevakompanii*. The HARILAID is now a spare vessel.

HIIUMAA, MUHUMAA, SAAREMAA Built by Fiskerstrand Verft A/S, Aalesund, Norway for *Saaremaa Laevakompanii*.

REGULA Built by Jos L Meyer, Papenburg, Germany for *Stockholms Rederi AB Svea* of Sweden for the service between Helsingborg and Helsingør operated by *Linjebuss International AB* (a subsidiary company). In 1980 she was sold to *Scandinavian Ferry Lines*. During Winter 1984/85 she was rebuilt to increase vehicle and passenger capacity. In 1991 ownership was transferred to *SweFerry* and operations to *ScandLines* on the Helsingborg - Helsingør service. Ownership later transferred to *Scandlines AB*. In 1997 sold to *Saaremaa Laevakompanii*. Now a spare vessel.

ST OLA Built as the SVEA SCARLETT for by Jos L Meyer, Papenburg, Germany *Stockholms Rederi AB Svea* of Sweden and used on the *SL (Skandinavisk Linjetrafik)* service between Copenhagen (Tuborg Havn) and Landskrona (Sweden). In 1980 she was sold to *Scandinavian Ferry Lines* of Sweden and *Dampskibsselskabet Øresund A/S* of Denmark (jointly owned). Initially she continued to serve Landskrona but later that year the Swedish terminal became Malmö. In 1981 she operated on the Helsingborg - Helsingør service for a short while, after which she was withdrawn and laid up. In 1982 she was sold to *Eckerö Linjen* of Finland, renamed the ECKERÖ and used on services between Grisslehamn (Sweden) and Eckerö (Åland Islands). In 1991 she was sold to *P&O Scottish Ferries* and renamed the ST OLA. In March 1992 she replaced the previous ST OLA (1345t, 1974) on the Scrabster - Stromness service. In September 2002 withdrawn and sold to *Saaremaa Laevakompanii*. In 2011 laid up.

UNITY LINE

THE COMPANY *Unity Line* is a Polish company owned by *Polish Steamship Company (Polsteam)*. The operator manages seven ferries on two routes: Świnoujście – Ystad and Świnoujście – Trelleborg. Three ships are owned by *Euroafrica Shipping* which was previously a partner in the company; the ships continue to be operationally managed by to *Unity Line*.

MANAGEMENT **Chairman of the Board** Jarosław Kotarski.

ADDRESS Plac Rodla 8, 70-419 Szczecin, Poland.

TELEPHONE **Administration** + 48 (0)91 35 95 795, **Reservations** + 48 (0)91 35 95 600.

FAX **Administration** + 48 (0)91 35 95 885.

INTERNET **Email** promy@unityline.pl **Website** www.unityline.pl *(Polish, Swedish)*

ROUTES OPERATED **Passenger Service** Świnoujście (Poland) - Ystad (Sweden) (6 hrs 30 mins (day), 9 hrs (night); *POLONIA, SKANIA*; 2 per day). **Freight Services** Świnoujście (Poland) - Ystad (Sweden) (8 hrs (day), 9 hrs (night); *JAN ŚNIADECKI, KOPERNIK*; 2 per day), Świnoujście (Poland) - Trelleborg (Sweden) (6 hrs 30 mins (day), 9 hrs (night); *GALILEUSZ, GRYF, WOLIN*; 3 per day).

1F+	GALILEUSZ	15848t	92	17.0k	150.4m	160P	-	115L	A	CY	9019078
2F+	GRYF	18653t	90	16.0k	158.0m	180P	-	125L	BA	BS	8818300
3F+	JAN SNIADECKI	14417t	88	17.0k	155.1m	57P	-	70Lr	SA2	CY	8604711
4F+	KOPERNIK	13788t	77	18.0k	160.1m	360P	-	60Lr	SA2	PL	7527887
5	POLONIA	29875t	95	17.2k	169.9m	920P	440C	145Lr	SA2	BS	9108350
6	SKANIA	23933t	95	22.5k	173.7m	1400P	430C	140L	BA	BS	9086588
7F+	WOLIN	22874t	86	17.5k	188.9m	370P	-	110Lr	SA	BS	8420842

GALILEUSZ Built as the VIA TIRRENO by Van der Giessen-de Noord, Krimpen aan den IJssel, The Netherlands for *Viamare di Navigazione SpA* of Italy. Initially operated between Voltri and Termini Imerese. In 1998 transferred to the Genoa - Termini Imerese route and in 2001 to the Genoa - Palermo route. In 2006 sold to *Euroafrica Shipping*, renamed the GALILEUSZ and in November introduced onto the *Unity Line* Świnoujście - Ystad service. In February 2007 transferred to the new Świnoujście - Trelleborg route.

GRYF Built as the KAPTAN BURHANETTIN ISIM by Fosen Mekaniske Verksteder, Fevag, Norway for *Turkish Cargo Lines* of Turkey to operate between Trieste (Italy) and Derince (Turkey). In 2002 chartered to *Latlines* to operate between Lübeck and Riga (Latvia). In 2003 chartered to *VentLines* to inaugurate a new service between Travemünde and Ventspils. In 2004 sold to *Polsteam*, managed by *Unity Line* and renamed the GRYF. Entered service in 2005. In February 2007 transferred to the new Świnoujście - Trelleborg route.

JAN SNIADECKI Built by Falkenbergs Varv AB, Falkenberg, Sweden for *Polish Ocean Lines* to operate between Świnoujście and Ystad. Now operates for *Unity Line* on this route.

KOPERNIK Train/vehicle ferry built as the ROSTOCK by Bergens Mekaniske Verksted A/S, Bergen, Norway for *Deutsche Reichsbahn* of Germany (DDR). Used on freight services between Trelleborg and Sassnitz. In 1992 modified to increase passenger capacity in order to run in passenger service. In 1993 ownership transferred to DFO and in 1994 she opened a new service from Rostock to Trelleborg. In 1997 she was used when winds precluded the use of the new MECKLENBURG-VORPOMMERN. Following modifications to this vessel in late 1997, the ROSTOCK continued to operate to provide additional capacity until the delivery of the SKÅNE of *Scandlines AB*, after which she was laid up. In 1999 she was sold to *SeaWind Line*, renamed the STAR WIND and operated in freight-only mode between Stockholm and Turku. Initial plans to bring her passenger accommodation up to the standards required for Baltic night service were dropped. In October 2002 replaced by the SKY WIND and transferred to the Helsinki - Tallinn route. She carried a limited number of ordinary passengers on some

Wolin *(John Bryant)*

Gryf *(John Bryant)*

sailings. In May 2005 returned to the Stockholm - Turku service, no longer carrying ordinary passengers, but was laid up after a few weeks. In October sold to *Euro Shipping OÜ* of Estonia, a company linked to *Saaremaa Laevakompanii*, and renamed the VIRONIA. In 2006 inaugurated a new service between Sillamäe (Estonia) and Kotka (Finland). In 2007 sold to *Euroafrica Shipping*, renamed the KOPERNIK and, in April 2008, placed on the Świnoujście - Ystad route, replacing the MIKOLAJ KOPERNIK.

POLONIA Train/vehicle ferry built by Langsten Slip & Båtbyggeri A/S, Tomrefjord, Norway for *Polonia Line Ltd* and managed by *Unity Line*.

SKANIA Built as the SUPERFAST I by Schichau Seebeckwerft, Bremerhaven, Germany for *Superfast Ferries* of Greece. Operated between Patras and Ancona (Italy). In 1998 transferred to the Patras - Igoumenitsa (Greece) - Bari (Italy) route. In 2004 sold to a subsidiary of *Grimaldi Lines*, renamed the EUROSTAR ROMA and placed on the Civitavecchia (Italy) - Barcelona (Spain) service. In 2008 sold to *Polsteam* and renamed the SKANIA. After modifications, she was placed on the *Unity Line* Świnoujście - Ystad service as second passenger vessel. In during the peak summer period in 2010 will operate a round trip between Ystad and Rønne for *Bornholmstrafikken*.

WOLIN Train/vehicle ferry built as the ÖRESUND by Moss Rosenberg Værft, Moss, Norway for *Statens Järnvägar (Swedish State Railways)* for the 'DanLink' service between Helsingborg and Copenhagen. Has 817 metres of rail track. Service ceased in July 2000 and vessel laid up. In 2001 sold to *Sea Containers Ferries* and in 2002 converted at Gdansk, Poland to a passenger ferry. She was chartered to *SeaWind Line*, renamed the SKY WIND and in Autumn 2002 replaced the STAR WIND on the Stockholm - Turku service. In 2007 sold to *Polsteam*, renamed the WOLIN and placed on the *Unity Line* Świnoujście - Trelleborg service.

VIKING LINE

THE COMPANY *Viking Line Abp* is a Finnish company Listed on the Helsinki Stock Exchange since 1995.

MANAGEMENT President & CEO Jan Hanses, Executive Vice President/Sales, Marketing & Products Pavlos Ylinen.

ADDRESS Norragatan 4, 22100 Mariehamn, Åland.

TELEPHONE Administration +358 (0)18 27000, Reservations +358 (0)9 1235300.

FAX Administration +358 (0)18 16944.

INTERNET Email international.sales@vikingline.com Websites www.vikingline.fi *(Finnish, English, Swedish)* www.vikingline.ee *(Estonian)* www.vikingline.de *(German)*

ROUTES OPERATED Stockholm (Sweden) - Mariehamn (Åland) - Helsinki (Finland) (14 hrs; GABRIELLA, MARIELLA; 1 per day), Stockholm - Mariehamn (day)/Långnäs (Åland) (night) - Turku (Finland) (9 hrs 10 mins; AMORELLA, VIKING GRACE; 2 per day), Kapellskär (Sweden) - Mariehamn (Åland) (2 hrs 15 mins; ROSELLA; up to 3 per day), Helsinki - Tallinn (2 hrs 30 mins; GABRIELLA, MARIELLA, VIKING XPRS, 3 per day), Cruises from Stockholm to Mariehamn (21 hrs - 24 hrs round trip (most 22 hrs 30 mins); VIKING CINDERELLA; 1 per day).

1	AMORELLA	34384t	88	21.5k	169.4m	2450P	450C	53T	BA	FI	8601915
2	GABRIELLA	35492t	92	21.5k	171.2m	2420P	400C	50T	BA	FI	8917601
3	MARIELLA	37799t	85	22.0k	176.9m	2500P	400C	60T	BA	FI	8320573
4	ROSELLA	16850t	80	21.3k	136.0m	1700P	340C	40T	BA	AL	7901265
5	VIKING CINDERELLA	46398t	89	21.5k	191.0m	2500P	100C	-	BA	SE	8719188
6	VIKING GRACE	57000t	13	23.0k	214.0m	2800P	556C	90L	BA	FI	9606900
7	VIKING XPRS	34000t	08	25.0k	185.0m	2500P	250C	60L	BA	EE	9375654

AMORELLA Built by Brodogradevna Industrija, Split, Yugoslavia for *SF Line* for the Stockholm - Mariehamn - Turku service.

Amorella *(Miles Cowsill)*

Rosella *(William Barham)*

GABRIELLA Built as the FRANS SUELL by Brodogradiliste Industrija, Split, Croatia for *Sea-Link AB* of Sweden to operate for subsidiary company *Euroway AB*, who established a service between Lübeck, Travemünde and Malmö. In 1994 this service ceased and she was chartered to *Silja Line*, renamed the SILJA SCANDINAVIA and transferred to the Stockholm - Turku service. In 1997 she was sold to *Viking Line* to operate between Stockholm and Helsinki. She was renamed the GABRIELLA.

MARIELLA Built by Oy Wärtsilä Ab, Turku, Finland for *SF Line*. Used on the Stockholm - Helsinki service. During 1996 additionally operated short cruises to Muuga in Estonia during the 'layover' period in Helsinki. In 2014, a daytime sailing from Helsinki to Tallinn was introduced.

ROSELLA Built by Oy Wärtsilä Ab, Turku, Finland for *SF Line*. Used mainly on the Stockholm - Turku and Kapellskär - Naantali services until 1997. From 1997 operated 21 to 24-hour cruises from Stockholm to Mariehamn under the marketing name 'The Dancing Queen', except in the peak summer period when she operated between Kapellskär and Turku. In Autumn 2003 transferred to a new twice-daily Helsinki - Tallinn ferry service. In May 2008 placed on the Mariehamn - Kapellskär route under the Swedish flag. In 2011 she was extensively rebuilt at Balti Laevaremondi Tehas in Tallinn, Estonia. Cabin capacity was lowered from 1184 to 418 and the restaurant and shop areas were increased.

VIKING CINDERELLA Built as the CINDERELLA by Wärtsilä Marine Ab, Turku, Finland for *SF Line*. Until 1993 provided additional capacity between Stockholm and Helsinki and undertook weekend cruises from Helsinki. In 1993 she replaced the OLYMPIA (a sister vessel of the MARIELLA) as the main Stockholm - Helsinki vessel after the OLYMPIA had been chartered to *P&O European Ferries* and renamed the PRIDE OF BILBAO. In 1995 switched to operating 20-hour cruises from Helsinki to Estonia in the off peak and the Stockholm - Mariehamn - Turku service during the peak summer period (end of May to end of August). From 1997 she remained cruising throughout the year. In Autumn 2003 she was transferred to the Swedish flag, renamed the VIKING CINDERELLA and transferred to Stockholm - Mariehamn cruises. She operates these cruises all year round.

VIKING GRACE Built by STX Europe, Turku, Finland. She operates between Stockholm and Turku. She is powered by LNG. Entered service in January 2013.

VIKING XPRS Built by Aker Yards, Helsinki to operate between Helsinki and Tallinn.

WAGENBORG PASSAGIERSDIENSTEN

THE COMPANY *Wagenborg Passagiersdiensten BV* is a Dutch private sector company.

MANAGEMENT **Managing Director** G van Langen.

ADDRESS Postbus 70, 9163 ZM Nes, Ameland, The Netherlands.

TELEPHONE **Administration & Reservations** *International* +31 85 4011008, *Netherlands* 0900 9238.

FAX **Administration & Reservations** +31 (0)519 542905.

INTERNET **Email** info@wpd.nl **Website** www.wpd.nl *(Dutch, English, German)*

ROUTES OPERATED *Car Ferries* Holwerd (The Netherlands) - Ameland (Frisian Islands) (45 minutes; *OERD, SIER*; up to 14 per day), Lauwersoog (The Netherlands) - Schiermonnikoog (Frisian Islands) (45 minutes; *MONNIK, ROTTUM*; up to 6 per day).

1	MONNIK	1121t	85	12.2k	58.0m	1000P	46C	9L	BA	NL	8408961
2	OERD	2286t	03	11.2k	73.2m	1200P	72C	22L	BA	NL	9269673
3	ROTTUM	1121t	85	12.2k	58.0m	1000P	46C	9L	BA	NL	8408959
4	SIER	2286t	95	11.2k	73.2m	1200P	72C	22L	BA	NL	9075761

MONNIK Built by Scheepswerf Hoogezand, Hoogezand, The Netherlands for *Wagenborg Passagiersdiensten BV* as the OERD. In 2003, on delivery of the new OERD, she was renamed the MONNIK. Used on the Lauwersoog - Schiermonnikoog route.

OERD Built by Scheepswerf Bijlsma Lemmer, Lemmer, The Netherlands for *Wagenborg Passagiersdiensten BV*. Used on the Ameland - Holwerd route.

ROTTUM Built as the SIER by Scheepswerf Hoogezand, Hoogezand, The Netherlands for *Wagenborg Passagiersdiensten BV* and used on the Holwerd - Ameland route. In 1995 renamed the ROTTUM and transferred to the Lauwersoog - Schiermonnikoog route.

SIER Built by Shipyard Bijlsma, Wartena, The Netherlands for *Wagenborg Passagiersdiensten BV*. Used on the Ameland - Holwerd route.

WASALINE

THE COMPANY *Wasaline* is the trading name of *NLC Ferry Oy Ab*, a Finnish company, jointly owned by the cities of Vaasa and Umeå.

MANAGEMENT Chief Executive

ADDRESS *Finland* Skeppsredaregatan 3, 65170 Vasa, Finland *Sweden* Blå Vägen 4, 91322 Holmsund, Sweden.

TELEPHONE Administration & Reservations *Finland* + 358 (0)207 716 810, *Sweden* + 46 (0)90 185 200.

FAX Administration & Reservations

INTERNET *Email* info@wasaline.com *Website* www.wasaline.com *(English, Finnish, Swedish)*

ROUTE OPERATED Vaasa (Finland) - Umeå (Sweden) (4 hrs; *WASA EXPRESS*; 1/2 per day).

| 1 | WASA EXPRESS | 17053t | 81 | 17.0k | 140.8m | 1100P | 450C | 84T | BAS2 FI | 8000226 |

WASA EXPRESS Built by Oy Wärtsilä AB, Helsinki, Finland as the TRAVEMÜNDE for *Gedser-Travemünde Ruten* of Denmark for their service between Gedser (Denmark) and Travemünde (Germany). In 1986 the company's trading name was changed to *GT Linien* and in 1987, following the takeover by *Sea-Link AB* of Sweden, it was further changed to *GT Link*. The vessel's name was changed to the TRAVEMÜNDE LINK. In 1988 she was purchased by *Rederi AB Gotland* of Sweden, although remaining in service with *GT Link*. Later in 1988 she was chartered to *Sally Ferries* and entered service in December on the Ramsgate - Dunkerque service. She was renamed the SALLY STAR. In 1997 she was transferred to *Silja Line*, to operate between Vaasa and Umeå during the summer period, and operated under the marketing name WASA EXPRESS (although not renamed). She returned to *Rederi AB Gotland* in Autumn 1997, was renamed the THJELVAR and entered service with *Destination Gotland* in January 1998. Withdrawn and laid up in December 2003. In 2004 chartered to *Color Line* to inaugurate a new service between Larvik and Hirtshals. Renamed the COLOR TRAVELLER. Operated in reduced passenger mode on this service but in summer peak period operated between Frederikshavn and Larvik in full passenger mode. In December 2006 returned to *Rederi AB Gotland*. In 2007 renamed the THJELVAR, chartered to *Scandlines* and placed on the Gedser – Rostock route. Renamed the ROSTOCK. In Autumn 2008 withdrawn and laid up. In June 2009 sub-chartered to *Comarit* of Morocco for two months. In September she resumed the name THJELVAR. In August 2008 she was chartered to *Fred. Olsen SA* of Spain, renamed the BETANCURIA and placed on the Las Palmas - Puerto del Rosario - Arrecife service. In September 2012 laid up. In October 2012 purchased by *NLC Ferry Oy Ab* and, in November, renamed the WASA EXPRESS. Entered service in January 2013.

Superspeed 2 *(Miles Cowsill)*

SECTION 7 - OTHER VESSELS

The following passenger vessels are, at the time of going to print, not operating and are owned by companies which do not currently operate services or are used on freight -only services. They are therefore available for possible re-deployment, either in the area covered by this book or elsewhere. Passenger vessels operating freight-only services outside the scope of this book are also included here. Exceptionally we have included two freight-only vessels possibly to be chartered to an operator serving the UK. Withdrawn vessels not yet disposed of and owned by operating companies are shown under the appropriate company and marked '•'.

Rederi AB Gotland

1	GUTE	7616t	79	15.0k	138.8m	88P	-	60T	BA	SE	7802794

GUTE Built as the GUTE by Falkenbergs Varv AB, Falkenberg, Sweden for *Rederi AB Gotland* of Sweden. Used on service between Gotland and the Swedish mainland. In 1988 chartered to *Brambles Shipping* of Australia and used between Port Melbourne (Victoria) and Burnie (Tasmania). In 1992 she was renamed the SALLY SUN and chartered to *Sally Ferries*, operating between Ramsgate and Dunkerque. In 1994 she inaugurated a Ramsgate - Vlissingen service, which was later changed to Dartford - Vlissingen. In 1995 she was chartered to *SeaWind Line*, renamed the SEAWIND II and operated between Stockholm and Turku. In 1997 she was chartered to *Nordic Trucker Line* for the Oxelösund - St Petersburg service and in 1998 she returned to *SeaWind Line*. In 1998, after *Rederi AB Gotland*-owned *Destination Gotland* regained the franchise to operate to Gotland, she was renamed the GUTE and resumed her summer role of providing summer freight back-up to the passenger vessels, but with a number of short charters during the winter. In Autumn 2002 chartered to *Amber Lines* for the Karlshamn - Liepaja service. In February 2003 chartered to *NATO* for the Iraq crisis. Returned to *Destination Gotland* in Summer 2003. In Autumn 2003 chartered to *Scandlines Amber Lines* to operate between Karlshamn and Liepaja. In 2004 lengthened by 20.3m by Nauta Shiprepair, Gdynia, Poland. In Autumn 2004 chartered to *Riga Sea Line* to inaugurate a freight service between Riga and Nynäshamn. In Autumn 2005 the service ended and the vessel was laid up. In January 2006 chartered to *Lisco* and placed on the Klaipėda - Karlshamn route, also undertaking two trips from Klaipėda to Baltiysk. In May 2006 chartered to *SeaWind Line*. In March 2007 chartered to *Baltic Scandinavian Line*. Charter ended September 2007. Apart from a trip to Cameroon, conveying Swedish UN Troops for Chad, she remained laid up until October 2008 when she was chartered to *Baltic Scandinavian Line* to operate between Härnösand and Kaskinen. In 2009 this service closed and she was laid up. She is currently laid up at Norrkoping, Sweden.

Sea Containers

1»	THE PRINCESS ANNE	-	69	50.0k	56.4m	360P	55C	-	BA	UK	-
2»	THE PRINCESS MARGARET	-	68	50.0k	56.4m	360P	55C	-	BA	UK	-

THE PRINCESS ANNE, THE PRINCESS MARGARET British Hovercraft Corporation SRN4 type hovercraft built at Cowes, UK for *Seaspeed*. Built to Mark I specification. In 1978/1979 respectively lengthened to Mark III specification. They underwent complete refurbishment at the beginning of 1999. Withdrawn in 2000 and laid up at the Hovercraft Museum at Lee-on-Solent.

Stena RoRo

1	STENA FERONIA	21856t	97	20.0k	186.0m	320P	100C	135T	A	UK	9136022

STENA FERONIA Built as the MERSEY VIKING by CN Visentini, Donada, Italy for *Levantina Trasporti* of Italy and chartered to *Norse Irish Ferries*, operating between Liverpool and Belfast. In 1999 the charter was taken over by *Merchant Ferries*. Purchased by *NorseMerchant Ferries* in 2001. In 2002 the service transferred to Twelve Quays River Terminal, Birkenhead. In September 2005 renamed the DUBLIN VIKING and in December moved to the Birkenhead – Dublin route. In August 2010 renamed the DUBLIN SEAWAYS. In February 2011 sold to *Stena North Sea Ltd* (a subsidiary of *Stena RoRo*). In April 2011 renamed the STENA FERONIA. In May 2011 chartered to *DFDS Seaways* to operate between Klaipėda and Karlshamn. In October 2011 withdrawn. In February and March 2012 operated between

Birkenhead and Belfast whilst the STENA LAGAN and STENA MERSEY were receiving major overhauls. Withdrawn for repairs on 7th March following collision with aggregates carrier UNION MOON and then returned to the Baltic to cover for *DFDS Seaways* refits. In July 2012 chartered to *FRS* to operate between Algeciras and Tangiers but could well return to Northern Europe at some time.

8 - SISTERS - A LIST OF SISTER (OR NEAR SISTER) VESSELS IN THIS BOOK

The following vessels are sisters or near sisters. This refers to 'as built' condition; some ships will subsequently have been modified and become different from their sister vessels.

AMORELLA *(Viking Line)*, ISABELLE *(Tallink Silja Line)*, GABRIELLA *(Viking Line)*, CROWN OF SCANDINAVIA *(DFDS Seaways)*.

ARGYLE, BUTE *(Caledonian MacBrayne)*.

ASK, URD *(Stena Line)*.

ATLANTIC VISION *(Tallink)*, DIEPPE SEAWAYS *(DFDS Seaways)*, STENA SUPERFAST VII, STENA SUPERFAST VIII *(Stena Line)*.

AURORA AF HELSINGBORG, HAMLET *(Stena Line)*, TYCHO BRAHE *(Scandlines)*.

EPSILON *(Irish Ferries)*, ETRETAT *(Brittany Ferries)*, NORMAN ASTURIAS *(LD Lines)*, NORMAN ATLANTIC *(LD Lines)*, SCOTTISH VIKING, STENA HORIZON, STENA LAGAN, STENA MERSEY, STENA FLAVIA *(Stena Line)*.

BALTIC QUEEN, BALTIC PRINCESS, GALAXY *(Tallink Silja Line)*.

BASTØ I, BASTØ II *(Bastø Fosen)*.

BEN-MY-CHREE *(Isle of Man Steam Packet Company)*, COMMODORE CLIPPER *(Condor Ferries)*, HAMMERODDE *(Bornholmstrafikken)* (Near sisters).

BERGENSFJORD, STAVANGERFJORD *(Fjord Line)*.

BERLIN, COPENHAGEN *(Scandlines)*.

BERLIOZ, RODIN *(MyFerryLink)*.

CANNA *(Rathlin Island Ferry Ltd)*, CLEW BAY QUEEN *(Clare Island Ferry Company)*, COLL *(Arranmore Island Ferries)*, EIGG *(Caledonian MacBrayne)*, MORVERN *(Arranmore Fast Ferries)*, RAASAY *(Caledonian MacBrayne)*, RHUM *(Arranmore Island Ferries)*.

CARRIGALOE, GLENBROOK *(Cross River Ferries)*.

COLOR FANTASY, COLOR MAGIC *(Color Line)*.

COLOR VIKING *(Color Line)*, STENA NAUTICA *(Stena Line)*.

COTE D'ALBATRE, SEVEN SISTERS *(DFDS Seaways France)*.

DAGALIEN, DAGGRI *(Shetland Islands Council)*.

DELFT SEAWAYS, DOVER SEAWAYS, DUNKERQUE SEAWAYS *(DFDS Seaways)*.

DEUTSCHLAND, SCHLESWIG-HOLSTEIN *(Scandlines)*.

EARL SIGURD, EARL THORFINN *(Orkney Ferries)*.

ECKERÖ *(Eckerö Linjen)*, POVL ANKER *(Bornholmstrafikken)*.

ERNEST BEVIN, JAMES NEWMAN, JOHN BURNS *(Woolwich Free Ferry)*.

EUROPEAN CAUSEWAY, EUROPEAN HIGHLANDER *(P&O Ferries)*.

FENJA, MENJA *(Færgen)*.

FINNCLIPPER, FINNEAGLE, FINNFELLOW *(Finnlines)*, STENA GERMANICA *(Stena Line)*.

FINNLADY, FINNMAID, FINNSTAR, NORDLINK *(Finnlines)*.

FINNHANSA, FINNPARTNER, FINNTRADER *(Finnlines)*.

FRIGG SYDFYEN, ODIN SYDFYEN *(Færgen)*.

FRISIA I, FRISIA V *(Reederei Norden-Frisia)*.

GOTLAND, VISBY *(Destination Gotland)*.

HARILAID, KÖRGELAID *(Saaremaa Laevakompanii)*.

HIIUMA, MUHUMAA, SAAREMAA *(Saaremaa Laevakompanii)*.

HJALTLAND, HROSSEY *(NorthLink Ferries)*.

HUCKLEBERRY FINN, TOM SAWYER *(TT-Line)*.

KAUNAS SEAWAYS *(DFDS Seaways)*, PETERSBURG *(Sassnitz - Ust Luga Ferry)*, VILNIUS SEAWAYS *(DFDS Seaways)*.

KING SEAWAYS, PRINCESS SEAWAYS *(DFDS Seaways)*.

KONG HARALD, NORDLYS, RICHARD WITH *(Hurtigruten)*.

Ben my Chree (*Miles Cowsill*)

Seatruck Power (*Gordon Hislip*)

KRONPRINS FREDERIK, PRINS JOACHIM *(Scandlines)*.
LANGELAND, LOLLAND *(Færgen)*.
LIVERPOOL SEAWAYS *(DFDS Seaways)*, STENA FERONIA *(Stena Ro-Ro)*.
LOCH DUNVEGAN, LOCH FYNE *(Caledonian MacBrayne)*.
LOCH LINNHE, LOCH RANZA, LOCH RIDDON, LOCH STRIVEN *(Caledonian MacBrayne)*.
LYNHER II, PLYM II, TAMAR II *(Torpoint Ferries)*.
MARIELLA *(Viking Line)*, PRINCESS ANASTASIA *(St. Peter Line)*.
MERCANDIA IV, MERCANDIA VIII *(Stena Line)*.
MIDNATSOL, TROLLFJORD *(Hurtigruten)*.
MIDSLAND, WESTFALEN *(Rederij Doeksen)*.
MONNIK, ROTTUM *(Wagenborg)*.
MÜNSTERLAND, OSTFRIESLAND *(AG Ems)*.
NILS DACKE, ROBIN HOOD *(TT-Line)*.
NILS HOLGERSSON, PETER PAN *(TT-Line)*.
NORBANK, NORBAY *(P&O Ferries)*.
NORDKAPP, NORDNORGE, POLARLYS *(Hurtigruten)*.
OERD, SIER *(Wagenborg)*.
OILEAN NA H-OIGE, SANCTA MARIA *(Bere Island Ferries)*.
PRIDE OF BRUGES, PRIDE OF YORK *(P&O Ferries)*.
PRIDE OF CANTERBURY, PRIDE OF KENT *(P&O Ferries)*.
PRIDE OF HULL, PRIDE OF ROTTERDAM *(P&O Ferries)*.
PRINCESS MARIA *(St. Peter Line)*, STENA SAGA *(Stena Line)*.
PRINS RICHARD, PRINSESSE BENEDIKTE *(Scandlines)*.
RED EAGLE, RED FALCON, RED OSPREY *(Red Funnel Ferries)*.
ROMANTIKA, VICTORIA I *(Tallink Silja Line)*.
SILJA SERENADE, SILJA SYMPHONY *(Tallink Silja Line)*.
SOUND OF SCARBA, SOUND OF SHUNA *(Western Ferries)*.
SOUND OF SEIL, SOUND OF SOAY *(Western Ferries)*.
SPIRIT OF BRITAIN, SPIRIT OF FRANCE *(P&O Ferries)*.
ST CECILIA, ST FAITH, ST HELEN *(Wightlink)*.
STENA ADVENTURER, STENA SCANDINAVICA *(Stena Line)*.
STENA BRITANNICA, STENA HOLLANDICA *(Stena Line)*.
STENA SPIRIT, STENA VISION *(Stena Line)*.
SUPERSPEED 1, SUPERSPEED 2 *(Color Line)*.
WIGHT LIGHT, WIGHT SKY, WIGHT SUN *(Wightlink)*.
Fast Ferries
CONDOR EXPRESS, CONDOR RAPIDE, CONDOR VITESSE *(Condor Ferries)*.
FJORD CAT *(Fjord Line)*, MAX MOLS *(Mols-Linien)*.
KATEXPRESS 1, KATEXPRESS 2 *(Mols-Linien)*.
RED JET 1, RED JET 2 *(Red Funnel Ferries)*.
WIGHT RYDER I, WIGHT RYDER II *(Wightlink)*.
Freight Ferries
ADELINE *(CLdN/Cobelfret Ferries)*, WILHELMINE *(P&O Ferries)*.
AEGEAN BREEZE, ARABIAN BREEZE, ASIAN BREEZE, BALTIC BREEZE *(UECC)*.
AMANDINE, OPALINE *(CLdN/Cobelfret Ferries)*.
ANGLIA SEAWAYS, FLANDRIA SEAWAYS *(DFDS Seaways)*.
ANVIL POINT, EDDYSTONE, HARTLAND POINT, HURST POINT*(Foreland Shipping)*, LONGSTONE, WILLIAMSBORG *(CLdN/Cobelfret Ferries)*.
ARROW *(Isle of Man Steam Packet)*, CLIPPER RANGER *(Seatruck Ferries)*, HELLIAR, HILDASAY *(NorthLink Ferries)*.
AUTO BALTIC, AUTO BANK, AUTO BAY *(UECC)*.
AUTOPREMIER, AUTOPRESTIGE, AUTOPRIDE, AUTOPROGRESS *(UECC)*.
AUTORACER, AUTORUNNER *(UECC)*.
AUTOSKY, AUTOSTAR, AUTOSUN *(UECC)*.
BEGONIA SEAWAYS, FICARIA SEAWAYS, FREESIA SEAWAYS *(DFDS Seaways)*.
BOTNIA SEAWAYS, FINLANDIA SEAWAYS *(DFDS Seaways)*, FINNHAWK, FINNKRAFT *(Finnlines)*.
BRITANNIA SEAWAYS, SELANDIA SEAWAYS, SUECIA SEAWAYS *(DFDS Seaways)*.

CAPUCINE, SEVERINE (*Stena Line*).
FRIEDRICH RUSS, PAULINE RUSS, SEAGARD (*Transfennica*).
CELANDINE, CELESTINE, CLEMENTINE, MELUSINE, VALENTINE, VICTORINE (*CLdN/Cobelfret Ferries*).
CLIPPER PENNANT (*Seatruck Ferries*), CLIPPER POINT (*DFDS Seaways*), SEATRUCK PACE, SEATRUCK PANORAMA (*Seatruck Ferries*).
CORONA SEAWAYS (*DFDS Seaways*), FINNBREEZE, FINNMILL, FINNPULP, FINNSEA, FINNSKY, FINNSUN, FINNTIDE, FINNWAVE (*Finnlines*), FIONIA SEAWAYS, HAFNIA SEAWAYS, JUTLANDIA SEAWAYS (*DFDS Seaways*).
CYMBELINE, UNDINE (*CLdN/Cobelfret Ferries*).
GENCA, KRAFTCA, PLYCA, PULPCA, TIMCA, TRICA (*Transfennica*).
MAGNOLIA SEAWAYS, PETUNIA SEAWAYS, PRIMULA SEAWAYS (*DFDS Seaways*).
MAZARINE, PALATINE, PEREGRINE, VESPERTINE (*CLdN/Cobelfret Ferries*).
NORSKY, NORSTREAM (*P&O Ferries*).
OBBOLA, ORTVIKEN, ÖSTRAND (*SCA Transforest*).
PAULINE, YASMINE (*CLdN/Cobelfret Ferries*).
SCHIEBORG, SLINGEBORG, SPAARNEBORG (*CLdN/Cobelfret Ferries*).
SEATRUCK POWER, SEATRUCK PROGRESS (*Seatruck Ferries*), STENA PERFORMER, STENA PRECISION (*Stena Line*).
STENA CARRIER, STENA FREIGHTER (*Transfennica*).
STENA FORERUNNER, STENA FORECASTER (*Transfennica*).
STENA TRANSIT, STENA TRANSPORTER (*Stena Line*).

SECTION 9 - CHANGES SINCE FERRIES 2014-BRITISH ISLES AND NORTHERN EUROPE
DISPOSALS

The following vessels, listed in *Ferries 2014 - British Isles and Northern Europe* have been disposed of - either to other companies listed in this book or others. Company names are as used in that publication.

ARROW (*Seatruck Ferries*) In April 2014 chartered to *Isle of Man Steam Packet*.

BEACHY HEAD (*DFDS Seaways*) In April 2014 sold to *C Bulk NV* of Belgium, an associated company of CLdN/Cobelfret Ferries and renamed the WILLIAMSBORG. In July she was chartered to to *Nordana Line A/S* of Denmark operating from Mediterranean ports to the USA and Latin America.

BIRKA TRADER (*Transfennica*) In July 2013 renamed the TRADER and the charter ended.

CARLINA (*Dartmouth Steam Railway & Riverboat Company*) No longer used as a ferry.

CAROLINE RUSS (*Finnlines*) In September 2013 charter terminated. In January 2014 chartered to *Transfennica*.

CELTIC HORIZON (*Celtic Link Ferries*) In March 2014 charter transferred to *Stena Line*. Renamed the STENA HORIZON.

CHAMPION (*Dartmouth Steam Railway & Riverboat Company*) No longer used as a ferry.

COTENTIN (*Brittany Ferries*) In October 2013 sold to *Stena RoRo* and renamed the STENA BALTICA. Chartered to *Stena Line* and placed on the Karlskrona - Gdynia service.

CRAGSIDE (*DFDS Seaways*) In January 2014 charter ended. Chartered to *US Military Sealift Command*.

DARTMOUTH PRINCESS (*Dartmouth Steam Railway & Riverboat Company*) No longer used as a ferry.

DOLPHIN JET (*Kattegatruten*) In November 2013 sold to *Conferry* of Venezuela and renamed the VIRGEN DE COROMOTO.

EDGCUMBE BELLE (*Dartmouth Steam Railway & Riverboat Company*) In 2013 sold to *Francis Knight*, Plymouth.

Edgcumbe Bell (*Andrew Cooke*)

Cotentin (*John Hendy*)

EMERAUDE FRANCE *(Sadco International)* In April 2014 sold to *SeaJets* of Greece. In April left Tilbury under tow and in May renamed the SUPERFAST CAT.

ESONBORG *(Wagenborg Passagiersdiensten)* In 2013 sold to *Waterbus BV* of Rotterdam.

FASTCAT SHANKLIN *(Severn Link)* In April 2011 sold to Russian interests. Moved to Sochi on the Black Sea. (not previously reported).

GARDENIA *(TransEuropa Ferries)* In October 2013 sold to *Oilchart International*, a creditor of the company. Renamed the ARDENIA. In April 2014 moved to Greece. May be chartered, sold or scrapped.

KATTEGAT *(Kattegatruten)* In November 2013 the service ended and she was transferred to FRS Group's Mediterranean operation. Renamed the MAROC EXPRESS.

KINGSWEAR PRINCESS *(Dartmouth Steam Railway & Riverboat Company)* No longer used as a ferry.

KINTYRE EXPRESS *(Kintyre Express)* In 2013 sold.

LARKSPUR *(TransEuropa Ferries)* In January 2014 sold to *Oilchart International*, a creditor of the company. Renamed the LARKS. In May 2014 moved to Greece. In July 2014 chartered to *Egnatia Seaways* of Greece to operate Brindisi - Igoumenitsa - Cefalonia - Zante. Renamed the ARK.

LONGSTONE *(DFDS Seaways)* In May 2014 sold to *C Bulk NV* of Belgium, an associated company of *CLdN/Cobelfret Ferries*. Charter to *DFDS Seaways* ended and she was chartered to *SeaRoad* of Australia to operate between the mainland and Tasmania.

MAI MOLS *(Mols Linien)* In February 2014 sold for recycling.

MIE MOLS *(Mols Linien)* In October 2013 sold for recycling.

MUIRNEAG *(Caledonian MacBrayne)* In October 2013 charter ended. Sold to *Kalyoncu Ro-Ro* of Turkey. She operates between Samsun (Turkey) and Gelendzhik (Russia).

NORDLANDIA *(Eckerö Line)* In June 2013 sold to *Isabella Cruise Co Ltd* of Belize and renamed the ISABELLA 1. Moved to Greece.

NORMAN VOYAGER *(DFDS France)* In March 2014 chartered to *Brittany Ferries* and renamed the ETRETAT.

OFELIA *(Saaremaa Laevakompanii)* In June 2012 sold to *Roris Maritime Co Ltd* of Portugal and renamed the TUIZIDI. She operates in Angola. (not previously reported).

OSTEND SPIRIT *(P&O Ferries)* In October 2013 sold to Turkish breakers.

RAPPAREE *(Severn Link)* In April 2011 sold to Russian interests. Moved to Sochi on the Black Sea. (not previously reported).

SEA-CARGO RENERGY, SEA-CARGO INNOVATION *(Sea-Cargo)* The order for these vessels has been cancelled.

STENA ALEGRA *(Stena Line)* In October 2013, charter to *Stena Line* ended. In November, chartered to *KiwiRail Interislander* of New Zealand to operate on the Cook Strait.

STENA CARRIER *(Transfennica)* In November 2013 charter ended.

STENA FREIGHTER *(Transfennica)* In December 2013 charter ended.

TRANSEUROPA *(Finnlines)* In October 2103 sold to *Grimaldi Lines* of Italy. In December 2013 renamed the EUROFERRY OLYMPIA.

TRANSLUBECA *(Finnlines)* In October 2103 sold to of *Paradise Cruise & Ferry* of Russia and renamed the POSEIDON EXPRESS. She operates between Novorossiysk (Russia) – Trabzon (Turkey) and Poti (Georgia).

SOLENT EXPRESS *(Hovertravel)* In 2013 withdrawn from service.

SOUND OF SANDA *(Western Ferries)* In October 2013 sold to *The Underwater Centre, Fort William* for conversion to a diving school pontoon. Renamed the LOCH SCAVAIG.

Ostend Spirit (*George Holland*)

Larkspur (*Miles Cowsill*)

SOUND OF SCALPAY *(Western Ferries)* In October 2013 sold to *The Underwater Centre, Fort William* for conversion to a diving school pontoon. Renamed the LOCH SUNART.

STENA CARRIER *(Transfennica)* In October 2013 charter ended.

TAMSIN *(C Toms & Son)* In spring 2014 withdrawn from ferry service.

VESSELS RENAMED

The following vessels have been renamed since the publication of *Ferries 2014 - British Isles and Northern Europe* without change of operator.

BIRKA CARRIER *(Transfennica)* In July 2013 renamed the CARRIER.

TRANSRUSSIA *(Finnlines)* In February 2014 renamed the FINNHANSA.

SEABUS *(Clyde Cruises)* In January 2014 renamed the CHIEFTAIN.

SILJA FESTIVAL *(Tallink/Silja Line)* . In February 2014 chartered to *Rio Tinto Alcan* of Canada and renamed the DELTA SPIRIT LODGE.

COMPANY CHANGES

Celtic Link Ferries In March 2014 the service was taken over by *Stena Line* and the company ceased trading.

Kattegatruten In November 2014 service ended.

Rømø-Sylt Linie Now listed under the name of *Syltfähre* rather than *FRS Group* following the ending of the Group's *Kattegatruten* operation and a change of trading name for *Rømø-Sylt Linie.*

Saaremaa Laevakompanii Now trades as *Tuule Laevad.*

Thames Clippers Now trades as *KPMG Thames Clippers.*

TransEuropa Ferries (in administration) Both vessels have now been sold and the company is no longer functioning.

LATE NEWS

Condor Ferries In July 2013 it was announced that Condor Ferries were to charter AUSTAL HULL 270. Built in 2010 and laid up ever since. Gross tonnage: 6231t, Speed: 39k, passenger capacity to be determined, 245 car or 12 lorries and 145 cars, Access: stern only, Flag: Bahamas, IMO: 9551363. To be renamed before entering service in spring 2015.

DFDS Seaways France In July the WILLIAMSBORG was replaced on the Marseilles - Tunis route by the BORE SEA. Spec as BORE SONG (see P&O Ferries). IMO: 9443554.

AG Ems During winter 2014/15 the OSTFRIESLAND is to be lengthened by 15.3 metres by BVT Brenn-und Verformtechnik Bremen GmbH, Bremen, Germany. This will increase gross tonnage to 2581t and car capacity to 70. She will also be converted to LNG propulsion.

LD Lines The Poole - Gijon and Rosslare - Gijon services are likely to end in September 2014.

FERRIES
ILLUSTRATED

Autosky *(FotoFlite)*

INDEX

Other books from Ferry Publications

Folkestone for the Continent 1843-2001

This new book covers the entire history of the Kentish port of Folkestone from its inception in the early years of the nineteenth century until its closure in 2001. Although the history of the port will for ever be linked with Boulogne, other services were operated to Flushing, Ostend, Dunkirk and Calais and are also covered. The book is enhanced with a complete fleet list, traffic statistics and maps of the port at different stages of its development. Published November 2014. Price £21.50 plus p&p

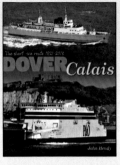

Dover-Calais

This will be an updated version of the Dover-Calais 2009 edition. Written by John Hendy, it covers the history of the most famous ferry crossing in the world but looks in detail at the development and expansion of the ferry operations and the new tonnage which has been introduced since the opening of the tunnel. The bookl includes DFDS and MyFerryLink operations. The title will be richly illustrated in colour and black and white. Now due to be published early 2015. Price £18.95 plus p&p.

TT Line

Since the introduction of the first Nils Holgersson in 1962, this German ferry has been both an innovative and reliable player in the southern Baltic ferry market. Their core Travemunde Trelleborg route has seen no less than six different generations of ferries so far. TT-Line is also known for Olau Line and for a service between Rostock. In 2012 TT-Line celebrated its 50th anniversary. This book captures the fascinating history of TT-Line, their routes and their ships. Price £16.95 plus p&p. Now available.

Order online from
www.ferrypubs.co.uk
By telephone on
+ 44 (0)1624 898445
By post from
PO Box 33, Ramsey, Isle of Man IM99 4LP
Please telephone or email for current postage costs.

The Ostend Ferry

This title traces the history of Ostend links with the UK. The publication covers the history of RMT and later the Dover Ostende Line. It also covers the history of the Ostend services to Folkestone Harwich, Ramsgate, Margate and also the other ports from Kent, Essex, and northern England. Also included are the local excursions from Ostend. Wealth of unpublished photos. Published early 2015. Price £22.00 plus p&p.

The SeaFrance Years

SeaFrance came into being on New Years Day 1996 afte splitting with former partners Stena Line. Although a late starter in the operation of vehicle ferries across the Channel, the fleet that eventually developed was a fine collection of purpose-built ships embodying the best examples of French design and technical advancement that frequently eclipsed their British contemporaries. This book traces the post-war development of French participation in the English Channel, also briefly looking at the Dieppe-Newhaven and Dunkirk-Dover operations which played such an important part in cross-Channel communications. Now available. Price £18.00 plus p&p.

Silja Line

Silja Line and Tallink are two of the world's best known ferry companies. This book gathers together for the first time in English their entire histories, from humble beginnings with small steamers to the leisure-oriented cruise ferries of today. Partial bilingual text in Finnish. Price £22.00 plus p&p. Now available.

Irish Ferries

In 1973, a newcomer to the Irish ferry scene began sailings between Rosslare and Le Havre. This company would grow from a single ship operator to become Irish Ferries. Today the company is the market leader on the Irish Sea to the UK and France. Price £19.75 plus p&p. Now available.